OPEN TO GOD

Brother Bernard, an Anglican Franciscan,
is the Guardian of Hilfield Friary, Dorchester.

Brother Bernard
of the Society of St Francis

OPEN TO GOD
The Franciscan Life

Foreword by John Austin Baker

COLLINS
FOUNT PAPERBACKS

First published by Fount Paperbacks, London in 1986

Made and printed in Great Britain by
William Collins Sons & Co. Ltd, Glasgow

For
Dave, Val, Richard and Jenny

To
Mary and Wyatt
and all who prayed

Deo gratias

Contents

Foreword

St Francis of Assisi is in some ways one of the best known of all Christian saints, yet in other and more important ways he is very little known. Millions will recognize his name who might be hard put to it to identify any other saint outside the Bible. By contrast, well-informed Christians who take him for granted as one of the great glories of the universal Church actually have very little precise knowledge or understanding of what he truly was.

This is a sad state of affairs, both because of Francis' place in the history of the Church and even more because of his enduring creative significance for Christian spirituality. During the past hundred years, however, a mass of first-class international scholarship has provided the materials for a faithful portrait of the saint and for an empathetic interpretation of his life and teaching which will speak to our own day; and as a result there have been some very helpful studies for a wider readership.

But what has been needed most of all is something which would combine three distinct strands: a sound and sympathetic account of the historical Francis: an authentic understanding of Francis' spirituality, such as only a life lived within the Franciscan tradition can provide; and an awareness of the modern world, sufficiently open, balanced and loving to enable Francis' legacy to speak to our condition. These strands come together in the author of this book:

someone who has the training and ability to make use of the
academic resources available; who has for twenty-seven years
lived as a Franciscan religious, and has been chosen to
exercise authority in his community; who has had a wide and
deep experience in the life of prayer which has made him a
much sought-after spiritual guide; and who is genuinely
open to and informed about the multi-faceted world in which
we live.

Brother Bernard interweaves the story of St Francis, his
own personal story, the story of humanity on the move in our
own day, and a profound insight into human nature in all its
variety, to create a unique document which brings past,
present and future together in a loving relationship. Written
with a light and engaging touch, springing from a Franciscan
love for joy in God's creation and all his children, it contains a
wealth of wisdom which not only draws us to new depths of
reflection but also challenges and encourages us to face the
reality of the world and of ourselves with courage and
humour, and to set out on the task of changing that reality
with faith, hope and love.

+ John Sarum
Salisbury, England

Introduction

The opportunity to write this came out of the blue as a pure gift, for which I am grateful. Francis, like the Lord Jesus Christ he followed, evokes many responses, inevitably subjective. I have tried to be faithful to his writings and to the early sources and to such critical work on them as I have managed to read. I have aimed to portray Francis as I perceive him, and as I try to follow him in our Anglican Society of St Francis. Of course, I am aware that I am only one among many and others would portray him differently.

Because Francis appeals way beyond Christian parameters, I have tried not to assume too much, but to explain the Christian, Catholic, medieval and scriptural terms that he uses. For some it will come as a surprise that he was such a clear-cut churchman; for others, that he ever put pen to paper. I have tried to relate what he wrote, both to his "story" (told in the first two chapters, together with my own "story" and that of the Society of St Francis) and to some of the wider considerations of our time.

I don't think that the appeal of Francis lies primarily in his churchmanship or in his writings, but rather in his wider humanity, his vitality, his discovery of God in all things, and his readiness to do wholeheartedly what he saw was for him. Yet his writings bear clear witness to the deep faith and openness to God which were at his core, and also to his profound gratitude to the Church which nourished him in the Word and in the Body and Blood of Christ. His deep and heroic commitment to the marginalized and the poor of his time, and his passionate peacefulness, also communicate to us over the centuries. Like Christ, he both encourages and challenges. He tells us something about being human: to be fully human is to be alive to God and willing to suffer for something bigger than ourselves.

I am very grateful for all who helped with this book in any way. I hope that you will enjoy reading it as much as I have enjoyed writing it.

Bernard SSF
Hilfield Friary
9 June 1985

Part One

Chapter 1
Crossing Over

I heard the story of St Francis and the leper for the first time in 1950 in a sermon on the love of God in Christ. One lovely sunny day, the young Francis, full of the joys of spring, rode out of Assisi into the glorious Umbrian countryside. His heart was full of the praise of God, a troubadour song on his lips. His future direction in the will of God was far from clear to him but at that moment it was the sheer delight in all God's world which filled his heart and mind. Ahead of him, from a ditch at the side of the road, he heard a cry for help. Francis was irritated at being interrupted; he prepared to ride by. But as he got nearer he saw that the man in the ditch was a beggar, filthy and in rags; and, nearer still, that he was a leper, his face partly eaten away. What a travesty of man "made in God's image"! Lepers were "unclean", highly infectious, so Francis pushed his heels into his horse's side to ride quickly by. But as he passed, he caught the words, "For the love of God, help me." The words struck home. Francis turned his horse's head, felt on his belt for coins to throw to the man . . . But then he paused . . . God's love did more for me, for us, than to throw a coin, Francis thought. He came to us in Jesus. Forgetting his fear, Francis went down into the ditch, gently lifting the beggar to his feet, and kissed his hand. "Brother Leper," he said, and went to serve lepers.[1]

The spoiling of the human image through the leprosy of sin, the coming of God in Christ to kiss our spoilt humanity, the change in our human lot because the God of heaven has called us "Brother" – these and other points the preacher no doubt made. But it was the story that took hold of me and it became a decisive point in my journey with God.

For Francis, meeting the leper was decisive. Shortly before he died in 1226, Francis wrote a final word for his followers (the *Testament*) expressing what his life had been about. This is how he began:

> This is how God inspired me, Brother Francis, to embark upon a life of penance. When I was in sin, the sight of lepers nauseated me beyond measure; then God himself led me into their company, and I had pity on them. When I once became acquainted with them, what had previously nauseated me, became a source of spiritual and physical consolation. After that I did not wait long before leaving the world.[2]

Francis met the leper on the road in 1205 when he was twenty-four. Up until then, much of his life had been light-hearted, enjoyable, fun. His father was a well-off cloth merchant, used to travelling to France and other places; cosmopolitan, he changed his eldest son's name from John to Francis.[3] Pietro Bernadone was ambitious for his boy and generous too, glad that he was master of revels among his peers and hopeful that he would take the family up a class by gaining a knighthood on some field of battle. Francis' first military escapade against Perugia ended with him as a prisoner for nearly a year.[4] It took a further year of convalescence before Francis regained his spirits, but then he was off to war again, his father decking him and his horse with fine clothing and armour. Disconcertingly, Francis gave a poor knight the finery,[5] but soon they were away, dreaming of glory to come.

The first night, near Spoleto, where they camped by the side of a river, Francis dreamed of a great hall in which all the armour of the world was displayed, and he heard the words, "Francis, which is the better to serve, the Lord or the servant?" "Lord, what will you have me to do?"[6] was his quick response, and he was told to go back to Assisi and find out. The abandonment of illusions about knights in shining armour, the scuttling of his father's ambitions, the flying in the face of what people saw as reasonable, were the first difficult choices which this new obedience involved; many more such choices were to follow. Francis seems to have taken them in his stride and to have been accepted back as full of fun, as abandoned as ever. Yet something was stirring. He had always been a bit wild, exhibitionist, whimsical: once he had a bizarre set of clothes made, in which the most expensive cloths were mixed with patches of sackcloth[7]; another time, on a visit to Rome, having thrown all his money into the Treasury, he changed clothes with a beggar outside St Peter's and joined those calling out for alms.[8] But now, too, he began looking for more opportunities for solitude and prayer, asking more what his life was for and where he was to go. One day in the middle of a party, when the gang were roistering down the street, Francis stopped, absorbed beyond himself. When they looked around, they mockingly said, "In love, Francis? Is that what's up?"[9] Francis answered seriously that he was in love with a bride more beautiful than they knew. Was the bride "True Religion" or "The Lady Poverty" – a character of Francis' imagination whom (in the tradition of the chivalry of his time) he made his lady and pledged himself to serve with all his being?

Francis saw the Spoleto incident and the "visitation" that day in the street of Assisi as the call and claim of God upon his life. Meeting the leper he knew that he would serve God by serving lepers. From now on, his time was divided between visiting the leper house near Assisi, and going out to a cave outside the city to find "a treasure". His companion (who some think was Brother Elias, who features in the story later on) failed to realize that it was the treasure of the Gospel story (Matthew 13:44) he was after, the sort that you sell all to buy.

The next "visitation" came to Francis in 1205 in a broken-down church, San Damiano, in Assisi. He was praying before a great painted Byzantine crucifix,[10] which still hangs in Assisi.[11] He heard the words, "Francis, build my church which is in ruins."[12] At once Francis obeyed, first giving the startled priest oil for a lamp to burn before the crucifix,[13] and then getting stones to begin the repairs. He wasn't fussy how he got the stones. Used to his father's indulgence, he took bales of cloth from the family store and sold them in Foligno (with the horse as well) and walked back to Assisi to buy the necessary materials.[14] Not unnaturally, Pietro didn't share the new enthusiasm, and the row culminated in Francis being summoned before the Bishop and ordered to give back to his father what he had taken. Francis gave back not only the money, but, to the consternation of the crowd and the shame of his father, he took off all his clothes and returned them saying, "I once called Pietro Bernadone 'father', now I say only 'Our Father in heaven'."[15] This terrible gesture started Francis on his journey further away from the world's norms. He set off "northwards" clad simply in a sackcloth garment signed with the cross: a poor religious man. He was beaten up by brigands, went to a monastery and worked in the kitchen for a few days, and eventually returned to his friends the lepers.[16] He began again to repair San Damiano[17] and other churches, begging his food and the materials. Somehow in the midst of all this Francis seems to have been full of joy, singing his praises to God.

A further event, in 1208 on 24 February, brought Francis, who must have been baffled by the direction his life was taking, to a further point of clarity. He was at Mass at the little church of St Mary of the Angels at the foot of the hill in Assisi, and the Gospel was read from Matthew 10:7–10 which describes the sending out of the disciples without purse, staff or shoes, to spread the news of the kingdom.[18] At once Francis recognized his vocation. "He cried out exultingly, 'This is what I wish, this is what I seek, this is what I long to do with all my heart' and, overflowing with joy, hastened to carry it out."[19] For Francis, then, the putting of his life under God's lordship meant a crossing over into a life of prayer, caring for people, sharing in the passion of Christ for the building of the Church and becoming an itinerant preacher of the Good News.

This may be the moment to examine more closely what Francis meant in his *Testament* by the phrases "in sin", "a life of penance" and "leaving the world", and to look also at the words "the flesh" and "the spirit", which we shall see he often uses in his writings. Some who write about Francis seem to me to have exaggerated the "sin" of his early life – a temptation to which all witnesses to conversion experiences are prone. Externally Francis wasn't any worse, I suppose, than his peers – indeed, his early life seems romantic and attractive, like that of Romeo in the Zeffirelli film, even though we hear of no great love affair. Within himself Francis came to recognize that in God's sight he had failed; indeed he calls himself (as Paul does) "the chief of sinners" (1 Timothy 1:15) and (as the Psalmist) "a worm, not a man" (Psalm 22:6). There is wide testimony that when we glimpse God in his beauty and love, we discover how much his image and likeness in us has been disfigured and distorted. There is a whole world of God's love in which we have an honoured place as his sons and daughters; but we choose to act as though things were ours by right, as if we can take or leave God as we choose. It is only when we come to see what the world is about, and what we are meant to be, that we recognize how wrong we have been. Like the prodigal in the parable we "come home" to the Father (Luke 15:20). Someone has said, "sin" is a "faith concept". That is, it follows from our understanding of God's nature, his purpose and our true place in it. Metropolitan Anthony Bloom says, "It is not the constant thought of their own sins, but the vision of the holiness of God that makes the saints aware of their own sinfulness."[20] The love of God opened Francis' eyes and he turned round. The New Testament calls the turning round to God *metanoia*, usually translated "repentance". "The kingdom of God is upon you; repent, and believe the Gospel" is Mark's summary of the message (Mark 1:15). Believing the message of God's love enables us to turn away from *all that* does not belong to it. The *all that* is called "sin". And the turning (though for some, like Paul, it starts dramatically), is a continual process. We are converted, we are being converted, and we hope that eventually all that we are will be converted into full fellowship with the God who made us.

The leper story symbolizes the process. Francis was afraid of the dark, leprous part of his nature – his Jungian shadow perhaps, his skeleton in the cupboard, the part of himself he would not acknowledge. He could only face it when he knew himself loved of God. When I discover I am loved I can bear to face "the very wounds that shame would hide".[21] I can let myself be loved into wholeness of life.

For Francis, of course, the event was not only symbolic: it was earthed in real experience. He crossed over from his world of privilege, careless extravagance, isolation from the feelings and problems of others, into the world of poverty, sickness, degradation, human alienation and hopelessness. He was impelled by the love of God, who had himself crossed over into humanness. Crossing the barrier, a whole new life opened up.

The new life he calls "*a life of penance*". "Penance" is not itself a New Testament word. It came to be used for the ecclesiastical punishment given to Christians who, having sinned after their baptism, repented and wished to be reinstated in the Church. At times penalties were extremely heavy; today they scarcely exist. In the sixteenth century they were highly suspect, both because "indulgences" in mitigation could be bought, but also for fear that the doctrine of God's free grace be compromised. No Christian can believe that we can buy God's forgiveness; forgiveness must always be a gift. The motive for the Christian life is not an attempt to atone for failure; it is a grateful response for pardon granted. God in Christ-crucified bears the cost of human sin. Our response, *metanoia*, isn't just a change of mind or heart, it is also a change of will and behaviour. "Bring forth fruits worthy of repentance" (Matthew 3:8). Francis, recognizing the poor quality of his Christian response, determines to live out his baptism totally. He wants to live in the fullest possible co-operation with the Lord Jesus Christ. It is this which he calls "a life of penance". In New Testament terms it is the life of penitence and faith, inaugurated when in baptism we share in the death and resurrection of Jesus (Mark 10:38–40; Romans 6:3–4), and worked out daily as we co-operate with the grace of the Holy Spirit. Bit by bit our full redeemed humanity is revealed. Francis is both a medieval man and a man of the Bible: he does penance; he is penitent. Anyway, it is clear that it is the life of faith that he has embarked upon in the closest possible identification with the Lord Jesus Christ. All this he terms "the life of penance".

"*Leaving the world*" conjures up ideas of becoming a hermit, like St Anthony of Egypt, or a monk, like St Benedict. Francis had a call to neither of these. "The world", in its New Testament sense, means society organized apart from and in defiance of God by men whose false desire for independence from God has alienated them both from him and from each other. "This world" is governed by the devil, "the prince of this world" (John 12:31; 14:30; 16:11). Jesus has entered it to establish a kingdom which "is not of this world" (John 18:36). The Church and each believer is delivered from this "present evil age" (Galatians 1:4) into the kingdom of the Son of God's love (Colossians 1:13ff). Like Christ then, the Christian is "not of this world" and, in fact, is the object of this world's hatred. The false values, false philosophies and vanities, are all shunned by the man in Christ. In Christ he is victorious over its evil power and saved from its coming condemnation. The conversion from "the world" (Romans 12:1–2), common to all, involves some Christians in going aside from the everyday world to deserts and monasteries to strive for true baptismal life. Francis' call was to continue to live in the everyday world, but yet to deny the world's "rebellion" against God and to live in the spirit of Christ who says "I have overcome the world" (John 16:33). This, of course, is the call of most Christians today.

Another crucial distinction in Francis, useful to clarify here, is between "*the flesh*" and "*the Spirit*". In the New Testament, "the flesh" means the whole human personality, not only the body. God made all things good. But because men sinned, "flesh" comes to mean the whole personality alienated from God. It is called elsewhere "the lower nature", "the sinful flesh".[22] Because wrong at its centre, it brings forth "fornication, impurity, and indecency; idolatry and sorcery; quarrels, a contentious temper, envy, fits of rage . . . jealousies; drinking bouts, orgies, and the like" (Galatians 5:19–20). The end of these things is death (Romans 6:21). On the other hand, the whole personality put right at its core and so directed towards God by the Holy Spirit brings its own harvest of goodness, love, joy, peace, etc. (Galatians 5:22). Paul finds right and wrong, the two natures, the flesh and the spirit, at war within himself (Romans 7:21–25). He finds deliverance from the flesh only through Christ. "Mortification of the flesh" (a thoroughly medieval phrase) comes to mean physical austerities, deprivals and even self-violence, but these are only helpful in so far as they contribute to the mortification of all in the human personality which draws it away from the will of the Holy Spirit. The *mind* of the flesh is the real enemy, but bodies collude with it. What must die is all that is not under the rule of God; "mortifications" are intended to bring this about. Francis clearly lived "in the Spirit" and although at the end he accuses himself of being over severe with his body (he called it Brother Ass),[23] we shall expect to find his bodily austerities governed by spiritual wisdom.[24]

If we put these concepts (which we shall meet often in the writings of St Francis) together in the story of Francis "crossing over" to kiss the leper, it works out something like this:

> Francis was inspired by the Holy Spirit and moved by the incarnate Christ: he therefore rejected this world. He put aside his fallen fleshly nature and turned his back on sin. He went to love and serve lepers in the love and compassion of Christ, as the Spirit directed him.

When I first heard that story, moved by the love of God in Jesus and how he came to embrace me in my sin, I was impressed by the action of Francis, his response to this love. I would like to explain where I was at in my personal story and why the Francis story became so important.

My father, too, was a businessman. We lived in Birmingham. We weren't all that well off, but I was privileged to go to a good school in the city and had many other opportunities. At the age of fourteen, after being evacuated (following a land-mine four doors away), I went to an evangelical camp and, on the last Sunday night, I had a conversion experience. It is difficult to describe its inwardness, but I came to see that I was refusing to let the Lord Jesus rule on the throne of my heart and I knew I must renounce the sin which kept him out. It was as simple as opening a door. Looking back, I suppose that at least some of the sins were sexual ones (disproportionately guilt-producing), but it was not so much the specifics that I remember as a blanket sense of unworthiness – unresponsive attitudes to God's love. The effect of opening the door was a whole new dimension of living, a new burst of energy, a desire to pray and to know and serve God. Though we were told this should include telling others about our conversion, I found myself shy of that, especially with my family – although they must have heard me singing the choruses, and certainly came across me kneeling by my bed.

For the next few years this religious "high" continued, though naturally not without some "lows". And though it did not quite cover all my behaviour, it altered me enough to be seen by others as a "godly man" (as I was once mockingly called), "a keen Christian". I was a member of a Crusader class, of the school Christian Union, and of an Evangelical Free Church. It survived my National Service in the Army, but there I met impressive Christians, both Roman Catholic and Anglican. My prayer and theology began to change into a more widely embracing, more human, less ghetto-like fervour. Just before I went to Cambridge, in October 1949, I was given as a twenty-first birthday present a book about an Anglican Franciscan priest who spent much of his life in Plaistow.[25] I was struck by his evangelical spirit, the Catholic framework to his faith and the way he lived it out among the poor. Before this I had no idea at all that the Anglican Church had religious communities. On my third day at college I met an Anglican friar, also new there, and we became great friends, co-operating in various student Christian activities. Through him I was led to more catholic understandings: to the daily Eucharist, for instance; a rule of life; my first (never to be forgotten) confession; and also to exciting activities like a youth mission to Newcastle, and a pilgrimage to Rome and Assisi. A whole new world opened up. We mixed with all types of people, from men straight off the road, to people who seemed to me extremely "precious".

At the same time as all this, I was studying medieval history and discovering the Christian tradition of religious communities, their spirituality, their role in society, their failures and renewals. I also began to see too some of the problems of the Church and society in the time when Europe was nominally Christian. I went, for instance, to the lectures of Professor Dom David Knowles OSB, on the history of Christian monasticism. In his simple, profound scholarship I found nourishment for soul as well as mind. I was getting the setting for Francis' life and I came to see what a radical, fresh spirit he brought into his world.

But his story met me at a deeper level still. "Converted" (and partly converted) in heart and mind and will, I was clear that my life was at the command of Christ. I was already accepted for ordination training and expecting to serve in the parochial ministry; now I saw in Francis and the Anglican Society of which he was patron, another way of serving Christ. The brothers had a strong, down-to-earth, practical caring, especially for the marginal and outsider, together with a sense of joy, *joie de vivre* even, based, I discovered, on a disciplined life of prayer. They were grounded in the Catholic tradition, had a questioning contemporary edge yet a warmly evangelical faith. I was attracted too by their itinerant, far-ranging mission.

After a further two years (during which I changed to studying theology), the penny dropped (with a thud of dismay which I have never quite lost!): I realized that my life was to be in the Society of St Francis. There were another two years at theological college, then ordination in Lincoln Cathedral and three more years as an assistant curate before I eventually entered the society. Looking back, I see the leper sermon as an important moment of conversion to the form my vocation has taken. For conversion is not just to God in the emotions of the heart, but also to God in the Church and God in the world, in people who need him, who want (and partly want) to know and love him and who already partly know him through the beauty and joy of this life and through the suffering, deprivals and oppression by which they share his passion.

I had been converted (and partly converted) to Christ. I was converted (and partly converted) to the Church. I was converted (and partly converted) to the world of men and women for whom Christ died. The Franciscan way brought these three together. But it's a long road: twenty-seven years a friar, I know I have barely started.

Chapter 2
Moving On

Francis' obedience seemed at first to bring him to a life of virtual solitude. He had burnt his boats with his family, was no longer a ringleader among his friends and was behaving oddly. He begged his food and the materials needed to rebuild churches; he spent long periods in solitary prayer; he went frequently to his friends the lepers. To such a gregarious character none of this could have been easy, and it continued for at least two years; yet the earliest stories all witness to his intense inner joy. It turned out that this period was the preparation for the coming of a whole group of men to this new life. First it was Bernard,[1] a wealthy merchant, then Peter Catani,[2] a canon lawyer, then Giles the mystic, and so on.[3] After a time together, they went off on preaching missions to the villages, just as they had heard in the Gospel, Francis taking Giles with him to the Marches of Ancona.[4] When their numbers reached twelve, Francis realized that the group needed a Rule and the acceptance of it by the Church.[5]

I think it is clear that Francis never set out to found an Order. He tried to live hour by hour in obedience to the guidance of the Holy Spirit, and brothers were given to him. As he said in his *Testament*: "When God gave me some friars, there was no one to tell me what I should do; but the Most High made it clear to me that I must live the life of the Gospel." He waited on God for guidance. His first biographer, Thomas of Celano, tells how one day, in great uncertainty, Francis went into the solitude of the wood and was away for a long time. When he came back "he seemed changed into another man."[6] "I have seen", he said, "a great multitude of men coming to us, and desiring to live with us in the habit of our way of life, and under the rule of our blessed religion. Behold, the sound of them is in my ears as they go and come according to the command of holy obedience. I have seen, as it were, the roads filled with their great numbers coming together to these parts out of almost every nation. Frenchmen are coming, Spaniards hastening, Germans and English are running, and a very great multitude of others, speaking various tongues, are hurrying."[7] And so it was that during his lifetime there were at least 5,000 friars and, by the end of the century, fifty houses in England, for instance, and over 500 houses in Italy.

Francis says that he had written down "briefly and simply" the core of the holy Gospel, by which the brothers were to live, and "His Holiness the Pope confirmed it for me."[8] It is a great pity that this "simple Rule", written in 1209, has not survived – the best we can do is to try to reconstruct it, as Dr John Moorman has done in his life of Francis.[9] We know from Celano[10] that when Francis was seeking guidance in 1208, he and Bernard went to St Nicholas' Church to look for a word of the Lord for them from Scripture.[11] Three times he opened the book:

> If you will be perfect, go and sell all and give to the poor . . . and follow me (Matthew 19:21).
> Take nothing for your journey (Luke 9:3).
> If any man will be a follower of mine . . . let him take up his cross and follow me (Matthew 16:24).

We know too what is contained in the draft *Rule of 1221* and the approved *Rule of 1223*. Moorman deduces from this data that "the primitive Rule" (1209–10) contains the three "foundation Scriptures", admonitions about food and clothing, authority and humility, work and begging, ministry to the poor and sick, loving one another, non-resistance and paying good for evil, fidelity to the Lord Jesus Christ and to the Catholic faith, the message of penance to be preached, and the reception and expulsion of brothers. Whether his reconstruction is correct is conjecture. What is not in doubt is that the Rule was simple, Gospel and direct. It may even have been more meagre than Moorman allows.

This simple, brave obedience which the early friars delighted in, not surprisingly did not seem to the Pope and his Curia an adequate Rule for a community. Indeed, the statesmanlike Innocent III (Pope 1198–1216), so keen on reforming and reordering the Church, had by then decided that further Religious Orders were not needed. Nevertheless, there was a debate in the Curia about these strange poor men. Objection was made that the Rule was too strict, that it was impossible to keep, and that relaxations, if not desertions, were bound to follow. But one Cardinal pointed out that to say that the following of evangelical perfection was impossible was a blasphemy against Christ, the Author of the Gospel. This view won the day and the brothers returned to Assisi singing.[12]

In the years to come, the Rule was, in fact, to be a source of great contention. Francis was adamant that their call was "to live by the Gospel" and he resisted attempts to modify the original understanding of what that meant. Even when in 1223 a new Rule, which in a masterly way incorporated much of the ideal, was approved by Honorius III (Pope 1216–27), there was further dissension. The process of institutionalizing a charism is never easy. What was possible for the founder and a few enthusiasts could not keep together the thousands who were to come after. Francis suffered as he saw his fidelity to the Lord threatened. Subsequent friars suffered as they tried to reconcile departures from the letter of the Rule and *Testament* with fidelity to their profession as friars. Some gave up the attempt: their abuses were scandalous.

In his simplicity, Francis actually pointed up three of the major distractions of the medieval Church. 1. By contrast with the strange rapaciousness even of Abbeys and other religious houses (many of which by now were considerable business corporations), Francis required absolute poverty, individual and corporate, even to the extent of forbidding the brothers ever to touch money.[13] 2. By contrast with the struggle for ecclesiastical privilege and exemption, and the litigation and chicanery that went with it, Francis refused to solicit or accept any privileges. 3. By contrast with the arid scholasticism of the time and the confining of sacred learning to an elite clerical class, Francis open-heartedly accepted the Scriptures, distrusting purely human learning. Francis made his challenge not by confrontation but by example. He got on with what he was given to do. If others saw in it a prophetic sign, or a rebuke, or a word of the Lord, that was fine; his job was to live the Gospel.

The Church in our time is being forced, in many places, to adopt a simpler form, nearer to the lives of the people it is called to serve. There is also a return to the Gospel. In places there is a new quest for Gospel poverty and simplicity of lifestyle. Many seek new forms of fraternity and, disappointed with established churches, seek for fellowship elsewhere. People look for new spirituality and go to the East or to sects, not finding it in Christianity. Francis' Gospel values need living again today in a way that is accessible and attractive. They need to be lived in the Church.

Innocent III is said to have seen in a dream his Cathedral of St John Lateran falling down. Only a little man in a simple habit held it up. The next day he met Francis and approved his Rule.[14] It is not "Franciscanism" that prevents the

Church falling down but Gospel living. If some of the Church's superstructure has to go, its essentials will be maintained by the Gospel life of humility, simplicity, poverty and prayer. The living of these values is what gives credibility to the Church of Jesus Christ.

The early days of any movement are easily idealized. Christians tend to look back to the New Testament Church in the idealized description of the Acts of the Apostles (Acts 2:42–47) rather than the scandalous party strife, sexual irregularities and legal squabbles which Paul's letters to the Corinthians indicate (I Corinthians 1, 5 and 6).

Certainly the life of early friars is very attractive. From the *Testament* we see that they *prayed*, "We who were clerics said the Office like other clerics" – and *did manual work*: "I worked with my hands and am still determined to work, and with all my heart I want all the friars to be busy with some kind of work. Those who do not know how to work should learn . . . to avoid idleness!" If necessary they were to beg from door to door without shame. They *cared for the lepers and the poor* and they *went around preaching*.

Francis and the first friars travelled extensively preaching in the towns and villages of Italy and, from 1217, friars crossed into France and Spain.[15] They were "sent out" by the Lord and had a simple, direct message about penitence and faith. Francis had a burning desire to go to Syria and the Holy Land, but was thwarted when he tried to go via Dalmatia in 1211 and via Spain in 1213 and only succeeded in 1219.[16]

An organization composed of itinerant friars was not easy to hold together. All the brothers, at first, returned to Assisi at least once a year at Pentecost. These Chapter meetings were times of great joy and fellowship as they told each other what God had done through them. No doubt, too, they spoke of the hardships and difficulties. Those who went to Germany, for instance, only knew one word: *Ja*. "Are you

heretics?" they were asked. *"Ja"*, they said, and they were
beaten up and thrown out of the town.[17] The sharing of
problems no doubt led to new understandings of the Rule:
modifications and additions were made – the introduction of
a noviciate year, for instance, as required by the Bull of 1220
– but at first this was done in an atmosphere of fraternal love
and under the inspiration of Francis himself. Celano waxes
lyrical:

> . . . a noble structure of charity arose, in which the living
> stones, gathered from all parts of the world, were erected
> into a dwelling place of the Holy Spirit. Oh, with what
> ardour of charity the new disciples of Christ burned! How
> great was the love that flourished in the members of this
> pious society! For whenever they came together any-
> where, or met one another along the way, as the custom is,
> there a shoot of spiritual love sprang up, sprinkling over all
> love, the seed of true affection. What more shall I say?
> Chaste embraces, gentle feelings, a holy kiss, pleasing
> conversation, modest laughter, joyous looks, a "single
> eye", a submissive spirit, a "peaceable tongue", a "mild
> answer", oneness of purpose, ready obedience, unwearied
> hand, all these were found in them.[18]

Francis' own love and gentleness inspired and led his
brothers. He taught them from the Gospels and kept before
them the ideal of their vocation. Nourished as he was in
Scripture, he nourished them. Yet caring and gentle as he
was, he was also single-minded enough to be stern and
uncompromising, as the *Admonitions* show. As news of sad
deviations from the ideal reached him and as pressure to
modify the ideal built up, he began to dig his heels in. His
draft of 1221 was rejected: a second version was even
reported to have been "lost by mistake".[19] Eventually, in
1223, the new Rule was approved.[20] Some have seen Francis'
Testament in 1226 as a bitter repudiation of this Rule, a kind

of rearguard action against the compromises involved; but I think this is simplistic.

Francis believed in obedience to the Lord, to the guidance of the Spirit, to the Gospel, and also to the Minister General (he himself resigned this office in 1220), the Ministers, his Guardian, the Chapter, the Catholic Church, the Bishop Protector and the Pope.[21] The way things developed, it was very difficult for him to keep all these obediences together. Undoubtedly he accepted the *Rule of 1223*; the *Testament* expressed another, and perhaps a deeper, part of his being.

There are a number of problems in all this which are still with us today. Few of us are so much of a piece that we have no conflicts within ourselves. No human group stays together without internal conflict and conflicts of loyalties. All of us have difficulty in living the challenging teaching of our Lord Jesus Christ. When people today say that they do not accept Christian dogma but live by the Sermon on the Mount (Matthew 5–7), I wonder if they have ever read the sermon: turning the other cheek, going the second mile, praying for those who persecute you, taking persecution and calumny with gladness and exultation, loving one's enemies, not being angry with a brother, not looking at a woman with lust, tearing out your eye if it offends, and so on. None of us can hope to live all this perfectly – least of all without the grace which the dogmas of Christianity express. The vivid and explicit descriptions of the life of the kingdom drive us back to penitence and faith that we may receive from God the power to live them. Isn't this what they are for? Francis had the best shot at living them out literally of anyone we know. His blatant, fearless, unashamed literalism rebukes our timidity and comfortable domesticizing of "the hard sayings" of the Lord. Francis was as blatant as an Englishman abroad who dresses himself up in a Union Jack – blatant, not to draw attention to himself, but only to Jesus whose colours he bore.

Conflicts developed when men of lesser calibre tried to live the Gospel together, in different settings, without having met Francis, with a weaker grasp of the Catholic faith, and in their fallibility.

The little band of Francis' most intimate stood with him in all the troubles: Leo, Angelo, Masseo, Rufino, Silvester, and above all Clare (1194–1253).[22] Clare (who had come to Francis on Palm Sunday, 1212), and the sisters who joined her, stayed inflexibly in her convent at San Damiano. The others, when the tide turned against them, lived quietly in hermitages and hidden places apart.

The election of Elias[23] as Minister General in 1221 (following the tragically early death of Peter Catanii who had taken the reins when Francis resigned in 1220), marks most clearly the turning of the tide. Elias shared with Cardinal Ugolino[23a] a vision of the Order: properly managed and directed, they believed it could renew the Church. With a degree of worldly-wisdom they sought to exploit its potential to the utmost. They led the movement in a way which saved it for posterity, but only, as some would argue, at the cost of its original greatness. The cost to Francis of obedience to Elias is hard to imagine, even though Elias cherished and protected him as a saint.

Saints in our world often appear in stained-glass windows – Francis most usually surrounded by birds. Why do we thus isolate them, making them remote from us, like God? Francis (like God) is better seen with the broken, the lepers, the oppressed, for that was his world – with the broken in heart (Luke 4:18) too, the poor in spirit (Matthew 5:3). The story of his valiance in the years 1220 to 1226, in extreme weakness and pain, brings us close (as he was) to the Passion of Christ. Ever since the San Damiano days before the crucifix, Francis had lived with Christ-crucified, saying, "I weep for the Passion of my Lord Jesus Christ and I should not be ashamed to go weeping through the whole world for his sake!"[24] He tells his brothers to say frequently: "We adore you most holy Lord Jesus Christ here and in all your churches throughout all the world, and we bless you because by your holy cross you have redeemed the world."[25]

Francis learnt that building the Church was not just a matter of getting stones and working hard, but rather of building living stones together in love, men and women who would together make a temple of the Holy Spirit. It cost him all he had. Beginning with the brothers, their relationship to Christ and to one another, and the relationship of the brotherhood to the wider Church, Francis spared no effort at reconciling. He was called on, too, to reconcile those in dispute in the wider community – the Mayor and the Bishop of Assisi,[26] for instance; the citizens of Arezzo[27] and Perugia,[28] and also individuals and groups. He even tried to reconcile the Saracens and Crusaders.[29] Travelling in his time must have been arduous and only when in serious illness did he allow himself mule or horse.[30] His martyrdom was not to be by speedy beheading by the Saracens, but "in torment and travail to serve the brethren". The cauterizing of his face with a red-hot iron (in the days before anaesthetics) and the near-blindness of his later years, together with what sounds like malaria, added to the general exhaustion of his emaciated body.[31] In his last months a novice asked him whether he would rather have to endure this sickness "so lingering and so long" or the most terrible martyrdom, and he replied: "That, my son, ever has been and is dearest, sweetest and most acceptable to me which is most pleasing to the Lord my God to do in me and with me . . . But compared with any kind of martyrdom, it would be more distressing to me to bear this sickness, were it but for three days."[32]

Francis eventually died at sunset on Saturday evening, 3 October 1226, when he was but forty-four years old.[33] He wanted to be buried obscurely, some say in the city sewer – yet over his tomb today is one of the finest churches in

Christendom. It was completed by Elias in 1230 as a basilica for Francis, newly canonized by Gregory IX (Pope 1227–41). It was an ironical tribute to "the homeless poor-one of Christ".

C. S. Lewis in *The Great Divorce*[34] describes a heretical Bishop going off from the threshold of heaven to address a theological society about the tragedy of the early death of Jesus, which, if avoided, could have given him so many more fruitful and mature years. The absurdity of this brings home the power and witness of the life laid down by faith. As we look at martyrs in our own time – Martin Luther King, Maximilian Kolbe of Auschwitz, Archbishops Luwum of Uganda and Romero of El Salvador, for instance – isn't their message somehow fulfilled in their being cut down before their time? Jesus said that if a seed falls into the ground and dies it yields a rich harvest (John 12:24). The harvest of Francis is in the stories of his life, in his writings, in Clare and her sisters, in the thousands who responded to his preaching, in those who joined the Third Order and in the millions who, in succeeding years, have seen in him the true reflection of the Lord Jesus.

The appeal of Francis, of course, is much wider than his own Communion. The Orthodox liken him to St Seraphim of Sarov (1759–1833); Protestants of different colours respond to his Gospel life. (It was Paul Sabatier, a French Calvinist, whose life of Francis in 1893 gave Franciscan studies a new fillip.) Anglicans, since 1894, when the Society of the Divine Compassion was founded, have established Franciscan communities, our Sisters of the Community of St Francis settling in Dalston in 1908. The story which follows is of an Anglican brotherhood begun in the early 1920s, which eventually became the Society of St Francis to which I belong. A fuller account is given in Barrie Williams' *The Franciscan Revival in the Anglican Communion*.[35] In the

Roman Communion there are many sisterhoods and groups of "Third Order Regular" as well as the three great expressions of Franciscan life: the order of Friars Minor Conventual, the Order of Friars Minor, the Order of Friars Minor Capuchin. By comparison our Society is tiny but, called into being by God, it has an ideal of primitive Franciscanism which we attempt to live out in an Anglican setting.

In an isolated part of Dorset, after the 1914–18 war, there was gathered a group of men determined in their discipleship of Christ and ready to express it in practical terms in the service of wayfarers. Wayfarers are marginal men, of "no-fixed-address", vagrants, tramps. Among them, Douglas Downes, soon to be known as Brother Douglas, exemplified single-minded devotion to Christ and to the service of the brethren.[36] He believed that the men who came to Flowers Farm could be retrained for work by a regular eight- or nine-hour day, with help in learning new skills. By being converted to Christ, their lives could be given direction and purpose. Such men he saw as his brothers, and he prayed with them night and morning, telling them of God's love for them in Christ. Some were converted and Brother Leslie Rose, for instance, in spite of his stammer, witnessed publicly to it in an open-air service in nearby Yeovil.[37] Others were not. Douglas had to speak for Brother Edward Furse at the Quarter Sessions. But together with those who knew themselves called by Christ to this service, Douglas built up a strenuous life of work, prayer and fellowship which has some of the spontaneity and delight of the early days at the Portiuncula in Assisi. By degrees they submitted their Rule to the Anglican authorities: they took the vows of poverty, chastity and obedience before Bishop St Clair Donaldson of Salisbury on 14 February 1931. The inspiration of Francis was recognized in their name: "The Brotherhood of St Francis of Assisi". Like the early Franciscans, they went out in pairs on the road, sleeping in doss-houses and casual wards, finding men for Christ through the simple witness of sharing friendship and work. If opportunity offered, they spoke of Christ. Like the early friars, too, they loved the Church and longed that it should return to its first love; they lived in great simplicity and poverty, depending on the divine providence.

Douglas' own purposefulness and devoted love for both his Lord and his fellow men was to reach heroic proportions. After the Second World War, for instance, when serving with the YMCA in Germany, he gave himself to some wounded, dispirited German ex-servicemen living in huts at Harburg near Hamburg.[38] Wherever he went – and this eventually included remote parts of Canada – there was the same unaffected friendliness, constant rapport, and readiness to help people practically and on their road to God. In London, St Martin-in-the-Fields crypt was often his lodging and he had the same pleasure in the company of the destitute as Francis found among lepers.

In the 1930s a new dimension to the life arrived in the person of Father Algy Robertson and his Brothers of the Love of Christ. He brought with him personal experience of evangelical Christianity, the Anglo-Catholicism of his Cambridge days, a wide ecumenical experience in the Student Christian Movement, the experience of an ashram in Poona and of his Little Brotherhood at St Ives. He had a great love for St Ignatius of Loyola and the early Jesuits and, of course, was a follower of St Francis. He had learnt a good deal about the timetable and customs of the Friars Minor; amalgamating with the brotherhood in 1937, he organized a noviciate, a liturgical timetable, and a more ordered life (which his own ill-health – the reason for his leaving India, and perhaps, too, his temperament – prevented him living fully himself). He had immense industry, considerable learning and great purposefulness of vision and it was through him that the Society of St Francis survived and grew. Many of us have personal reasons to be grateful to Algy. More of his life can be found in *The Life of Father Algy* by Father Denis.[39]

After the disruption of the 1939 war, there were houses in Cambridge, Hooke Court in Dorset (a school for maladjusted boys), and, in 1952, East London where the mission district in Plaistow was taken over from the Society of the Divine Compassion. In 1961 a new friary was established at Alnmouth in Northumberland. The work was not active alone: a firm Rule of Life with frequent Eucharist, the Anglican Offices, the Lesser Hours of the Church and a daily hour of private prayer was encumbent on all. Glasshampton Monastery was taken over in 1947 for the spiritual deepening of the brothers and the training of novices. The Community of St Clare, where sisters followed the way of contemplation in enclosure, was established in 1950 at Freeland near Oxford. Soon, too, came the beginnings of work overseas: at first in Central Africa, and then a house in Papua New Guinea was established. This new little Franciscan adventure in the Anglican Communion continued to grow. The Fellowship of the Way, founded in the late twenties, became the nucleus of a growing Third Order; the Sisters of the Community of St Francis formally affiliated in 1964; and the Episcopal Friars in the USA, founded by Father Joseph in 1919, amalgamated in 1967, so that by that year there were the three traditional Franciscan Orders existing in three provinces – the Pacific, the United States and the United Kingdom. Today there is further extension and growth. The growth is for us a sign of "God with whom the little ones go forth as the mighty"; we come back to him with our failures but with gratitude and hope.

The last three Archbishops of Canterbury have visited Chapters and conferences of the Society and have been generous in their appreciation and encouragement. But they have challenged us to keep the early spirit of adventure and poverty. Archbishop Coggan, when asked what he saw as the greatest danger to the Society, said, "that you become respectable". Archbishop Runcie said, in 1981, that he looked for reassurance that "your heroic efforts in Plaistow, in Belfast and Liverpool, are going to be the shape of things to come and not front-line positions which will be abandoned".[40] Indeed, in the last fifteen years the emphasis has been away from the more settled life of the larger friaries to small inner-city groups sharing more fully the lives of the people. Edinburgh, Birmingham, Stepney, Scunthorpe and Paddington could now be added to the list. But however much real poverty we meet in inner cities it is nothing compared to the constraints of life in Tanzania, Papua New Guinea or the Solomon Islands. All of us are enjoined by the Principles "to eschew all extravagance and superfluity and to study strict economy"; in these places there is little choice.

In the desire for simple brotherhood, the General Chapter in 1966 returned to the earlier usage of the term "brother" for all friars, whether they were ordained or not. This, now fully accepted, has been beneficial to the common life. The next major change was to include our active Sisters of the Community of St Francis (the Second Order, the Community of St Clare, is for enclosed sisters) in the First Order of our Constitution, although this is a departure from traditional Franciscan categories. The sisters have their own Chapter and elected leaders but are closely parallel to us in every way. We work together in some of our houses and on missions. Overlapping in many parts of our work we see our life together as a sign of the new and more natural relationship between women and men in our century and culture. Most of our brothers and sisters welcome the new closeness, and probably a majority too the possibility of the ordination of women to the priesthood as a step nearer to the fulfilment of the new humanity which St Paul describes in Galatians

3:28: "Baptized into union with him, you have all put on Christ as a garment. There is no such thing as Jew or Greek, slave or freeman, male and female; for you are all one person in Christ Jesus."

In these post-Vatican II days it has been easier for Roman Catholics to see in Anglicans at least "residual catholic elements" and many warm friendships and ecumenical understandings have sprung up.[41] Fidelity to a particular calling is the message of Francis. This involves us both in working at our vocation in the Anglican Communion and reaching out towards a wider Catholic fellowship. Through an initiative of Father Pedro Arrupé, the former General of the Jesuits, Brother Michael (now our Minister General) and Mother Elizabeth have been involved in consultations in Rome and in the establishment of an Ecumenical Commission for Religious. The statement published in 1983 recognized the particular fellowship in the vows of religion. Likewise, in this country and abroad, Catholic friars have included us in their fellowship and prayers.

It was a relief to me to discover that fidelity to the calling didn't mean an anxious attempt to follow the saint in every detail, nor indeed to conform to the life in one of its forms developed in the Order since his time. It is rather to drink deeply of the Spirit he drank of and to co-operate with that Spirit as he reproduces the life of Christ and its fruit in us. The expectation that studying the writings of St Francis and the early stories about him will forward that work of grace encourages me to attempt it. If the fruit of the Spirit has some particularly Franciscan marks, then glory be to God.

Just as the appeal of Francis is so much wider than any Christian group, so the discovery of what he actually said and taught – though it may come as a shock to those who know him only as a friend of animals, or as the author of the prayer that carries his name[42] – can, through penitence and true faith, bring us to deeper sharing in the new humanity for

which Christ died. Francis did not hesitate to address one of
his letters to "All Christian, religious, clerics, laymen, men
and women, to everyone in the whole world".[43] He says,
"Brother Francis, their servant and subject, sends his
humble respects, imploring for them true peace from heaven
and sincere love in God." As we look more closely at his
message, may his prayer be fulfilled.

Part Two

Chapter 3
Knowing

From stories written to celebrate and inspire sanctity, it is difficult to discover the real man. Did Francis ever make bad decisions? Was he ever difficult to live with? Did he ever doubt that he was doing the right thing? Did his confidence in God ever waver? There are no data to provide answers, except the common experience of being human. When we know a person's vulnerabilities and temptations we appreciate better his achievements. Nevertheless, we can but go to the stories we have and to Francis' own writings to discover him.

The most astonishing thing is Francis' apparently continuous awareness of God. It has a directness, simplicity and confidence very different from our modern self-consciousness and tentativeness. Yet he is not a bit "cocky". Where did Francis find this? How did he sustain it? And what about us? We shall hope to discover by looking first at Scripture and seeing how "faith comes by hearing, and hearing by the Word of God" (Romans 10:17); then at the reasons why Francis was cautious about book-knowledge, "knowing God by living rather than from books" (and taking note of the new emphasis today on "contextual theology" and on "orthopraxis"); and finally by trying to glimpse his intuitive knowledge of God which goes beyond both the Bible and books.

Knowing God through the Scriptures

The form of Francis' knowledge of God, and the nourishing of it, clearly comes from the Christian Scriptures, the Bible. His writings reflect Scriptures deeply digested, as well as directly quoted. Thomas of Celano says:

> Although this blessed man had been educated in none of the branches of learning, still, grasping the wisdom that is of God from above, and enlightened by the rays of eternal light, he had a deep understanding of the Scriptures. For his genius, free from all stain, penetrated the hidden things of mysteries and, where the knowledge of the masters is something external, the affection of one who loves enters within the thing itself. At times he would read the sacred books, and what he put into his mind once, he wrote indelibly on his heart. His memory substituted for books, for he did not hear a thing once in vain, for his love meditated on it with constant devotion.[1]

Francis' knowledge of Scripture was part of his worship of God, and no doubt it was often in a liturgical context that he heard and read it. It was part too of his intimate relationship with God in meditation. It was to Scripture that he turned when he wanted to know what God wanted him to do.[2]

There were in his times sects, like the Waldensians, who relied heavily on Scripture, and though he never refers to them or to any heretics, he must surely have come into contact with them, especially as they were often associated with the cloth trade.[3] The Waldensians were originally an orthodox movement but increasingly moved away from the Catholic Church. Certainly, from somewhere, he found an approach very different from the Schoolmen, or even the spiritual writers of his time. As Dom David Knowles says:

> The absolute freshness and originality which were characteristic of his mind . . . can perhaps be appreciated

adequately only by those long familiar with the religious
literature of the early Middle Ages and of the renaissance
of the eleventh and twelfth centuries . . . Francis [has] a
more direct, personal view, in which the human life of
Christ on earth is the centre of the world's history and the
model of all lives . . . Nor is there with him any trace of
that literary culture which clothes even the most intimate
utterances of such wholly sincere voices as those of
Anselm, Bernard and Ailred. Compared with the limpid
freshness of Francis, the letters and dialogues of the abbots
of Clairvaux and Rievaulx seem artificial and rhetorical;
they are of a school and of a date; the most characteristic
utterances of Francis have something of the dateless purity
of the Gospels.[4]

In Chapter 22 of the *Rule of 1221*, we have an example of
Francis expounding a Scripture passage, in the way that he
must often have done for the brothers. It is a sustained
meditation on Luke 8:11–15, the Parable of the Sower. We
shall examine it in some detail.

It opens with the injunction to "love your enemies and do
good to those who hate you" (Matthew 5:44). The brothers
are exhorted to be like the Lord in this matter: "We are to
love and to love very much those who, for no reason, cause us
trouble and suffering, shame or injury, pain or torture, even
martyrdom and death . . . They are our friends; for all they
do to us we are given eternal life."

He then passes on to what we must hate: "Our lower
nature with its vices and sins"; "the worldly life"; anything
that pulls us away from eternal life. He illustrates this from
Mark 7:21–22, listing the things which come from the heart
and make a man unclean: "evil thoughts, adulteries, immora-
lity, murders, thefts, covetousness, wickedness, deceit,
shamelessness, jealousy, blasphemy, pride, foolishness".

He then moves into direct commentary on the parable,

saying, "We have left the world now, and all we have to do is to be careful to obey God's will, and please him. We must be very careful or we will turn out to be like the earth by the wayside, or the stony or thorn-choked ground, as our Lord tells us in the Gospel." Building on the phrase, "the devil comes and carries off the word from their hearts" (Luke 8:12), he says that man's mind and heart can be drawn away from God, "even by some good and useful interest, and by the anxieties and cares of life, by which the devil tries to dull man's heart and make a dwelling for himself there". Matthew 12:43–45, about the devils coming into the house that has been swept and garnished, is quoted. He concludes the paragraph: "And so we must keep close watch over ourselves, or we will be lost, and turn our minds and hearts from God, because we think there is something worth having or doing, or that we shall gain some advantage."

A great catena of verses follows, describing what is meant to be the good ground from which the Word bears its fruit with patience. Putting aside every attachment and anxiety, we are to make a dwelling place for God in ourselves, watching and praying (Luke 21:36, Mark 11:25, Matthew 6:9, Luke 18:1) and worshipping God in spirit. This leads to John 4:24: "Those who worship him must worship in spirit and in truth." It is to the Good Shepherd that we should turn, who lays down his life "for the sheep" (John 10:15). We should know ourselves as brothers, with no father or master save God and Christ (Matthew 23:8–10).

An exposition of our union with God and Christ follows. We are to abide in him, as his words abide in us (John 15:7) and pray to him who is in the midst (Matthew 18:20), who will be with us always (Matthew 28:20). We are to receive his words, which are spirit and life (John 6:63), for he is "the way, the truth and the life" (John 14:6). He concludes with: "And so we must hold fast to the words, the life and the teaching and the holy Gospel of our Lord Jesus Christ. Of his own goodness he prayed to his Father for us and has made his name known to us as he said . . . " and here he quotes twenty verses of Christ's prayer in John 17 (6–26).

This passage shows that Francis quotes Scripture very extensively.[5] Its thought has deeply penetrated him. The core of his spiritual teaching is here: our hearts apart from God bring only wickedness, but if we allow God to live in us, he will bring forth goodness. Our part is to co-operate with him by open-hearted humility. We are to be the good earth (humus) in which the seed of God's Word will germinate and grow. By simplicity and poverty we stay open to God: be simple, be poor. In his *Praises of the Virtues*, Francis links simplicity with wisdom thus:

> Hail, Queen Wisdom! The Lord save you,
> with your sister, pure, holy Simplicity.

and again:

> Pure and holy Simplicity puts
> all the learning of this world,
> all natural wisdom to shame.

One of the exciting things of our times has been the rediscovery of the Bible by so many Roman Catholic lay-people. Encouraged by the hierarchy, and by the publication of the excellent Jerusalem Bible,[6] a whole world, long closed to ordinary people, has been opened up. Before the divisions of the sixteenth century, the Bible was assumed to be normal spiritual food amongst the small minority that could read. In the monasteries, for instance, *lectio divina*, the private reading of Scripture, was a basic part of the day's spiritual exercises. Such reading was reflective, "chewing the cud" on Scripture ("reading, marking, learning, and inwardly digesting"[7]); or, to change the metaphor, staying like a bee on each word and sentence until its nectar had been taken in. In the sixteenth century, when printing made the Bible widely available (and in the vernacular too), the Church became anxious, not unnaturally, that heresy would spread through the misunderstanding of Scripture by untrained minds. Consequently some Catholics even came to think of the Bible as "a Protestant book". But not so Ignatius of Loyola (1491–1556), the General of the Counter-Reformation, for he based his *Spiritual Exercises* on the contemplative and personal use of Scripture; his tradition lived on in Catholic piety.[8] Among Protestants there was a long tradition of reading the Scriptures daily, sometimes in households: to some extent this continues today. The charismatic renewal, among both Catholics and Protestants, has also greatly stimulated biblical devotion.

But in our century too, new challenges have arisen to scriptural assumptions. "Non-scientific", "non-historical", means to the popular mind, "non-reliable". The Bible is a closed book, old-fashioned and superseded. Scholarly application of modern literary and historical methods has also tended to undermine the authority of Scripture: not everyone is able to use these methods and still come to the understanding of the scriptural message, that it is God who is to be the authority in their lives. It is argued too that the different thought-forms and assumptions about the universe make it impossible for the modern reader to hear the biblical message without doing violence to his understanding of today's world. Yet is this true? I think we have the apparatus within us to listen behind the different context of the words and come to the heart of the matter. We can then go on to our own situation. But for any understanding of Scripture we need the help of the Holy Spirit (cf. 2 Peter 1:20–21). "The Spirit of truth", Jesus promised his disciples, "will guide you into all the truth . . . Everything that he makes known to you he will draw from what is mine" (John 16:12–15). He makes Jesus known to us and Jesus reveals the Father.

Francis several times makes a distinction between the "letter which kills, and the Spirit which gives life" (2 Corinthians 3:6). The distinction is from St Paul, whom Francis quotes (out of context) in *Admonition* VII. Paul argues that the Jewish people still read the Scriptures with a veil over their eyes (like that which Moses put on after he had been on the mountain with the Lord) and that it prevents them from seeing the Gospel and believing. He says that for those who turn to the Lord, there is no veil and "we all reflect, as in a mirror the splendour of the Lord; thus we are transfigured into his likeness, from splendour to splendour; such is the influence of the Lord who is Spirit" (2 Corinthians 3:18). Francis takes the kernel of this and links with it John 6:63: "The spirit alone gives life; the flesh is of no avail; the words which I have spoken to you are both spirit and life"; and Mark 4:12: that the people's hearts are hard and their minds dull, so that they do not see and believe. Because God is spirit (Francis says in the first of the *Admonitions*), he can only be known in the spirit; and the Son, who is equal to the Father, can only be known in the same way. The knowledge of God is clearly, then, more than a cerebral matter. The simplest person, with little education, is not more handicapped in knowing God than the university professor.

But if knowledge of God is a gift of the Spirit, how do we put ourselves in the way of it? Those who seek God may need help in understanding the kind of book the Bible is, and how it can be used to make God known to them. Some have been converted simply by reading Scripture with a heart that seeks him. Reading the Bible with other Christians, hearing it read in worship, and hearing it expounded may all be a necessary part of the discovery. In one way or another people move from "knowing about God" to "knowing God"; the mode differs with the person.

A simple Russian peasant, a saint of Mount Athos, Staretz Silouan, who died in 1938, says: "To believe in God is one thing; to know God is another." And again:

> The Father so loved us that he gave us his Son; and he became incarnate and lived with us on earth. And the Holy Apostles and a multitude of people beheld the Lord in the flesh, but not all knew him as the Lord; yet it has been given to me, a poor sinner, to know that Jesus Christ is God.
>
> O Lord, grant to all nations to know thee, by thy Holy Spirit. As thou didst give the Holy Spirit to the Apostles and they knew thee, so grant to all men to know thee by thy Holy Spirit.[9]

Francis is also quite sure that *knowing about* is not the same as *knowing*. In his seventh Admonition he says:

> A man has been killed by the letter when he wants to know quotations only so that people will think he is very learned and he can make money to give to his relatives and friends. A religious has been killed by the letter when he has no desire to follow the spirit of sacred Scripture, but wants to know what it says only so that he can explain it to others. On the other hand, those have received life from the spirit of sacred Scripture who, by their words and example, refer to the Most High God, to whom belongs all good, all that they know or wish to know, and do not allow their knowledge to become a source of self-complacency.

Knowing by doing

There are many stories about Francis and books.[10] He recognized a danger in learning and feared the privilege that book-learning represented. He kept to the ideal of poor and dependent itinerant brothers – "the lesser ones". A book was expensive (about the price of a horse); books could fill their

owners with a sense of importance. To the novice who asked
if he might have a psalter, Francis said, "When you have a
psalter, you will want a breviary, and then you will sit on a
high seat like a great prelate and say, 'Brother, bring me my
breviary.' "[11] By contrast, Francis says in the *Testament*,
"we made no claim to learning", and, in the *Rule of 1223*,
Chapter 10:

> Those who are illiterate should not be anxious to study.
> They should realize instead that the only thing they should
> desire is to have the Spirit of God at work within them,
> while they pray to him unceasingly with a heart free from
> self-interest.

In the *Rule of 1221*, Chapter 17, where he writes of
preachers, he says:

> I entreat all my friars, whether they are given to preaching,
> praying, or manual labour, to do their best to humble
> themselves at every opportunity; not to boast or be
> self-satisfied, or take pride in any good which God says or
> does or accomplishes in them or by them . . . We must be
> on our guard against pride and empty boasting and beware
> of worldly or natural wisdom. A worldly spirit loves to talk
> a lot and do nothing . . .

It isn't that Francis despises knowledge or true wisdom; on
the contrary, in the *Testament* he writes: "We should honour
and venerate theologians too, and the ministers of God's
Word, because it is they who give us spirit and life."[12] The
point is that what we *do* shows what we believe. "If you were
so clever that you knew everything and could speak every
language, so that the things of heaven were an open book to
you, still you could not boast of that. Any of the devils know
more about the things of heaven and know more about the
things of earth than any human being, even one who might
have received from God a special revelation of the highest

wisdom."[13] Francis himself was not ignorant; he called himself "idiot",[14] meaning unlearned, but he had learned to read and write at his Church school[15] and we see how clearly he understands the Scriptures. He wanted only to be the "clay vessel" of 2 Corinthians 4:7, "that the excellency of the power should come from God". He is more than ready to be a "fool for Christ's sake" (1 Corinthians 4:10) so that people should come to worship and adore the God from whom alone good comes. And he wants God's power to be known and seen in the lives of his followers.[16]

By the middle of the thirteenth century, less than twenty-five years after his death, the Order had moved into scholarship. The new universities, like Bologna, Paris and Oxford, all had flourishing Franciscan houses. The best of the Franciscan scholars kept to the ideal of simplicity. To many of the early friars, however, the new development was a betrayal. "O, Paris, Paris," said Brother Giles, "you have destroyed Assisi."[17] St Bonaventure (Minister General 1257–1274), himself a product of the University of Paris, wrote in one of his letters:

> Do not be upset that in the beginning the friars were simple and unlettered . . . it resembles the beginning and growth of the Church. As the Church began with simple fishermen and afterwards developed to include renowned and skilled doctors, so you will see it to be the case with the Order of the blessed Francis. In this way God shows that it was not founded by the prudence of men, but by Christ.[18]

In the light of the deep divisions in the Order about learning, his words may seem a little bland. It is at least arguable that the development was a betrayal of the specific vocation of the friars. In his last sentence, however, he shows that he understands the essential Francis.

Knowledge in the Holy Spirit was right at the heart of the

protest made by the group of friars who came to be called "the spirituals".[19] It separated them both from those who stressed learning, and from those who believed in a life much more like traditional monastics. It led many of them, too, towards the teaching of Abbot Joachim (1132–1202) of Fiore, who prophesied that the age of the Holy Spirit would dawn in the mid-thirteenth century (c.1260), and that the friars were to be the Order by which the corrupt Church was replaced by the New People of God. The terrible battle against what came to be heresy dragged on well into the fourteenth century. We, in our time, can see the dangers which arise from those who claim special revelation and privilege, as "God's own". We see, too, that often their faith is based on their "special understanding" of Scripture. Those who rejoice in the new life in the Holy Spirit which characterizes parts of our Church today, should take warning: the "evil one" can corrupt even the best. Worshipping God with the mind is one of the ways of combating evil's influence. Mindless religion easily moves to superstition; cultures which have rejected Christian understandings as "superseded" seem to me very prone to new incredulities. We need a new robustness today among Christians, a knowledge which is thorough and exact but which does not overestimate its importance in the scheme of things. We need to perceive the God who is greater than any knowledge of him, and recognize all knowledge as partial (1 Corinthians 13:12).

There are three reasons then why Francis was cautious about study: whereas books represented wealth and privilege, the brothers were to be the "lesser ones" who travelled light; whereas study easily leads to pride, worldly-wisdom, vanity and self-importance, the Holy Spirit leads the humble in heart to know God; whereas knowledge in the head confers status and respect, true knowledge in the Holy Spirit leads to action.

In *The Mirror of Perfection,*[20] which among the early

writings is the most critical of learning, Francis says:

> The Emperor Charles, Roland, Oliver and all the other
> paladins and men of valour were mighty in battle, they
> fought the infidels until death, with great sweat and toil,
> and they gained a famous victory. And the holy martyrs
> themselves gave their lives in battle for the faith of
> Christ. But in these days, there are many who wish to
> win honour and praise . . . by merely reciting the deeds
> of the saints. [As though to say, "Our concern is not
> with books and learning, but with holy deeds, for learn-
> ing brings pride, but charity edifies."][21]

Francis knew that people needed to see the Gospel lived if
they were to believe it. Jesus had warned of the catastrophe coming to those who heard the Word but failed to
do it – their house on its sandy foundations falls (Matthew
7:26). "Be ye doers of the Word, and not hearers only,
deceiving your own selves" (James 1:22). Francis, as we
have seen already, was quick to obey the word he heard
from God.

It is a sign of our "untogetherness" that we can *think* one
thing, *feel* another, *say* a third and *do* something quite
different. Jesus was integrated, his words and actions were
one, they carried weight. The world today is quick to spot
the credibility gap in Christians. Our inconsistency may
not be so apparent to us. The "liberation" theologians,
many of them from South America, challenge us to see
that by our spiritualizing and privatizing of religion we
have betrayed the Gospel. Christ came not only to preach
but to liberate mankind from oppression. He said, "[God]
has sent me to announce good news to the poor, to
proclaim release for prisoners and recovery of sight for
the blind; to let the broken victims go free, to proclaim the
year of the Lord's favour" (Luke 4:17–19). I heard of a
missionary in China who quoted this passage to Chairman

Mao Tse-tung, when he asked what she was about. "Oh, I see," said Mao, "and where is this happening today?"

I think the first time I ever seriously questioned my liberal, bourgeois assumptions (though I had worked for ten years in East London and had always voted Labour!) was during the six months I spent alone in the Hong Kong New Territories near the China border. Below me was the vast activity of a free capitalist economy; to the north, Chairman Mao was working so that the 800 million Chinese (one-third of the world's population) should "stand up". I was reading Gustavo Gutiérrez's *A Theology of Liberation*[22] and began to realize how conditioned we are in our understanding by the particular social climate in which we live. Reading the Scriptures and adopting the Christian faith from this standpoint we often fail to look beyond it. Distinguishing the essential Gospel from our own assumptions and discerning how the Gospel is best expressed in our society is the task. If liberation from oppression leads to the kinds of oppression we see in Eastern Europe, of course, then further liberation, continual revolution, is necessary. My English temperament prefers gradualism yet I long for a clearer programme and strategy into which I can put Gospel energy. Francis demonstrates how "he who does the will of God will know the doctrine" (John 7:17). Ortho-praxis should lead to ortho-doxy, as well as the other way round.

Intuitive knowledge

While in Hong Kong I was also reading about Zen Buddhism and the Taoism which lies behind it. I would exhaustedly put down the barrage of Mao's exhortations and turn to writers who told me to watch the wind on the bamboo leaf and let my pond become so still that it would reflect the moon without distortion. The hill on which I lived was called Tao Fong

Shan. Tao (the way: the mysterious flow in all things); Fong (the wind: reminding me in Christian terms of the Holy Spirit); and Shan (the hill – and what a place holy hills have in all traditions!) I sensed more than ever before the mystery of life in all that is. I discovered myself as part of it, the more so if I let myself go into its rhythms. I came to see that I mustn't force myself on to things, or force them to be what I wanted them to be, but that I must let them be themselves, which was only possible as I came to accept myself. I spent long hours in Zen meditation, and much time too looking at the way things are in the natural world. As I entered into dialogue, letting things come into me and giving myself to them, I discovered a communion greater than either of us. I tried to give myself in every activity in such a way as to lose myself in it. None of these things is easy to describe. I am trying to do so because I think that all of us have some sense of them. Especially aware people, of whom Francis was undoubtedly one, sense it intuitively and live in harmony scarcely noticing it. And I think for many people it is this awareness in Francis which they find appealing.

We get glimpses of it in the way Francis reassured animals[23] and made friends with them, in his affinity with the birds, and with the little things like the earthworms[24] that most people ignore. He has a reverence and respect for things as they are and seems at home in his Father's world. It is his relationship with God whom he knows as Father that enables him to discover all things, inanimate as well as animate, as his brothers and sisters.

There is for all of us a way of knowing which is non-cerebral. Feeling comes before thinking in human development, and talking much later than either. People know far more than they think they know. They may know God under many names or none. More primitive cultures know many things we have lost touch with, among them how to listen to what our bodies are telling us. People in some

cultures listen to the music behind all that is and sing their
song in harmony with it. If we have stopped listening, we act
with a violent independence. Leonardo Boff helps us
discover this reality when he tells of Brother Bonaventure, a
present-day friar in Assisi, and with this quotation from his
Saint Francis: A Model for Human Liberation I conclude.

On one occasion, Brother Bonaventure, the gardener of
the friary at the Portiuncula, climbing Mount Subasio
with a brother from a faraway country, was asked what
Franciscan spirituality is. Brother Bonaventure, a simple
and very spiritual man, in a sweet voice, made more so by
his Umbrian accent, responded: "Franciscan spirituality
is St Francis and who is St Francis? It is enough to utter his
name and everyone knows who he is. St Francis was a man
of God, and because he was a man of God he always lived
what is essential. And so he was simple, courteous and
gentle with everyone, like God in his mercy."

The little old Fiat bounces along the rocky road that
leads to the friary at the Carceri. There below, spread out
and lit by the pleasant autumn sun, is the peaceful valley of
Assisi, like a woven tapestry of houses and farms. Suddenly Brother Bonaventure stops the car and jumps out;
but it is not to contemplate the wide panorama before him,
from the height above the cliffs to the valley below.
Rather, with his Franciscan eyesight, he has discovered
little white flowers among the abundant greenery. "Look
at how beautiful they are!" says the brother, rough but
with a refined spirit, as he leans over them, like someone
leaning over the crib of a newborn child.

The brother from the faraway country discovers some
mulberries, green and ripe, and he tastes them. "Why do
you take the green mulberries, brother?" interrupts
Brother Bonaventure. "Don't you see that they suffer?
Would you cut someone down in the prime of life? Only

when they are older do they offer themselves gladly for our enjoyment."

The descent is as slow as the climb. The small car descends the mountain smoothly. "Why don't we go a bit faster, Brother Bonaventure?" He answers, "There is no reason to abuse the good nature of the car. For eighteen years it has carried me to and fro, and it has always been good to me. Should I not show it some consideration by avoiding rough braking with so many curves?"

Then back at the Portiuncula he shows me his garden, full of vegetables, grapevines, fig trees and many flowers. I also see a disorderly bush, bright green in colour. "Brother Bonaventure, what is that?" He says, with an innocent smile, "They are our sisters the weeds, I let them grow there because they too are daughters of God, and they sing the beauty of God."

It is Sunday, and there is a celebration in the friary because the new Superior of the house begins his term of office. A special wine is served. Brother Bonaventure drinks his wine in silence and with deep respect. He does so as if he was taking part in a ritual of some sort. "What is it, brother?" And he, in almost a whisper, says, "I must honour Brother Wine. I myself made it six years ago and it too is joyful in our joy."

. . . Francis lives and is among us, hidden within each one of us. I saw him born again in the attitudes of Brother Bonaventure.[25]

Chapter 4
Praying

From about the age of eleven it became for me a daily practice (or anyway intention) to read a passage of the Bible each morning or evening, to mull it over inside myself and then to pray. The spontaneous kind of praying, which some prayer groups of the evangelical or charismatic kind foster, no doubt influenced the very personal, "subjective" form my prayers took, but I suppose there were ingredients of adoration, confession, thanksgiving and prayer for others, which we call supplication. Many Christians, of all schools, use the Bible, pray daily, something along these lines, and most would consider this, with weekly Communion, a normal basis for a serious Christian life.

When I was a young subaltern in the Army in Germany in 1948, I discovered a different and supplementing way for morning prayer, namely to use a set-form from the *Book of Common Prayer*. It happened partly because we had no Padre for a time and I was roped in to conduct parade services; partly because, after trying to catch what prayer and reading I could in barrack-room conditions, a room to myself was a privilege, giving new scope; and partly because, feeling rather alone, a sense of "sharing in the prayer of the Church" made the Office valuable. The structure was psalms, introduced by Psalm 95[1] daily, two readings from Scripture, with responsive canticles following them (then it was Te Deum and Benedictus), followed by the Lord's Prayer, petitions and collects. I discovered that the form gave shape to my prayer-time, that it was possible to extend or ponder on any part of it, and that its definiteness and corporateness and enriching language gave continuity and strength. On "good days" the Office was a joy and rapture, on "bad days" something of the good ones was remembered through the familiar words. And when subsequently I came to use Offices with other people – in the college chapel, the parish and now in community – I found that we strengthened each other. Of course, Offices can be so rushed, and so insensitively said, that those who abandon personal prayer-time for them might end up with meagre nourishment indeed. But the new forms of the Office, as in Morning and Evening Prayer,[2] The Alternative Service Book (1980), the Taizé Office[3] and our new SSF Office Book (1981), do give opportunity for disciplined, but reflective, prayer. As in all human skills, freedom can be discovered within form, and I have found greater freedom in praying through liturgical form than from having to find my own words, or adjust to the words of others in the group. For me now the Offices (in our Society we use the new Morning and Evening Prayer from the *Alternative Service Book* and a short midday and night prayer) are the bass drum beating beneath whatever music is playing.

It comes as a surprise to many that Francis and his first followers "said the Office". The surprise is perhaps because he is seen as being so spontaneous and free. This indeed he was, but his commitment to the "prayer of the Church" underpinned the rest and rooted him in the Scriptures. In his time the Office was undergoing change (as today) and (as today) there was pluriformity. He went for the Curia Office, the new breviary followed in the Pope's household, and the friars helped to make this more generally familiar.[4] It comprised seven Offices, one of which was more substantial with Scripture readings and readings from the Fathers. Francis took the Office seriously, composing opening praises to be said before it. They begin:

Holy, holy, holy, Lord God Almighty
Who was and who is and who is to come
Let us praise and glorify him for ever.[5] (Revelation 4:8)

Four further stanzas from the Book of Revelation of St John and one from Daniel follow, with the same response between each (Revelation 4:11; 5:12, 13; 19:5; Daniel 3:57). Adoration, praise and thanksgiving characterize all Franciscan prayer. Christian prayer has long been seen as a sharing in the eternal exchange of love between the Son and the Father and hence the "Glory be to the Father . . ." refrain which occurs so frequently. Christians see themselves incorporated into Christ and in him are offered to the Father. As St Paul says to the Corinthians, "we are indeed the incense offered by Christ to God" (2 Corinthians 2:15). It is the Holy Spirit who brings us into that union and sets free in us the sacrifice of praise and thanksgiving which in our new humanity in Christ, the new Adam, is offered to the one from whom all things come.

One way of entering this ceaseless dialogue of praise is through the words of Jesus in which the Father's name is "hallowed" (Matthew 6:9) and prayer made that his kingdom come and that his will, already done in heaven, may be done on earth. (Those brothers in Francis' time who couldn't read repeated the Lord's Prayer a number of times in place of the Office.)[6] Often a silent entering into union with the prayer which Jesus, while on earth, prayed to his Father in heaven, is made before an Office, in which the words of the "Our Father" may be recalled. There is some evidence that Francis followed this practice and even made a paraphrase of the prayer to focus the mind, but the paraphrase isn't accepted by many as authentically his.[7] The recognition that only in Christ can we come before God is expressed in Chapter 23 of the 1221 Rule in these words:

> We are all poor sinners and unworthy even to mention your name, and so we beg our Lord Jesus Christ, your beloved Son in whom you are well pleased [Matthew 17:5; Mark 1:11], and the Holy Spirit, to give you thanks for everything, as it pleased you and them; there is never anything lacking in him to accomplish your will, and it is through him that you have done so much for us.

If we stand in Christ before God we stand with all redeemed humanity, with the whole Church both in heaven and on earth. So Francis goes on in the same chapter of the Rule to name the company of heaven, asking that in Christ we may join with them in the ceaseless praise and thanksgiving.

> And we beg his glorious mother, blessed Mary, ever virgin, Saints Michael, Gabriel, Raphael, and all the choirs of blessed spirits, seraphim, cherubim, thrones and dominions, principalities and powers; we beg all the choirs of angels and archangels, St John the Baptist, St John the Evangelist, Saints Peter and Paul, all the holy patriarchs, prophets, innocents, apostles, evangelists, disciples, martyrs, confessors, virgins, blessed Elias and Enoch and the other saints, living and dead or still to come, we beg them all most humbly, for love of you, to give thanks to you, the most high, eternal God, living and true, with your Son, our beloved Lord Jesus Christ, and the Holy Spirit, the Comforter, for ever and ever, Amen.

And he goes on to invite all living people to join in the song of the universe.

Today there is a new freedom in the Church which encourages people to make their own liturgy, choosing elements, or at least selecting from alternatives, so as to bring something of their own into the prayer of the whole. Francis likewise composed an Office, not designed to displace the Curial Office, but to be said in addition to it. Though it is called *The Office of the Passion* it has five seasonal variations and an invariable antiphon before the psalms (which are selected verses of many psalms, put together), addressed to blessed Mary. The warm, intimate devotion of Francis to the Mother of the Lord comes out here as elsewhere in his writings. We may note that the ascription, "spouse of the Holy Spirit" (a clear reference to the "overshadowing" in Luke 1:35), is not a phrase previously found in the Western Church.

> Holy Virgin Mary, among all the women of the world there is none like you, you are the daughter and handmaid of the Most High King and Father of heaven, you are the Mother of our most holy Lord Jesus Christ, you are the spouse of the Holy Spirit. Pray for us, with Saint Michael the archangel and all the powers of heaven and all the saints, to your most holy and beloved Son, our Lord and Master.

The similarity to the form of the Angelus (a devotion of the Incarnation kept three times a day at approximately 6 a.m., 12 noon and 6 p.m. in the Western Church) will be noted by those familiar with it.

If further evidence of this delighted intimacy is needed, all agree that *The Salutation of the Blessed Virgin* was written by St Francis.

Some Christians believe that prayer to Mary is to put her in the place of God, and is therefore idolatry. No doubt there have been mistakes and dangerous excesses at times. These are best corrected by understanding what is so clear in the writings quoted above, that it is because we are incorporated into Christ by the Holy Spirit that we stand before God with the whole company of heaven. From that stance, to wave to other members of the Body ("hail") is naturally human and fun. Above all, it is the solidarity of the new humanity in the corporate nature of our redemption, which corrects the distortions of a "me-and-Jesus" individualistic piety. Francis is so deeply united to Jesus our Brother and aware of his human nature given us by the glad co-operation of Mary's humanity, that he rejoices to pray with Mary and to ask her to augment what in his poverty he offers. The theocentric essence of Francis' prayer is shown by his concluding prayer at each Office:

> Let us bless our Lord and God, living and true:
> to him we must attribute all praise, glory, honour,
> blessing, and every good for ever. Amen.

There are many stories of how seriously Francis took the Office – the brothers are to stand and not lean against the wall to say it; Francis on a journey stands in the open air and pouring rain to say it, and so on.[8] It became one of the great debates among his followers as to how far the obligation of the Office made it preferable to live in settled "convents" where a well-ordered routine facilitated the devout recitation. It is clear that Francis saw the world as his friary and never went back on the itinerant vocation described in the Gospels, yet he was committed to considerable prayer of this kind. People vary. In our Society there are those who worship best in larger friaries, where the Office can be sung and regularly shared, while others know their worship to be among the poor or deprived in inner cities or Third World situations, in small houses and cramped conditions, where the Office is said informally and often alone. For any Christian, the form of prayer has to be integrated into the demands of life around. For some there are few possibilities of privacy; for others little or no chance of praying with small groups of other people; for most the ideal is some blend of each.

Prayer exercises, of which the Office is a prime example,

certainly bring the exercitant to points of recollection through the day (and in this sense "sanctify time"), but their aim is to train up the muscles of praise and thanksgiving, which continue behind and within all the other activities of the day. To think of the life of prayer as consisting of such exercises is to mistake the means for the end. One danger of too much formal prayer is the sense of "now that I've got that over, I can get on with . . . " Actually, the "that" is just a focusing and expressing of what is inherent in all. It is not only when they are reciting prayers that human beings are "the priests of nature".

What in the writings of Francis is most obviously central to all Christian prayer and worship is the service variously called by Christians, the "Eucharist", the "Mass", the "Lord's Supper", "Holy Communion".

Most of its ingredients have been mentioned above: it is a Scripture-based service, a service of praise and thanksgiving, a service in which our unworthiness is taken into the worthiness of Christ, a celebration combining heaven and earth and the whole of restored humanity. It concerns the essential union, communion, of men and women with Christ in the blessed Trinity. But there is an additional factor, unique to this service, a factor which Francis highlights in almost all his writings. All other religious exercises are concerned with words, ideas, feelings. This alone involves material things, bread and wine, the stuff of life, the physical focuses of all that is. They are used by God to nourish our being because, intimately received through our mouths, they become part of our bodies. For Francis, God is as tangibly present in the Sacrament as He was in the human body of Jesus on earth.

Here is how he expresses it in the first of his *Admonitions:*

Because God is a spirit he can only be seen in the spirit; it is the spirit that gives life; the flesh profits nothing [John

6:63], but God the Son is equal to the Father and so he too can be seen only in the same way as the Father and the Holy Spirit. That is why all those were condemned who saw our Lord Jesus Christ in his humanity, but did not see or believe in spirit in his divinity, that he was the true Son of God. In the same way now, all those are damned who see the Sacrament of the body of Christ which is consecrated on the altar in the form of bread and wine, by the words of our Lord, in the hands of the priest, and do not see or believe in spirit and in God that this is really the most holy body and blood of our Lord Jesus Christ. It is the Most High himself who has told us "This is my body . . . and blood of the new Covenant" [Mark 14:22–24] and "He who eats and drinks of my blood has life everlasting" [John 6:54].

Leaving aside, till a later chapter, the "condemned" and "damned", there are three other crucial points to notice: the invisible God is made visible in Jesus and in the bread and wine of the Eucharist; he is made present by his words ("This is my body, this is my blood") at the hands of the priest;[9] just as the truth of the incarnation is spiritually perceived, so is the truth of the Eucharist.

All these points Francis makes time and again in practically every one of his writings – in his *Letter to All the Faithful*, his *Letter to All Clerics*, his *Letter to a General Chapter*, his *Letter to All Superiors*, his Rules and his *Testament*. And he goes on to say that he will reverence everything that goes with the Sacrament, primarily the priest (however much he may be careless or sinful[10]), then the altar vessels, ornaments and linens, the place where the Sacrament is housed (and the housing should be glorious), the churches, and everything that relates to it. He speaks too of the fearfulness of any disrespect or violence. He points out (for instance in the *Letter to a General Chapter*) that if Mary is revered who bore him in her womb, and if the tomb where he lay for only a short time is venerated, and if John the Baptist (at the baptism) trembled to touch his sacred head, "how holy and virtuous and worthy should not a priest be: he touches Christ with his own hands, Christ who is to die now no more, but enjoy eternal life and glory, upon whom 'the angels desire to look' [1 Peter 1:12]. A priest receives him into his heart and mouth and offers him to others to be received."

But Francis is moved above all by the humility of our God.

Every day he humbles himself, just as he did when he came from his heavenly throne (Wisdom 18:15) into the Virgin's womb; every day he comes to us and lets us see him in abjection, when he descends from the bosom of the Father into the hands of the priest at the altar. He shows himself to us in this sacred bread, just as he once appeared to his apostles in real flesh. With their own eyes they saw only his flesh, but they believed that he was God, because they contemplated him with the eyes of the spirit. We too, with our own eyes, see only bread and wine, but we must see further and firmly believe that this is his most holy body and blood, living and true. In this way our Lord remains continually with his followers, as he promised, "Behold, I am with you all days, even unto the consummation of the world" [Matthew 28:20].[11]

There is no doubt that Francis was accustomed to daily Mass and frequent Communion,[12] but he warns continually about unworthy, unspiritual reception of the Sacrament, urging true penitence, penance, turning from the "lower nature", from the "mind of the world", from all the vices of the unregenerate heart, into faith in God. He specifically enjoins "we should confess our sins to a priest", in his *Letter to All the Faithful* and elsewhere.

The mention of Eucharist and penance points inevitably to

the Passion of Christ which is central to the teaching and prayer of Francis, as in all Christian theology. Crucial in his spiritual journey was the experience before the crucifix in San Damiano,[13] and he speaks of "going through the world weeping for the suffering of Christ",[14] and of seeing in every tree[15] the sign of God's crucified love. He returns continually to the Good Shepherd who lays down his life for the sheep (John 10:15) – "to save his sheep he endured the agony of the cross",[16] "to redeem us from our captivity, by the blood of his Passion and death".[17]

The sacrifice of Christ on the cross, the joyful self-giving even to death, is indeed at the centre of Christian faith and is, of course, central to the Eucharist. Francis speaks of the *sacrifice* of the Eucharist, for it is by sharing in the action of the Eucharist that our poor response of praise and thanksgiving is taken into the eternal holy exchange of love. That dialogue of praise and thanksgiving, endlessly continuing between the Father and the Son, is (because of the detestable enormities of man's rebellion and sin) expressed in the event of the cross, where it continues despite the terrible weight of mankind's rejection. He who says, "Father forgive them; for they know not what they do" (Luke 23:34), says also, "Father, into thy hands I commit my spirit" (Luke 23:46). Whatever mysterious exchange occurs between these two moments in the story, the effect for believers is the liberation made known in the resurrection (about which Francis says little directly, but which he shows in his profound spirit of joy[18]) and celebrates with praise and thanksgiving in the Eucharist.

In our times the Eucharistic rites among almost all Christians have been reshaped to clarify the celebration in thanksgiving of all God's mighty works, in creation, in Jesus, in the Holy Spirit. Surprisingly, this now-familiar shape of prayer is followed in Chapter 23 of the *Rule of 1221*, part of which is quoted above. With but few adjustments, this could

be a Franciscan Eucharistic prayer; from the rest of his
writings all the other essentials of the Eucharistic prayer
could be completed. And it is worth noticing, too, that
almost never when Francis is writing about the Mass or
priests, does he fail to refer also to the Word – words and the
priest's ministry by word. The recovery of the Word in
relation to the Sacrament is another much welcome feature of
our time.

At Christmas 1223, Francis brought together many of
these Eucharistic insights with characteristic originality and
joy. Celano and the other biographies tell how he arranged
that the Mass should be celebrated at Greccio in a stable with
some beasts and the straw there.[19] Francis (a deacon) sang
the Gospel of the Lord's nativity and recalled the saving
sacrifice of the incarnate Lord, born in a manger, dying on a
cross; the brothers exulted in songs of praise and thanksgiving. No wonder that a great light blazed from that manger
(the origin of the Christmas crib) – it was as if morning had
come.

We move finally to the third mode of Francis' praying, his
prayer in solitude. His early experience of seeking his true
treasure in a cave outside Assisi never left him, and he loved
little, hidden, solitary places, and hermitages.[20] Pilgrims to
Assisi today may find the spirit of Francis more readily in the
Carceri (a series of small caves outside the city where
brothers sometimes lived) than in the Portiuncula at the foot
of the hill, a holy place indeed, now safely enshrined in a
great church.[21] Francis would withdraw to solitary places for
long weeks, intimately alone with the Lord.[22] He encouraged
the brethren to do the same, not least by drawing up a Rule
for *Religious Life in Hermitages*. Four brothers are to take it
in turn, two by two, to be the "Marys"[23] (Mary sat at the feet
of Jesus. He said, "[Mary] has chosen the better portion,
which shall not be taken away from her" – Luke 10: 38–42),

and "Marthas", who look after the others. The Marthas are called "mothers". After a suitable time, "sons" and "mothers" are to change round. There were many such hermitages, especially in the Marches of Ancona, and this aspect of Franciscanism was greatly valued, especially by the "spirituals".

The spirit of ecstasy in the ministry of Francis clearly flourished in these settings, but it remained with him in the activity of preaching, caring and journeying which his life entailed. Celano says:

> He always sought a hidden place where he could adapt not only his soul but also all his members to God. When he suddenly felt himself visited by the Lord in public, lest he be without a cell, he made a cell of his mantle. At times when he did not have a mantle he would cover his face with his sleeve so that he would not disclose the "hidden manna" . . . "the bridegroom's touch" . . . He was absorbed in God . . . filled with flourishing fervour of spirit . . . he would taste the sweetest manna in frequent snatches.[24]

Celano tells how, when alone, Francis would burst out into song, or with sighs share himself intimately with the Lord so that "he not so much prayed as he became himself the prayer".[25] He would weep aloud,[26] repeat a phrase, "God be merciful to me a sinner",[27] or (as when he thought Bernard, his host, was asleep) *"Deus meus et omnia"*, "My God and my all", which he repeated throughout the night.[28] Snatches of psalms, or names of God lovingly repeated,[29] filled him with ecstasy. Caught up in the Holy Spirit, he was set alight from a burning heart into the rapture of adoration. Such prayer got well beyond words, but can be heard in these words of Francis (again from the *Rule of 1221*, Chapter 23):

> With all our hearts and all our souls, all our minds and all our strength, all our power, all our understanding, with

every faculty and every effort, with every affection and all
our emotions, with every good wish and desire, we should
love our Lord our God who has given us and gives us
everything, body and soul and all our life . . . we should
find no pleasure or delight in anything except our Creator,
Redeemer and Saviour, he alone is true God, who is
perfect good, the true and supreme good, and he alone is
good, loving and gentle, kind and understanding; he alone
is holy, just, true and right; he alone is kind, innocent,
pure, and from him, through him, and in him is all pardon,
all grace and all glory for the penitent, the just, the blessed
who rejoice in heaven. Nothing then must keep us back,
nothing separate us from him, nothing come between us
and him. At all times and seasons, in every country and
place, every day and all day, we must have a true and
humble faith, and keep him in our hearts where we must
love, honour, adore, serve, praise and bless, glorify and
acclaim, magnify and thank, the most supreme and eternal
God, Three and One, Father, Son and Holy Spirit,
Creator of all, Saviour of those who believe in him . . .

Here is an expression of an exchange of love which is the
whole secret of the life of Francis. The Spirit of God catches
him up into the mystery of the God who is beyond all, yet
within all that he has made. He is especially in men and
women who give themselves over to ceaseless prayer (1
Thessalonians 5:17)[30] with which the Holy Spirit links them
to God.

Two aspects of this mystical prayer need to be noted. The
first is the approach to the invisible God dwelling in light
inaccessible (1 Timothy 6:16); the second, the God alive in
all that is.

Of the first, "one who knows doesn't speak, one who speaks
doesn't know"[31], yet from all traditions, men and woman
have approached the otherness of God, which is beyond

knowing. Significantly, Francis describes God in a series of negatives: "without beginning or end, unchangeable, invisible, indescribable and ineffable, incomprehensible, unfathomable".[32] We take the shoes off our feet for we know the ground we stand on is holy ground (Exodus 3:5). We can talk *about* it as the *via negativa*, "the apophatic way", the Dionysian[33] tradition in Christian spirituality, or "the cloud of unknowing"[34], or the "dazzling darkness", and, when we have said all, we know we have trespassed beyond our knowledge. The merciful Lord puts his hand over our eyes as he passes in his glory, for "My face you cannot see, for no mortal man may see me and live" (Exodus 33: 18–23). No one has doubted that Francis was in this kind of prayer (and St Bonaventure doesn't hesitate to expound his prayer-life in Dionysian terms[35]), but even if a lot more is said about it, its essential mystery remains.

Finally, however, there is *The Canticle of the Creatures* (sometimes called *The Canticle of Brother Sun*) – the best known of Francis' writings.[36] It points us to God alive in all that is. It is written in Italian and is one of the earliest surviving poems in the vernacular. It was written towards the end of Francis' life, after the summer of 1225 when he was in great spiritual and physical agony, in darkness, nearly blind. It is the praise of God coming from a heart of perfect joy in the midst of crucifixion.

The first section praises God for the basic elements of his world – earth, air, fire and water, together with the sun and moon and stars. There are two special features in this. It is in praise of God not only *for* these things, but *through* (per) them. They are praising; we join in their praise. "The spirit of God fills the whole world" (Wisdom 1:7); the whole world, all that is in it, is caught up in the song of praise. Praise is inherent in all that is, and little Francis gives tongue, catching the spirit of praise in all. Secondly, he finds himself so intimately related to all things in Brother Jesus, that he addresses the praise to the Father, the Most High God, giving relational terms to all things – brother Sun, sister Moon, our mother the Earth, sister Water, brother Fire and so on. The God beyond all is known in all that is, and he is known as personal. The sensitive delight of Francis to all this is evident. He has, for instance, an affinity and fearlessness with animals. Things are not themselves God (pantheism), but he sees God in all things and all things in God (pan-en-theism).

The profound significance of this for the whole theology and way of life of a Christian cannot be underestimated. Christian faith is "this worldly", "material", "earthy", because all is made by God. It is made good by God, to be enjoyed, thankfully received, celebrated, cared for, used responsibly in such a way as to allow its inherent praise to be offered unhindered. No wonder Francis is patron of ecology, as well as many animal-rights groups. No wonder Francis is a Catholic worshipping with material things and delighting in word and form, as well as freedom and spontaneity. No wonder Francis' spirituality is distinguishable from any taint of that part of Manichaeism which calls material things "bad" and spiritual things "good", whether it is the Manichaeism of the sects of his time (Albigensian or Catharist) or any others of days to come, be they Puritan or Jansenist. In our times, at least in many cultures and ideologies, "material" and "spiritual" are separated, so that the "spiritual" is represented as an irrelevant, pious hobby for the few, and the "material" the only concern of the many. Yet matter and spirit, earth and heaven, are one in Christ; their marriage is salvation.

Francis' *Canticle of the Creatures* goes on to recognize human beings' enmity with each other. It is thought that there was a specific quarrel in Assisi between the Mayor and Bishop,[37] which prompted the dying saint's intervention.

The stanzas "Praised be my Lord by those who pardon one another for love of thee" (which were added at that time) bring us to the heart of the Gospel. Men and women find freedom; the barriers melt; the free-flow of praise and love for which they are made is restored. Later Franciscans speculated that God would have become incarnate in creation even if mankind had never sinned.[38] But we have. When we recognize it and accept the grace which God gives us in Christ, our feet are taken out of the "miry clay" and set upon a rock (Psalm 40:2) and he puts a new song on our lips, even "a song of praise to our God" (Psalm 40:3).

The last stanzas of the *Canticle* about physical and spiritual death, and the awful possibility of refusing to join the festival of praise which God invites us to, though prominent in all Francis' writings, must be left till Chapter 8. "Praised be my Lord by our Sister the death of the body from which no one escapes: woe to those who die in mortal sin . . . " It is only by facing the darker truths that we can emerge into fullness of life; Francis never shirked that recognition.

Overall, Francis rejoices in God, despite all that makes most of us draw back, or give up, or react half-heartedly, hedging our bets. And he does so not apart from, but in the midst of life in the material world, in his own body, in the realities of the way things are between people, groups and nations. In it all, with realism and hope, the message of Francis is "praise God".

Chapter 5
Loving

However satisfying, comforting and integrating our times of prayer may seem (and, of course, they sometimes seem anything but that), and however deeply we sense God and feel a response of love move in our whole being, the test of the reality of the exchange will be in how we live. Francis "did not consider himself a friend of Christ unless he loved the souls that Christ loved".[1]

I can remember in my teens returning from a prayer meeting or a worship service in time for Sunday dinner and being thoroughly bad-tempered. It was as though all the beauty and harmony that I knew in prayer was contradicted by how things were around me in the world. And though I felt loved and nourished in prayer and with Christian friends, and though I felt I could give love in response both to God and them, when I got back home it all went – other people were them and I was me, and not a nice me at that. The gap between the vision of a happy world where everyone is a good self and it all works out right, and the everyday world most of us experience, can be very daunting. I always warn people at the end of a spiritual retreat, not to expect things at home and work to be different, but rather to expect a kind of counter-attack from the devil, who will suggest that the blessings of the retreat were an illusion.

Such experiences do make us ask how far we are using prayer as a withdrawal into a place of consolation, away from the hard realities of daily life. No doubt we all need escapes or respites: I suppose religion is at least less harmful than others. The secular humanism of our culture sees religion as a relatively harmless crutch for those who can't manage without it. A sensitive, musical and religious teenager was angrily told by his father that "religion is for the weak". The boy told me that when he was sure he could get into the door of his room and lock it before his father caught hold of him, he shouted from the landing, "It isn't!" When I was talking with a solicitor about a man facing serious charges, he said, "And you think his religion will be a solace to him?" "No," I said, "a strength." It is, in fact, extraordinary what a wide range of personality types, strong and weak, find in the Christian faith both solace and strength. We all need both consolation and challenge. I used to despise the more needy side of myself and try to present only the tougher side, until I came to see that most other people, too, have a soft underbelly, beneath their hard shells and spikes.

Living in community helps us to discover these things. It is easier the more one can get behind other people's hard outer layer and find the real person; this is one of the ways that prayer can help. To pray for someone is to try to see them as God sees them and to love them as he loves them. Not surprisingly, when that happens the relationship with them changes. Prayer can also keep you close to someone even though you are separated from them for long periods. I spent six years in Australia at our friary in Brisbane. Sometimes I would get so deeply into prayer for people I knew in England that when I finished praying I wasn't sure which country I was in, and I find the same true in reverse now. There is a way of loving in prayer which brings you into the depths of things. Sometimes you start with the person, thinking about him, imagining, caring for him, and find that you move through to God. Sometimes you begin with God and it is his love for people that moves you to pray for them.

Finding each other in God is the heart of community life.

Unfortunately, we can be very complicated about how we express the love we discover. English people tend to disguise deep feelings, bringing out love (if at all) upside down in jocular aggression. We were having a general conference of brothers and sisters in which a Japanese brother, whose English wasn't always easy to follow, spoke in our small group about the "crushes" that happen between us. Several of us blinked, swallowed and tried to do our best with his words. As he went on about "crushes", which he said happened just as easily in large houses as small, and so on, it suddenly dawned on me that the "r" and the "l" had got confused and that he was talking about "clashes". We invented a new word, "clushes": strong feelings of affection and strong feelings of aggression come from a common base. It is sometimes because of a genuine, God-given love for another person, about which we are embarrassed or ashamed, that we give them an unfriendly or ambiguous message. Coming to know ourselves and our feelings better is one of the points of being in community. Certainly, growing into giving clearer messages, and the ability to receive the message of others more exactly, is a skill to develop.

When listening to members of communities talking about their life, I sometimes feel an ambiguity, an unreality even. Sometimes they seem to idealize it as though because we all love God so much and love each other, life flows on happily and peacefully (and how strange it seems when visitors tell us that that's how peaceful it feels to them coming in, even when at the time we know ourselves to be at each other's throats!), and sometimes they seem to fall over backwards to destroy the ideal image by saying how horrid community life really is and how heroic we are to tolerate it. In fact, community life is just like all life – marvellous and terrible.

I find in myself a conflict about playing out the range of feelings. Should I show either my anger or my love, or should

I modulate both? In the group, too, how far should the underlying difference of opinion or conflict be brought out into the open? As the chairman of the meeting I often find myself anxious to harmonize and modulate, even at the risk of driving things further underground. I think we have moved away a bit lately from too much confrontation in group meetings. I can remember in the past sometimes feeling that the young liberation-orientated brothers had to see people like me as the oppressors, so that there was something to be liberated from! I can remember, too, very angry rows in our meetings when a great deal of the anger was articulated by me. What does it mean to love in these situations? I have often to ask myself. There can be a façade of love which conceals deep animosity; "love" can be used to manipulate as much as silence, or "humility", rage or spite. Ideally, we act towards another in the way we think most likely to build him up as a person. We seek to cross over from ourselves to him. Francis says we should treat the other as we should like to be treated ourselves (Matthew 7:12).[2] I have found in prayer that I can sit on my prayer stool looking (I imagine) as serene as any buddha, while inside there is a riot of angry, lustful or hurt feelings. I believe one use of praying is to listen to and come to terms with feelings. Once we know them we have more choice in what we do with them.

"True prayer", it has been said, "is to stand before God stripped of my illusions about myself and daring to ask him to strip me of my illusions about him."[3] Community life, as well as prayer, is a place where this can happen.

But if prayer is a stripping, it is also a building up – a place where we learn to let ourselves be loved and where we learn to love. And I believe that this is also part of what community life is for. We can only know ourselves in relationship to others – we are made for love. Just as the God we worship is an interaction of love – not a superhuman being in the sky, but a mystery of being underpinning the inter-relatedness of everything – so we are made in his image and likeness for inter-relationship, the give and take of love. And none of us reaches wholeness until we are wholly at one with each other and with all the world in God. It follows from this that it is in my own interest to help others to grow into their true fullness – though without putting my expectations on to them – for only with them can I be whole. I once said to a brother, "I suppose one of our functions here is to have people in for a re-tread." I felt a bit rebuked by his reply: "As one who has been re-trodden . . . " The old language about breaking people so that they can be re-made is perilous on both counts: both the breaking and re-making are the work of God; we should take the shoes off our feet on such holy ground.

Mention of something being "in my own interest" raises questions about "dying to self", "losing one's life to find it" and "taking up the cross". Clearly there has to be a letting go into the community life and we lose some of our own preferences, accept the limitations of the group's decisions and its lifestyle. This is true of any human and group relationship. I don't imagine it is any easier because in marriage, say, you choose your particular spouse and the children are yours. Nor do I think the group relationships at work or in the sports or recreation club, political party or any enterprise, differ much from group relationships in a religious community. Where I think we differ is that our "family loving" and our "work or activity-group loving" are brought together. Novices fresh from secular jobs tell me that when they had finished work at 5.30, the rest of the day was their own (at home, at the pub, or wherever), but that the friary day doesn't finish at 5.30. The love and work sides of us come together in community (though of course we have friends outside and some of us go out to work). Some hide their loving by "workaholism", others dissipate their application to work by "majoring in relationships". A lot of loving is needed to give oneself to the mind of the group: fortunately it is true that "in losing our life" in this way, "we find it".

But the language of modern psychology about "self-fulfil-ment", "individuation", etc., isn't easy to hold together with the language of Jesus and Francis about "dying to self". The greatest help I have found is from St Bernard of Clairvaux's fourfold stages in loving.

> We love ourselves for ourselves.
> We love God for what he gives us.
> We love God for himself.
> We love ourselves for God's sake.[4]

Dying to self comes through falling in love with God and finding everything and everybody in him. Loving him for his own sake means risking all. As Francis says, "Nothing must be kept back, nothing separate us from him, nothing come between us and him."[5] This is the radical death for which Franciscan poverty ultimately stands. It leads to finding everything, including ourselves, in him. Mother Julian of Norwich says: "God, of your goodness give me yourself for you are sufficient for me." She also says: "God, of your goodness give me yourself, for in you alone have I all."[6]

It's only as we come to love God for himself, willing to lose all, that we can come to love everything in him. That is the place where we find God as the ground of our being, the source of all life (cf. Acts 17:28), purpose and hope, the affirmation of who we are and the freedom to be ourselves with others in his world. This true self is something I can never let the group swallow up, for it is eternal in the heavens (1 Peter 1:4), but, as I am surer of it, I can let down the defences which try to protect it. I can even be reckless in self-giving to others. The principle I experience in my relationship with God – "losing life to find it" – I can experience, too, in my relationship with others.

All this often comes together in discovering how to accept forgiveness. René Voillaume,[7] of the Little Brothers of

Jesus, writes in their magazine *Charitas*:

It is only after having been disgusted, furious, spiteful, repentant, humiliated and forgiven, only after having quarrelled and been reconciled (by Christ and with Christ) that we become truly brothers in Christ.

God calls us into community that we may be stretched in our loving beyond our narrow preferences and cliques, into wider, more open loving, like that of Jesus stretched on the cross. It is at the cross that Piers Plowman says, "Blood brothers we became there and gentlemen each one."[8]

In the lives and writings of St Francis the fruit of prayer expresses itself in love – love of the brothers, of enemies, of lepers, of the poor. Structural, political and other institutional forms of love are less prominent – but are becoming more so today.

The descriptions of the early life of the friars at the Rivo Torto[9] and the Portiuncula in Assisi,[10] have a romantic attraction about them which might suggest that the friars didn't experience these human problems. Certainly Francis always speaks of the brothers with affection and tenderness: for instance, he calls them "my beloved brothers",[11] and there is a reciprocation and gentleness, with an instance of Francis being called "Mother".[12] He loves each brother differently, for himself, showing special affection for Brother Leo.[13] Life was very tough. Food was uncertain and was often the result of going out and begging. Any indulgence or attempt to settle down in comfort, Francis sternly rebuked, more by what he did than by what he said. They slept on the floor, often so close together that Francis marked on a ceiling beam the area for each below.[14] He was also very fierce about any sign of possessiveness,[15] never allowing anything, however simple, to be called his own. Yet tough as it was, there was room for gentleness and concern. The brothers are

told in the Rule to "make their needs known to each other"[16] –
indeed, openness in our vulnerabilities builds community
more than the self-sufficiency which can never receive but
only give help. Francis goes to great trouble for the sick
brother, sharing grapes with one, for instance,[17] and making
a meal for a brother who cries out in the night because of the
hunger pains in his stomach.[18] Francis' personal charism
obviously did much to hold the brothers together. Celano
describes him as a "very kindly person, easy and affable, even
making himself foolish because of it",[19] and "courteous"[20]
and "charming in his manners, serene by nature and affable
in conversation".[21] The *Rule of 1223* says:

> Whenever the friars meet one another, they should show
> that they are members of the same family. And they should
> have no hesitation in making their needs known to one
> another. For if a mother loves and cares for her child in the
> flesh, a friar should certainly love and care for his spiritual
> brothers all the more tenderly. If a friar falls ill, the others
> are bound to look after him, as they would like to be looked
> after themselves.[22]

They are to work hard together, none of them is to claim
ownership of place, they are to welcome "everyone who
comes to them (friend or foe, rogue or robber), everyone
must be welcomed".[23] They are to be spiritually minded
enough to show reverence and honour to one another without
murmuring (1 Peter 4:9). Also, in the *Rule of 1221*, Chapter
7, we get these words:

> They should let it be seen that they are happy in God,
> cheerful and courteous, as is expected of them, and be
> careful not to appear gloomy or depressed like the
> hypocrites.

But, *Admonition* XXI distinguishes joy from flippancy:

Blessed the religious who finds all his joy and happiness in the words and deeds of the Lord and uses them to make people love God gladly. Woe to the religious who amuses himself with silly gossip, trying to make people laugh.

Joy is the fruit of the Spirit listed after love in Galatians 5:22. Like all fruit it comes from the heart rooted in Christ.

Christian fellowship is a unique and recognizable gift of the Holy Spirit. Tertullian (160–225) reports a pagan's comment: "See how these Christians love one another."[24] The recapturing of this fellowship was a goal of many reformers and founders throughout the twelfth century and certainly there was a great flourishing of it in Franciscanism. Fellowship can be stimulated in many ways: often unity and a common task bring it as a by-product, more than when it's worked for as an end in itself. Such fellowship does not mean that personality differences are ironed out into some sort of conformity. Leo, Juniper, Bernard, Masseo, are all delightfully themselves, different but friends. The purity of their love, underpinned by a strict discipline (a brother, for instance, is to be dismissed for fornication[25]), makes them free from the fear of "particular" friendships. Yet for all the idyllic stories of these first days, Francis warns in his *Admonitions* against such things as anger, envy, impatience, speaking evil of others, murmuring, quarrelsomeness, detraction, disputing, boasting, greed, the cares and anxieties of the world. I think that these warnings suggest that the brothers were made of the same stuff as we are. Community life then (as now) wasn't all roses.

Father Leonardo Boff sees in Francis "a model of human liberation". He cites gentleness and care as the two signs of a mature and "free" human being.[26] Using Eros in the sense of elan, vitality, life-force, he shows how, when it is disciplined by Logos – that is, reason, concept, judgement – and held in balance with it, it becomes strong gentleness and purposeful caring. He likens Logos to the wall of a dam which enables the water to build up in such a way as to provide energy for the great turbines. Too easily the old ascetic theologies drove vitality underground and produced a common life, artificial and depersonalizing. On a new psychological understanding, community life is being recreated, and fortunately many of the young come to it with freshness, freedom and hope. Boff sees in Francis the attractiveness of one fully alive and delighting in all that is: a dedicated man who has not lost his humanity. People can identify with his inner vitality and positiveness.

The remarkable friendship of Francis and Clare shows all the delight of lovers who deeply valued each other in the Holy Spirit, with all the restraint of the single-minded who "will one thing" in the service of God and Lady Poverty.[27] How little time they spent together, yet they were never separated. And at crucial points Francis consulted Clare,[28] who, for her part, upheld with inflexible grace the vision and principles that she saw in Francis. Part of maturing is to discover the *animus* and the *anima* in both men and women and to delight in their complementarity. It is a mistake to exaggerate the sexually differentiated roles; anyway, they are partly socially conditioned and almost always biased in favour of men. Sometimes, in communities, "butch" women and "effeminate" men become evident and are ugly or embarrassing (and they have a very heavy burden to bear). But, in fact, strength of purpose and caringness, reason and feeling, objectivity and intuition, are not opposites appropriate only to men or women; they all belong together. Great damage and violence has been done to religious women by past segregations: men have become absurdly inflated, especially when their male dominance has claimed justification from their priesthood. Often, under it all, there has been devastating hollowness. In our times, much freer, more wholesome human relations predominate in communities and, when these are grounded in a deeply affective spirituality, the potential for human loving burgeons. The cost of belonging to community and of its sexual deprival need neither be denied nor made a virtue of. Rather, they can best be undertaken, like all asceticism, in the spirit of Jesus, "who for the joy that was set before him endured the cross, despising the shame" (Hebrews 12:2). There is a choice: either to bemoan the deprival or to celebrate the gift.

Any human group with a common purpose and belief can become a clique. The easiest way to unite a group is, in fact, to find something *against* which everyone can unite – hence the wartime camaraderie. Francis' brothers, on the other hand, were to be open not only to each other and to life, but to the world, to people everywhere; they were also exhorted to love their enemies (Matthew 5:44). Francis goes so far as to say that the person who calumniates you is actually doing you a good turn.[29] Such people should be shown love in a clear and practical way.[30] Francis calls the robbers "Brother Robber" and advises the brethren to take good food to them.[31] If the brothers are well received the first time, perhaps they might gently mention that they hope the robbers won't be violent to their victims. They should go again, with even better food, and gradually perhaps, through such friendship, the robbers will be converted. Boff says that in each brother is a robber and in each robber a brother. Similarly in the story from *The Little Flowers* of the fierce wolf which was terrifying Gubbio: Francis looked into his eyes without fear and, understanding him in his hunger, called him "Brother Wolf"[32] – the wolf was tamed and he licked Francis' hand. Francis looked at the citizens of Gubbio with like compassion and urged them to be penitent for their sins, then their terror and belligerence subsided. So it came about that the citizens looked after the wolf, and the wolf served the citizens.

With the belligerence of most people of Western Christendom towards the dreaded Moorish infidels (against which at intervals popular solidarity and enthusiasm had been exhorted and crusades raised), Francis went, not to fight, but to share his faith.[33] Finding himself before the Sultan, he fearlessly and courteously spoke of the Lord God. Impressed, the Sultan let him go in peace. Indeed, "may the Lord give you peace" was the greeting Francis urged his brothers to use.[34] He pursued the work of reconciling those in dispute, like the citizens of Perugia and Assisi.[35] He went behind the current cause of conflict to the common factors: God is the Father of all, who gives his gifts, sun, rain, etc., to all, irrespective of whether they are deserved; we are all sinners; Jesus loves us and calls us all brothers and sisters.

Knowing himself to be a sinner, Francis was able to avoid the sentimentality which refuses to recognize evil; knowing himself loved enabled him to be forgiving and accepting of others, free from any Pharisaism or superiority; knowing himself a son of the Father enabled him to recognize and love all people as his brothers and sisters in that great new humanity (2 Corinthians 5:17) which Brother Jesus came to inaugurate.

The way for Francis is littleness, poverty and humility. Humility is openness to God, openness to receive the gift he gives. Humility towards other people is a difficult virtue. Uriah Heep doesn't help: any virtue self-consciously acquired is unpleasant.

When I was in the Army, we were once to have a royal inspection. We "bulled" everything up, painting the kerb stones and everything else in sight. We even dug the gardens round our barrack rooms for the first time in over six months. On the afternoon prior to the inspection, the Company Commander remarked to the Sergeant Major that the gardens looked a bit bare. First thing in the morning the

Sergeant Major arrived from the market with boxes of cut daffodils, so that we could have an instant Wordsworthian display of dancing flowers. But, alas, flowers for show without roots don't last in the sun; neither do rootless virtues. Humility is a God-ward attitude before it is man-ward. It is the unconscious virtue of the man who is open and attentive to God. Francis sees humility in the poor. He loved them because of their lack of self-sufficiency, their dependence on the divine providence and their lack of pretence and affectation. They were for him "the little ones", those who knew their need of God, the poor in spirit.

In the New Testament the rich are characterized as self-sufficient, closed to God, preoccupied with themselves and with their worldly concerns. Like Dives they ignore Lazarus at the gate. It was Lazarus, however, who was raised up, Dives who was put down (Luke 16:19–31). The poor, the *anawim* of Scripture are, like Mary of Nazareth, open to God, ready, attentive, willing to co-operate with his will. The kingdom of heaven is theirs – it belongs to the poor in spirit (Matthew 5:3).

Is it the poor in spirit or "the poor" (Luke 6:20) who inherit the kingdom? After all, not all those who are poor in this world's goods are open to God. Grinding poverty saps energy and awareness and, if accompanied by anger (however justifiable), by resentment and bitterness, the ground of the heart must be very hard indeed. Such poverty is certainly an enemy. It has to be combated, together with its evil brothers hunger, disease, exploitation and oppression. The poor Christ has led the assault and won the victory. Our part is to make the victory actual. In the actual poor and powerless ones we see Jesus crucified; in the vision of the poor "standing up" we see Jesus glorified. Those who undertake voluntary poverty believe it will both keep them open to God and also identified with those he came to save. Francis shows us that the poor and the lepers are our brothers, one family with us in Brother Christ. He treats them respectfully, is at their service, is courteous and tender. He tells a friar who implies a slight on a beggar, to go and lie at his feet and beg his pardon.[36] This is true poverty of spirit, openness to God and man, more readily accessible to poor people than to rich.

The way we are with the poor for Christ's sake is as important as the task. St Vincent de Paul (1580–1660) used to say: "To forgive you your gift of bread, the poor must feel your love." It is hard to be always on the receiving end of other people's kindness. My mother, who was chair-bound for fifty years, used to say that she was a target for other people's good works. St Francis identified with the poor as equal, ready to receive from them as friend to friend. He says in the *Testament*: "But when I made friends with them they were a source of great consolation, physical and spiritual." Bishop Helder Camara,[37] the great friend of the poor of South America today, says, "No one is so poor that they cannot give, nor so rich that they cannot receive." The brothers were to wear poor clothes, have no possessions, accept no money, avoid prestigious jobs, give to those who asked, be as near to the poor in their insecurity as possible. Francis wanted to be not only *for* the poor and *with* the poor, but *as* the poor; to be *minores*.[38]

Leonardo Boff, writing from Brazil (where 50 per cent of the resources are owned by 5 per cent of the population) sees in the acquisitiveness of capitalism a focus of great evil. He lists the evils as: work directed towards accumulation, nature seen as something to be exploited, goods as a means of exchange rather than use, knowledge as power, power as dominion by those who control. His vision is of a participatory democracy where the poor are agents of their own liberation, making their own decisions and living their own lifestyle. They are to move from a place of exploitation, and of paternalist pity, to a place where they can forge their own destiny. The Bishops' Conference in South America, both at Medellín in 1968 and at Puebla in 1979, declared the Church's option for the poor. Many Christian leaders (clergy and religious especially) have worked to make the people conscious of their position. They have helped them organize grass-roots groups, in which, gathered around the Word of God, they reflect upon their real situation in life and organize themselves to change it. Many have paid the price which the forces of "law and order" impose: disappearance, imprisonment, torture, death.

Will structural wickedness be best overthrown by violent confrontation or by building up alternative communities? Most Christians are opposed to violence, both the institutionalized violence of the oppressors and the violence of revolutionaries. But not all have the vision and patience of a Gandhi, nor are they in a position to determine the means of change. Moral decisions in the world as it is are nearly always a choice of the lesser evil. Christ did not join the Zealots. He undermined the Establishment of his time by living and teaching what the Law was designed to do – keep people at one with their God. Francis was a man of peace. He showed by his own life the world he believed in. With these examples we have to pick our way. As our world polarizes, those who believe in the middle ground – in government, armament negotiations, economic issues – will be forced to choose. In places where the Church has buttressed the status quo and only preached "law and order", a more confronting role comes as a shock to authorities. The membership and attitudes of such a Church will also change as new challenges disturb old consolations. But I take a tip in all this from Bishop Desmond Tutu who is a Third Order member of our Society. In his book of addresses, *Hope and Suffering*,[39] I see a tough, fearless confidence that God will set his people free, and that the white minority in South Africa cannot withstand God's might for ever. I see no hatred of the white people themselves, but only of their racist practices. "We must love the whites," he says, adding humorously, "whether they like it or not." From his solidarity with the poor he loves the rich: of such, reconcilers are made.

We have looked at how love proceeds from prayer. I sum up with two quotations. The first is from Bishop Frank Weston, a prominent Anglo-Catholic of the 1920s.

> You are Christians . . . Your Lord is one and the same: Jesus on the throne of his glory, Jesus in his Blessed Sacrament, Jesus received into your hearts in Communion, Jesus who is mystically present to you as you pray and with Jesus enshrined in the hearts and bodies of his brothers and sisters . . . Now go out into the highways and hedges and look for Jesus in the ragged and naked, in the oppressed and sweated, in those who have lost hope, and in those who are struggling to make good. Look for Jesus in them; and when you find him, gird yourselves with his towel of fellowship and wash his feet in the person of his brethren.[40]

And finally, Francis wrote (in the spirit of St Paul, who said, "Do not be overcome by evil, but overcome evil with good" (Romans 12:21)):

> Where there is LOVE and WISDOM, there is neither
> fear nor ignorance;
> Where there is PATIENCE and HUMILITY, there is
> neither anger nor annoyance;
> Where there is POVERTY and JOY, there is neither
> cupidity nor avarice;
> Where there is PEACE and CONTEMPLATION,
> there is neither care nor restlessness;
> Where there is the FEAR of GOD, to guard the
> dwelling, there no enemy can enter;
> Where there is MERCY and PRUDENCE, there is
> neither excess nor harshness.[41]

Chapter 6
Obeying

Leonardo Boff explains how Logos needs Eros to give it vitality, and Eros needs Logos to save it from running away with itself.[1] Eros alone he likens to an over-watered seed; Logos alone to a dried-up one. In daily life we hope to find a balance between spontaneity and order. A question prominent in religious communities today is what kind of obedience keeps a person in immature dependence and what kind aids maturity. The same question arises in many different situations and groups, especially in our rapidly changing society.

Changing attitudes to authority and freedom

We live in times when the understanding of authority, in all parts of society, is undergoing change. Of course there is nothing new in that: I'm told that Eve, as she left the garden of Eden, said to Adam, "Darling, don't you see we're living in an age of transition." What is unprecedented today is the speed of change. Whenever I pass the little road bridge between our friary and our school at Hooke, I notice an eighteenth-century iron notice prescribing deportation as the penalty for defacing it. Tolpuddle and its deportations (1834) are only a few miles further on. They remind me of how far our society has moved from authoritarianism and from the heavy penalties of disobedience to a much freer way of life. In Francis' time, too, society was changing – from settled feudalism towards a merchant and capitalist culture. The balance of authority and freedom in all cultures is subtle. Boff sees our world moving from capitalist-dominated culture to a new world where all the people are free participants in working out their own destiny. In this century we have seen such brave visions resisted by strong authorities and then controlled by new authorities just as strong. The Church, looking for the good in the societies around it, seeks to baptise the kingdoms of this world (Revelation 11:15); sometimes Christians hold on to the sacralizing of yesterday's good and are not open to today's.

At a different level, this can be true also in religious communities. Some of our Anglican communities, for instance, founded in the last century, have had great difficulty in distinguishing Gospel values from Victorian ones, finding it hard to break away from the model of the unmarried daughters at home with mother, father being an unfamiliar and awesome visitor. Similar problems are described by Sister Prue Wilson as she traces the changes in the understanding of authority which she has experienced in the last forty years within a large Roman Catholic congregation.[2] What may be a virtue in one context can be an obstacle to growth in another. There is a certain opportunism in the Church's strategy towards the world, and within the Church attitudes vary. Some personalities find this difficult to take, preferring clarity, the cut-and-dried (or at worst "what we've always done"), to the new responsibilities of choice. Others, of course, go overboard the other way. In our world I think it is hard to find what true obedience to God and each other means: we are required to be adults before God.

Obeying God and obeying each other

Francis, in his time, is in no doubt about where true

obedience is to lie. We are to undo the arrogance of Adam by
co-operating with God, accepting the limitations which his
love requires. All lesser obediences are for this greater end:
they are helpful if they enable us to be more open to God,
rejecting what is not his will; they are unhelpful if they
increase our pride. Francis gives individual conscience more
scope than many of his predecessors. He had had to discern
for himself what the Holy Spirit wanted him to do, and he
expected his brothers to do the same. After all, much of their
time would be spent out of reach of their Superiors as they
moved in pairs over the countryside. In a *Letter to Brother
Leo* he says, "In whatever way you think you will best please
our Lord God and follow in his footsteps, and in poverty,
take that way with the Lord God's blessing and my
obedience."[3] And in *Admonition* III: "Any good that he (a
brother) says or does which he knows is not against the will of
his Superior is true obedience." He goes on to give advice for
when conscience and obedience are in conflict:

> If a Superior commands his subject anything that is
> against his conscience, or our way of life, the subject
> should not spurn his authority even though he cannot obey
> him. If anyone persecutes him because of this he should
> love him all the more for God's sake. A religious who
> prefers to suffer persecution rather than be separated from
> his confrères certainly perseveres in true obedience
> because "he lays down his life for his brethren".[4]

The primacy of conscience is fundamental to all moral
theology, for in the end there is no higher authority. Francis
means the conscience to be alive to God, in tune with the
Spirit and instructed in true doctrine. A man who stands in
God need not fear lesser authorities: after all, Christ
submitted to the lesser powers in co-operating with his
Father to overthrow the great powers of evil. So we might
actually gain from submission to authorities as long as it is a

matter of preferences rather than conscience. In the same Admonition, Francis says, "A subject may realize that there are many courses of action that would be better and more profitable to his soul than what his Superior commands. In that case he should make an offering of his own will to God and do his best to carry out what his Superior has enjoined. This is true and loving obedience which is pleasing to God and one's neighbour." He has grounded this attitude in the renunciation of all a man possesses to follow Christ, and in losing his life to save it (Luke 14:33, Matthew 16:25). He says: "A man takes leave of all that he possesses and loses both his body and his life when he gives himself up completely to obedience in the hands of his Superior."[5] Many religious today would find this strong stuff, capable of dangerous, immature misinterpretation by the subject and of exploitation by the authority, but (with the essential safeguard of conscience) it is congruent with what Francis says everywhere about humility.[6] In practice, a Superior who perceived such renunciation in a subject would have to be very careful what he asked him to do.

I prefer people who can articulate their positive and negative response to a proposed course of action, and with whom a conclusion can be genuinely worked out together. Even more, I prefer those who make an initiative rather than wait for a directive, for I was brought up on the dictum "initiative is doing the right thing without being told: obedience is doing it on being told once". But that kind of independence does need to be checked out with another and related to the group; "the right thing" isn't always apparent and acceptable to all concerned. In whatever way it is interpreted, in the end a vow of obedience means that I do what my Minister (when he is acting within the constitution and understandings of our way of life) asks of me. And if I can do this without resentment, without feeling hard done by or martyrish, such a subjection of my own preferences can develop me towards God, to whom alone ultimate obedience belongs. And in love towards my Superior, were he to require such strong discipline of me, I would hope to sympathize with his having to put me in that position. I think love might also require me to say if I did not agree with his judgement in the matter, and to ask if he thought we should take the matter to Chapter or the Bishop Protector; but in the end I would hope, unless it were against my conscience, to do it cheerfully without breaking fellowship with him or the community.

I am glad to say that such an extreme situation is purely hypothetical – necessary perhaps to see what obedience might in the end require, but outside my experience. The nearest I have got to it was going to serve in a house which was not my preference. But then I find myself so divided in my preferences and ambivalent in my choices that any conclusion reached would leave part unsatisfied. I did choose the community; I didn't choose any place I've served in. I have tried to give myself to each with as little projection of my dissatisfaction on to my Superior as I could manage. And I do believe that, through all this, parts of me have developed, and parts of me that can have no place in the kingdom have been revealed and begun to be dealt with. If it all sounds very heavy and difficult, I would have to say that for some temperaments these things are more difficult than for others. Whatever choices one makes in life involve limitations which have to be lived through and used as fully as possible. Fortunately I have never suspected malice or a deliberate attempt to humiliate in what my Superiors have asked. I have almost always thought that what they asked was both in the best interests of the community and just about manageable for me.

The work of the Minister

Francis says much in the Rules about the work of a Minister

and the spirit in which he should do it. He is to receive those who wish to join the Order and explain to them the way of life, check that they are Catholic in thought and practice, that they are free for celibacy, and then advise them to dispossess themselves (but without influencing how, or requiring it of absolute necessity). He clothes them and, after a novice year, professes them in obedience. All this is in Chapter 2 of the 1223 Rule. Thereafter he cares for their material needs, especially in sickness, and prescribes what clothing they need, taking into account place, climate and other circumstances.[7] But his main work is their spiritual care: there is warning about his accountability for them to God. He is to visit, encourage, admonish them and correct them humbly and charitably.[8] He is to be ready to forgive the brother again and again if only he will look him in the eyes.[9] He is not to be angry or upset if they fall into sin, for these attitudes make it difficult to be charitable.[10] Ministers are to receive those who come to them because unable "to observe the Rule spiritually" with kindly charity and sympathy (as they would wish to be received themselves), so that the friars can speak and deal with them "as with their servants". "This is the way it ought to be; Ministers should be the servants of all the friars."[11]

Francis here highlights the curious ambiguity in the word "Minister". The man in charge is the servant. Jesus taught that clearly when he washed his disciples' feet at the Last Supper and said, "If I, your Lord and Master, have washed your feet, you also ought to wash one another's feet . . . I give you a new commandment: love one another; as I have loved you . . . " (John 13:14,34). Francis is very clear that the brothers should not seek power nor hang on to it, and when they have it they should put it at the service of the brothers.[12]

The working out of this at all levels of community is very much the stuff of daily life and, of course, what we do in "micro", men and women in all kinds of groups do too,

sometimes in "macro" in industry, government and international relations. The word "Minister" is used for heads of
government. In his 1221 Rule, Francis gave conditions for
the deposing of a Minister;[13] in both Rules the Minister is
subject to the Minister General and required to attend
Chapter meetings.[14]

Both in Church and State (and in micro and macro),
power easily corrupts and authority is misused. It is very
much a current political question under what circumstances
a government should be deposed or resisted and what form
such resistance should take. Ways by which power can be
better shared is also high on some agendas. In religious
communities, too, decision-making is increasingly a corporate matter – our community, for instance, is governed at
every level by an elected leader and a group, and some
smaller houses prefer not to have a named leader at all.

Obedience to the group, and the task of its leader

Perhaps the biggest change in community life in our times is
this heightened emphasis on the group. The religious life has
its origins in the solitary eremitical life where an individual
went out from the ordinary world to seek God. Community,
or coenobitical life, developed around a spiritual teacher as
training for this. The tension between the individual and
corporate search for God remains. Some people are naturally
more "clubable" and for them the daily routine about times
of getting up, going to meals and chapel and spending time
with others, is easily accepted. Others function better with a
more individual, idiorhythmic style. Some find too much
sharing in decisions about daily life a distraction from their
work of prayer and can fit into such secondary matters with
comparative indifference; others work hard at the push and
pull of getting a situation right.

Some are happier in smaller houses, others in larger. Some value stronger, clear authority, others find this irksome. Some find God more readily in solitary prayer, others in liturgical, and so on. But each group has to establish its own norms, as suitable as possible to the range of individuals and faithful to the tasks and visions of the congregation and of the particular house. These norms can easily become absolutes, and new people coming to the group have to accept them, or try to change them, or both. Ideally the situation is kept open enough for change to happen gradually and without great upheaval. The group has to keep together God's calling, the charism of the foundation (with its Principles and Statutes) and the guidance of the Spirit now.

The place of discernment and leadership is crucial in all this. Francis says that the Minister General of the Order is the Holy Spirit.[15] But how is the Holy Spirit's will discerned? A charismatic leader like Francis seems to know it intuitively in a way that his followers can accept. Without such a leader (and groups, anyway, are wise to keep a sharp eye on people who make such a claim), the group itself must confer and seek together and try to come to a common mind. The early Chapters (held, significantly, at Pentecost, the celebration of the coming of the Spirit) were that sort of conferring, more for spiritual sharing than for legislation, a time for building one another up in the life to which they were called.[16]

When every member has opportunity to participate in such sharing it is easier for all to accept obedience to the group decisions. Research has shown that time spent in groups discussing a task (and it can seem a very extravagant use of time) actually speeds the task, for everyone is able to give themselves freely to carrying out what has been agreed. If one objects that surely the nature of the task must determine the time taken deciding it, one is brought into questions of what life is really about – achievement, efficiency, creation of wealth, relationships, or what? Not finding answers, weariness, or the sense that my opinion won't make any difference anyway, or that all this is beyond me, can make us capitulate to the "thems" with strong authority, preferring to complain rather than take responsibility for change.

Christian leadership, ideally, has the task of enabling the group to exercise its responsibility towards the life and task of the kingdom. Life in the kingdom is about loving each other in the Spirit: if we seek to spread the kingdom to others it must be in that Spirit that we do it. But the pressures and contradictions of the world alienated from God (and, alas, that world is still inside us) incline us to over-strive, to force, to impose, to damage, not letting each person and thing be its true self in relation to the whole. Christian leaders confront the group with its ideal and goal in a way which enables the members to amend and gain new power and hope; example and encouragement are prime means to this end. Another function of leadership is to relate a small group to a larger, by representing it at the larger meetings (as the Order grew, the Ministers represented their province at the Pentecost Chapter) and representing the larger meeting (and its decisions) to the smaller.

The place and form of a Rule

One way the authority questions in the early Franciscan movement surfaced was concerning the Rule. Francis was a bit caught. On the one hand he always argued for the spirit not the letter.[17] On the other, he had to remain faithful to what God had given him. His simple obedience to Gospel words had a cutting edge and he disliked glosses and ways round things. The fiercest expression of this is in the *Testament*: "In virtue of obedience I strictly forbid any of

my friars, Clares, or lay-brothers to interpret the Rule or
these words saying, 'This is what they mean.' God inspired
me to write the Rule and these words plainly and simply and
to live by them doing good to the last."[18] The difficulty comes
from writing down the ideal and making it law in the sense of
an enforceable code of practice. Perhaps this is why Francis
was originally against any other Rule than the Gospel, for the
imperatives of the Sermon on the Mount could never be the
law-code of the Church.

In our Society we distinguish the Principles from the Rule
of Life and from the Constitution, Statutes and Customaries.
The Principles seek to enshrine the spiritual ideals of our
community charism and they remain to us a constant
challenge; the Rule of Life prescribes our commitment to
specific acts of prayer and practice which we normally expect
to live by each day; the Constitution spells out the
government and procedures for election, the noviciate, the
taking of vows, leave of absence, release, ecclesiastical
allegiance – things common to the whole Society; the
Statutes apply to provinces and the Customaries to houses.
At profession, therefore, a brother or sister makes a vow of
obedience:

> I . . . . do hereby dedicate myself for my whole life,
> in company with the brothers and sisters of the First Order
> of the Society of St Francis, to the service of our Lord
> Jesus Christ, to follow him under the conditions of
> poverty, chastity and obedience in the way of blessed
> Francis; and I promise and vow in the presence of
> Almighty God that I will live according to the Rule of this
> community, God being my helper.

Obedience, then, is to the service of our Lord Jesus Christ in
the way of blessed Francis according to the Rule (Principles,
Rule of Life, Constitutions, etc.), and the daily experiencing
of life together.

Obedience as yielding in love

Some of the harsh, repressive overtones of obedience – which have, unfortunately, been ground deeply into some personalities – need the sweetening and liberating power of love. In *The Praises of the Virtues*, Francis writes:

> Lady Holy Love, God keep you
> with your Sister, holy Obedience.

Love is the creative exchange between people; obedience regulates and shapes its expression. Just as love is essentially mutual, so is obedience, and both are based on trust. There is joy in yielding. The relief of trusting, of the letting go, complements the striving and controlling. Looking at this more widely than in the context of a religious community, we can discover it when absorbed in work, or in sport, or in music, or in making love, or in the contentment of being with someone we love. Rather than "putting us down" these experiences build us up; rather than robbing us of our identity they make us more "us". It is as though what we anxiously strive to maintain as essential to our identity, maintains itself when we let go towards another, or the wider world. At the deepest part of all of us there is that which can only be itself when it lets go beyond itself. So, in relation with God we become ourselves. He does not destroy what he has made but gently enables it to be itself. The union of our spirit with his, or rather his with ours, is life itself. Letting go into that reality relieves us, renews us, reinvigorates us, excites us, equips us with energy for whatever the task. The difficulty we find in calling that yielding "obedience" shows how far we have misunderstood obedience. We hate it through fear, misunderstanding the God who invites us to it (1 John 4:18–19).

Learning again how to yield can come through many experiences. What we learn with people can show us what we can know with God. Knowing it with him, we shall learn it better with others – a partner, a family, a community. Rightly related to them, the yielding and the receiving happen as simply as breathing. Difficulties can be used to move us towards right relationships, back to the discovery of the unhealed in ourselves, which, coming to the light, we can let God heal. Moving through being forgiven and forgiving, we move towards wholeness and in our wholeness with God we can discover the wholeness of others and of the world and our true relatedness to all.

Is this what Francis knew?

The renouncing of everything to be a disciple of Christ is possible in the confidence that Christ, who gives us all that we possess, does not wish to waste it. The life I want to save I must lose, because to try to save it apart from Christ (through not trusting him) is already to lose it, for my "life is hid with Christ in God" (Colossians 3:3). Giving myself to the Superior's will, going along with a group decision, knowing that others may indeed be more right than I am, these experiences and the enduring that may follow them train my "give-and-take muscles" which can keep me open to God. It might actually be a relief to me, as well as to everyone else, if I sometimes move out of the driving seat and surrender the controls. Such passivity quenches my false individualism to make me more aware of myself as part of the Body of Christ, and I can come to delight in what God does through someone else as much or more than in what he does in me.[19] And it is only as I grow in the skills of yielding to others that I'm safe in allowing others to yield to me.

Getting with the flow of things

Some people, of whom Francis was one, have a well-developed intuition about the way things are in the natural world and are able to bring themselves with apparent ease into co-operation with it. Others find it more difficult. Can the skill be developed? I believe that reflectiveness and the silence of prayer is one way. Francis loved solitude.[20]

Our Sisters of St Clare spend much of their day in silence. They rarely go beyond the enclosure of house, chapel and gardens, and work hard in a variety of activities. Though they read (including the newspapers) and receive letters from many parts of the world, much of their data about life comes from their life together. I find them acute, perceptive of what matters and, curiously, more in touch with the real issues than most people I meet elsewhere. Part of the explanation is that in their prayer they listen and pay attention to God; part, certainly, is the silence which lets them listen through the day to what the news, or the liturgy, or their reading, or the garden, or the chickens, or the printing press, or the paintbrush, or the rising dough, or their bodies, or the sun, or their sister, is telling them. They listen with uncluttered minds; that listening is a form of obedience. It rebukes our self-importance which easily falls into creating a world which revolves around ourselves; it corrects our desire to fit other people into our constructs. Perhaps our forefathers, who were closer to the soil and far less mobile, knew these things better than we do. In a quieter world, perhaps, they listened more. But of course a lot of the noise comes from inside us and we may fear silence in case we hear it.

I have come to see that listening to "the sound of silence" within myself and, as far as I can, around me, enables me to live better with others and to be more creative. Lowering the anxiety level can help me to let go co-operatively. I am not very good at a lot of the practical jobs which make up our life (and we hope never to employ others to do them). The brothers tell me I am a disaster in the kitchen, not because I can't usually (just about) manage to produce a meal, but because the anxiety and panic while I do it make me unbearable to be with. Cooking requires knowledge of how things work – how to ensure that the custard doesn't go lumpy, for instance – and the confidence to let ingredients work according to their own principles. I can impose unreasonable, unscientific anxiety-based demands. Again, in the garden (where, alas, I am not much better) there is much to learn about soil, seed, plant, water, about when to intervene and when to let be; disobedience, or disregard of these principles prevents or destroys growth. When I was in Australia we looked after a small herd of Friesian cows. I was terrified and showed it by shouting and shoving. But one day, someone who knew better showed me what to do and gradually I began to make signs that the beasts understood. When I came back to England I discovered that my friend's animals would come when he called them, that they rubbed against him and licked him. They served and loved each other because he understood and loved them and was obedient to the way things are for them. "Obedience", says Francis, "subjects a man to everyone on earth. And not only to men but to all beasts as well as to wild animals. So that they can do what they like with them as God allows them."[21]

This attitude in Francis of obeying the principles of creation is greatly appealing to people today, perhaps because we recognize how out of touch with it we are. Francis applies this to all relationships with people – letting them be themselves, learning how to fit in with them, to contribute to their endeavour, to become part of them without dominating. If a friar works in a household he is not to allow himself to be in charge, especially not of the money or the cellar![22] Franciscan humility is to be at one with all, taking the lesser place. Francis found all relationships within the relatedness to God – everything was brother and sister to him because there was one Father of all.

Letting go into this obedience is the inner secret of every human skill and achievement, whether God is named or known or not. In various ways we recognize that there is that beyond our effort. Struggling with the scales on the piano, loosening the fingers, developing the touch, learning to read the notes, playing a piece of music over and over – will it ever come? – then one day, perhaps, we don't only "play" the piano, we "make music". Struggling with the human voice and the whole personality that comes through it, so that it is relaxed in a way that allows all its strength to come out with control, seems to require even more of a person, but still it happens beyond our own efforts – in fact, to try too hard is one of the biggest obstacles, maddening though that is. Or again, coping with the massive amounts of data necessary these days for research projects can bring the student to the depth of despair and to feelings of worthlessness. On a lesser scale, preparing a sermon can feel the same. But there is also the hunch, the lucky find, the missing bit, and hopefully the *Gestalt* of it all coming together. A lot of work has to go on before the spark leaps across the gap and it "happens". In human loving too, the married couple can't force each other to be "turned on" and delightedly and ecstatically to be taken beyond themselves. There are things to learn but, in the end, it either happens or it doesn't; sometimes it happens unexpectedly after lots of frustrating trying.

I was talking to an artist about painting. Her master was rigorous about seeing the subject accurately and thoroughly mastering its dimensions, proportions, spatial relationships and the rest. He required, too, flawless technique, mastery of the materials and absolutely the right tools. But in none of these things did the painting's truth reside, however hard to achieve they were – it came with its own self-authenticating reality.

The principle behind all this came to me when I was in Hong Kong as I read a book by Eugen Herrigel, *Zen in the Art of Archery*.[23] He tells how he went as professor to Sophia University in Tokyo and wanted to take up archery as a hobby. He looked for a Zen teacher but found them reluctant saying, "You academics want more to know about a thing than to do it." However, he was eventually lucky. He found his teacher as silent as he was relentless – he would only demonstrate and tell his pupil to practise. When the teacher did it, the bow seemed to dance into the firing position with its string taut but with no tautness in any of the teacher's muscles. When the professor did it, however, jerks and tugs continued for many months. But that was only the beginning: the letting go of the arrow was to be far more difficult. First it whizzed way over the target, then it plopped down only a few yards ahead; yet for the Master it flew directly, without apparent effort, straight to the target's centre. A holiday with his wife was ruined in the professor's desperation to master the art; a crafty method he devised caused the Master to turn on his heel in disgust and only very reluctantly agree to take on his pupil again. Sheer cussedness alone kept him at it, though he got to the point of thinking that he didn't care if he ever fired the thing, or if he ever saw a bow and arrow again. In desperation he asked the Master for a word. "The right shot at the right moment", his teacher said, "does not come because you do not let go of yourself. You do not wait for fulfilment but brace yourself for failure. So long as that is so you have no choice but to call forth something of yourself that ought to happen independently of you, and so long as you call it forth your hand will not open in the right way – like the hand of a child: it does not burst open like the skin of ripe fruit."[24] But one day it did! The professor whooped; the Master bowed gravely; it had happened. The professor had mastered the art of archery; or should we not rather say that it had mastered him. There is an obedience in realizing that we can't order things: our application is part of what it takes; another part is pure gift.

Freedom within a Rule

A friend of mine, who is a sculptress, had a phase of making beautiful sensuous figures and suspending them in metal frames so that they swung. She had discovered a framework for her own life – the rediscovery of her Christian faith and the value of form and rule in worship and personal discipline. The acceptance of limits can be a freeing thing: within them we can swing.

Francis, in his *Letter to All the Faithful*, called on people of all sorts to bring themselves under the rule of God. Addressing them as their servant he says: "To all Christians, religious, clerics and layfolk, men and women: to everyone in the whole world." He spells out what God has done for them in Christ and what their response should be. He plays on a wider keyboard the same tune he played to his brothers and incidentally says, "Religious especially are bound to make greater efforts, without neglecting the duties of ordinary Christians, because they have left the world." "Ordinary Christians" have often been demoted to "second-class" by clergy and religious and by elite groups of the "spiritually enlightened". But "ordinary Christians" are the great majority and Francis longs that they, together with all men and women, and all creatures, should give to God "praise, glory, honour and blessing". Indeed, that desire bursts forth in the *Rule of 1221*: he begs and implores everyone to persevere in the true faith and in the life of penance. Following the list of clerics he says:

We beg all children, big and small, the poor and the needy, kings and princes, labourers and farmers, servants and masters; we beg all virgins and all other women, married or unmarried; we beg all layfolk, men and women, infant and adolescents, young and old, the healthy, the sick, the little and the great, all peoples, tribes, families and

languages, all nations and all men everywhere, present and
to come; we Friars Minor beg them to persevere in the true
faith and in a life of penance.[25]

For those from all this range of humankind who felt
particularly drawn to the Franciscan way, but not to the First
or Second Order, Francis founded an "Order of Penance",
the Third Order, often now called Secular Franciscans.
They live out their Christian discipleship with a Franciscan
inspiration under obedience to their Rule of Life, drawn up
with and monitored by their spiritual director, who seeks to
coach them and encourage them towards God. In our
Society, the Third Order continues to grow, calling men and
women of very different social status and responsibility and
from many parts of the world. They live a Gospel way amidst
the everyday decisions, making subtle discernments and
costly sacrifices. Our Principle bids those in the First Order
to remember "how much greater often are the sacrifices and
difficulties of those engaged in the ordinary professions of life
and how much more nobly they face them." Many tertiaries
have found the strength which comes from binding themselves together in the love of a common Franciscan commitment. They draw inspiration from meeting together and
from their magazine and intercessions.

Each individual, taking into consideration all his obliga-
tions, has to decide about where, when and how he is going to
pray, and what other disciplines, like stewardship of his
money and time, fasting, reading, service of others, he will
take on himself as a Rule of Life. I always counsel tertiaries
and others drawing up a Rule to make it less than their
current norm, lest their guilt in not keeping it brings them
into bondage to the law. The Rule should be a frame to swing
in. A "soul friend" or "a spiritual director" can be useful in
helping me discern what the Holy Spirit is indicating, both
about the swinging and the frame. There is a particular kind

of commitment and obedience in such relationships. It is not about subservience, servile dependence and the refusal to take responsibility for myself. It is about the acceptance of who I am in God, the recognition that it is his life in me and in all things, and that he has a place for me as a son within it. As I grow in all this, I grow into my proper place within the whole redeemed humanity and redeemed creation, finding my true place within the relationships and groups of which I am part. My spiritual director (guide or soul friend) is a gift to me now for this part of the journey to wholeness, and together we listen to the voice saying, "This is the way, walk ye in it" (Isaiah 30:21).

The search for close Christian fellowship

The Franciscan Third Order is but one manifestation of a need (very obvious in our times) to belong in deep relationship within human groups. Perhaps it is because of the smaller family units and because the extended family rarely lives round the corner. Perhaps, for Christians, it is also the pressure of unbelief and apathy in the world. But the result is that Christians in all traditions are seeking closer fellowship than anonymous churchgoing or the superficial camaraderie after a Sunday service. Housegroups for study and prayer meet the needs of some; some find their way into house churches in which the Word is heard and the Eucharist celebrated and the participants pledge themselves to share goods and time in continued fellowship. Others live together in communities of families and individuals with a whole range of norms, as David Clark illustrates.[26]

In other parts of the world, notably South America, groups called "basic" or "grass roots" are an integral part of the Church of the People. They exist within the framework of the institutional Church and include some Bishops, clergy and religious, but they are lay-orientated and more radical than most established Christian groups. They gather round the Word of God, seeking to understand it and to apply it to their situation and society. They care for each other and work towards a common mind about action. Their members expect to be agents of change in society. Some see such groups as the Church which is to come – not only in South America, but everywhere – believing that the old Christendom concepts which followed from the conversion of the Emperor Constantine (306–337) have run their course, and some would say "not before time". For others, such groups are subversive and threatening, divisive of the unity of the Church and damaging to the proper witness of the Church in society. In this contemporary debate questions of vision, dogma, authority, power, obedience, hope, initiative, relationship with the world, spiritual insight, are raised in critical and often very painful forms. Out of such debate the coming Church will emerge; its form will be greatly influenced both by what it borrows from the society around it and by what it chooses to confront and oppose in the name of Christ.

In Francis' time the Church was reformed and organized under Innocent III in the heyday of its temporal power. Groups striving for Gospel or New Testament perfection easily come to see themselves as "real Christians", the wheat in a field of darnel (Matthew 13:24–30). The decision to break away and form "pure Churches" some take in conscience, with all the risk of spiritual pride and disproportionate doctrinal emphases which heresy implies. Such groups often live the Gospel with a simplicity of intention and with heroism and fidelity. They show the truth and power of Christ and fellowship in the Holy Spirit. They claim truth in their action (ortho-praxis) which Christ taught as much as right understanding of truth (orthodoxy). There is a truth in love as well as a love of truth.

Francis gathered such a "renewal group" around him, but kept it firmly within the Catholic Church. Though he lived a radical Christian life, following the Gospel, he pledged his allegiance to the Pope and his successors, as the brothers pleged their allegiance to him.[27] The "grass roots" and the hierarchical, the Gospel and the institutional Church were not separated.

The greater Church

Many Roman Catholics ask how we can call ourselves Franciscans if we do not accept the Pope. We could answer that Francis lived in an undivided Western Church (and he says nothing of the Eastern Church which he must have met in the Holy Land) whereas we live in a more divided Christendom. We are pledged within our Anglican Communion to work for the unity which Christ wills and which belongs to the fullness and perfection of the Church. Like many Anglicans we see ourselves as in continuity with the historic tradition; many of us stand with the Orthodox against the distortion of the nature of the Church which the developed Papacy represents. Anglican Reformation insights, like vernacular liturgy, the Scriptures available to the laity, frequent Communion in both kinds, the place of the Bishops, have now been implemented in Churches of the Roman obedience. Some more modern developments, like synodical government which includes the laity, begin to develop there too. And in relation to truth, the Anglican experience of comprehensiveness by which a variety of opinion about the Christian mysteries can be held together within the fellowship of love, is highly prized. The desire not to confine Christian truth within one philosophical framework but to go on interpreting it as far as possible through the prevailing thought-forms of our times, all remain valuable attitudes despite the range of diversity which sometimes disquiets and confuses the faithful. In matters of moral judgement, too, Anglicans prefer authority to say less rather than more, and are not impressed by detailed authoritative pronouncements on current issues which, though claiming to be binding on all the faithful, are in fact widely ignored. The confusing of moral guidance, law and the politics of ecclesiastical authority remain a difficulty.

Anglican Franciscans (who, of course, don't claim continuity with the original foundation or to be following the *Rule of 1223*) come from a variety of traditions within our Communion. All our provinces have a Bishop as Protector and we serve on synods and other organizations of the formal Church. We vary greatly about how much churchly questions and structures concern us and also vary about how much attention we give to the work of bringing Christians back into the unity of the one Body. For instance, some of us would accept the universal authority of the Pope and try to follow his guidance exactly, looking for the corporate union to come; others look for corporate reunion but only following changes in the way that the Papacy works in the Church. We vary; but one good thing about being Anglican is that we could never think we were the only Church or the model of the whole of redeemed humanity! Catholicity of doctrine and order we do believe we have in all its essentials. Few of us could expect Anglicanism to have an indefinite future – it was Archbishop Michael Ramsey who said, "The Church that lives to itself, dies by itself" – but many of us believe that the Anglican experience and tradition has its own contribution to bring to the whole Catholic Church. As Franciscans, we point beyond our own Communion and many of us are deeply committed to the negotiations which we hope will follow from the new Anglican Roman Catholic International Commission (ARCIC 2) which hopes to find proximate steps towards reunion based on the "sufficient convergence" which

Anglicans find in the doctrinal statements of ARCIC 1. Most Anglicans think that more work has to be done on such questions as authority, the place of the Bishop of Rome in the economy of God, the collegiality of Bishops, and the place of the laity in the Church. We take heart at the dramatic changes of our century and while believing in the one Holy Catholic and Apostolic Church, recognize that sin has damaged it (just as it has damaged the "new man in Christ" we know ourselves to be by baptism – 2 Corinthians 5:17; Ephesians 4:24). As we experience the Church, then, it is not perfectly *holy*, nor fully *catholic* (in embracing all mankind). It is imperfectly *apostolic* (both in the quality of its lifestyle and its zeal to share the faith) and so regrettably is not manifestly *one*.

Would Francis have found our position strange? For him, Jesus was the life of God incarnate on earth (though not all men recognized him), the Eucharist is his life incarnate now (to the eye of faith), and the Church and its priests should be reverenced and obeyed for they bring us the Eucharist and Word of life, and so (by implication) are an extension of the incarnation. All that most of us would accept, but we look for Christ incarnate in the pluriformity of both ecclesial bodies and persons. Christ longs to bring all into unity in the truth.

Ecumenical dialogue and the sheer hard work which has involved so many theologians, leaders and ordinary Christians in this century, are the attempt to find a way back from the sin and scandal of division into what obedience to the truth of Christ means in our present divided situation. Some – especially the young and many charismatics – feel it a waste of time. "If only we received Holy Communion from each other," they say, "the rest would follow." I even heard Church unity likened to "an arranged marriage between senior citizens". I don't believe there are shortcuts. But changes in the wider human scene may make our ecclesiastical concerns look quite different. Clearly new obediences await us.

As well as trying to see the inner dynamic of obedience and its relation to life together, in the wider world and in relation to God, a great variety of obedient responses have been noted – in marriage, in political life, in religious communities (active and enclosed), in the Third Order and other basic groups, with spiritual directors and in the wider Church. As the Zen Master said, "Life would be simple were it not for picking and choosing." And the underlying choice for all is whether we are going God's way, co-operating, yielding to him by whatever name or none we know him, or whether we choose independence in a world of our own constructing. I believe that getting ourselves right with God opens the way for discovering the inner harmony and congruence and unity of all that is, and the significance of each part of it. Francis, I believe, discovered more about all this than most human beings have. From higher up the mountain of glad obedience he beckons us on.

Chapter 7
Telling

The core of spiritual obedience is willing co-operation. All mankind is created to offer it back to God. Francis is so filled with the song of praise and thanksgiving in the Holy Spirit that he hears it everywhere and longs that none should withhold their share in it. In his exhortation in the *Rule of 1221*, he calls on all kinds of people, lay and clerical, to hold nothing back from God, but with all their being "to love, honour, adore, serve, praise, bless, glorify and acclaim, magnify and thank, the Most High Supreme and Eternal God, Three in One, Father, Son and Holy Spirit, Creator of all and Saviour of all who believe in him, who hope in him and who love him . . . "[1] He has a vision of everything thanking and praising God and he begs everyone and everything to join in. Thanksgiving and self-giving go together.

One of the ways of bringing people to do this was by preaching. The brothers were apostolic men, sent out to preach the kingdom; the preaching was simple, fervent. Celano says:

Francis began to preach penance to all with great fervour of spirit and joy of mind, edifying his hearers with his simple words and his greatness of heart. His words were like a burning fire, penetrating the inmost reaches of the heart, and it filled the minds of all the hearers with admiration . . . In all his preaching, before he proposed the Word of God to those gathered about, he first prayed for peace for them, saying "The Lord give you peace".[2]

But the peace Francis preached was no easy peace. He carried so strong a conviction of God's goodness and love that he was able to point out fearlessly all that impeded or damaged that love. Celano continues:

> . . . preaching peace, teaching salvation and penance unto the remission of sins, not in persuasive words of human wisdom, but with the learning and power of the Spirit. He acted boldly in all things because of the apostolic authority granted to him, using no words of flattering or seductive blandishments. He did not know how to make light of the faults of others, but he knew well how to cut them out; neither did he encourage the life of sinners, but he struck hard at them with sharp reproof, for he had first convinced himself, by practising himself what he wished to persuade others to do by his words; and fearing not the censurer, he spoke the truth boldly.[3]

Francis preached the peace which comes from sins forgiven. Time and again in his writings he recognizes that all goodness comes from God and that all of us in ourselves are spoilt, sinners in need of God's mercy. Accepting that so deeply in himself, he was able simply to share it. He loved people in the spirit of the Christ who loved them and died for them: "He preached peace to you who were far off and peace to those who were near" (Ephesians 2:17).

His words carried weight: they changed people. Francis came as a bright light into the profound darkness of people's sins and forgetfulness of God; he moved them to bring their sins to its light. And so says Celano: "In a short time the face of the region was changed and it took on a more cheerful aspect everywhere, once the former foulness had been laid aside." Even the crops and the vines burgeoned![4] "Thanksgiving and the voice of praise resounded everywhere so that many put aside worldly cares and gained knowledge of themselves from the life and teaching of the most blessed Francis and they longed to attain love and reverence for their Creator."[5]

There is an attraction in holiness. Preaching in the power of the Holy Spirit does convict of sin: it leads people to the joy of new life in Christ. In the authority and spontaneity of Francis' sermons, we see the signs of the Spirit.

> When he so very often preached the Word of God to thousands of people, he was as sure of himself as though he were speaking with a familiar companion. He looked upon the greatest multitude of people as one person and he preached to one as he would to a multitude . . . without thinking about it beforehand, he spoke wonderful things to all . . . [sometimes] without embarrassment he would confess to the people that he had thought of many things, but could remember nothing at all of them; and suddenly he would be filled with such great eloquence that he would move the souls of the hearers to admiration.[6]

Indeed, he got quite carried away in the Spirit at times.

> . . . indeed, he spoke with such great fervour of spirit that, not being able to contain himself for joy, when he spoke the words with his mouth he moved his feet, as though he were dancing, not indeed lustfully, but as one burning with the fire of divine love, not provoking laughter but drawing forth tears of grief. For many of them were pierced to the heart . . .[7]

The occasion of this sermon was a meeting with the Pope and Cardinals. Francis had been carefully briefed by Cardinal Ugolino, but forgot every word of his learnt sermon. He begged their pardons and asked if they would give him a few moments to wait on the Holy Spirit. Soon the Spirit burst forth.

Without the Holy Spirit, a sermon is lifeless. The Holy Spirit helps the preacher to prepare and also to deliver the Word. Brother Douglas used to prepare his sermons on his knees and to deliver them in a forthright but simple and challenging way. I remember, too, some of Algy's sermons, simple but powerful. And for me, Brother Kenneth[8] still never fails in his Franciscan preaching style: there is a homeliness, an intimacy even, a use of stories, and he allows the words of Scripture to carry weight. We cannot command the Spirit, we wait on him. As Father Robert Llewelyn says: "It is ours to bind the wood of the sacrifice on the altar: his to send the fire from heaven. It is ours to fill the water-pots to the brim, his to make the wine drawn from them. Ours to roll away the stone; his to say, 'Lazarus, come forth.' "[9]

A lively, contemporary book on preaching the Gospel today is that of John Fenton and Michael Hare Duke, entitled *Good News*.[10] They suggest a fivefold test to ensure that what is being preached is the Gospel. First, is it new? Does it come with freshness? "There is a parallel with the way that beauty always comes in a fresh disclosure. We do not say of the trees of autumn, 'It is just like last year all over again', but we are astounded every time it happens." When Jesus preached, people were amazed, they recognized his authority and they saw that he pointed to a new covenant, a new age and new hope. Secondly, does the preaching offend, disturb, upset? Is it offensive, upsetting those who hear it? For when Jesus preached, many were scandalized and went away (cf. John 6:61,66). Paul preached Christ crucified, a stumbling block to Jews (1 Corinthians 1:23). As Fenton and Hare Duke say: "The Gospel strikes us first as offensive; it takes faith to receive it." The third test for the Gospel is, does it take our breath away, is it greater than our hopes and worse than our fears? The Gospel words of Jesus, as we have already seen, are extreme, challenging, and those who respond to them, like Francis did, live lives which most think are excessive. The fourth of these tests is, does it bring joy? The Gospel is not only news, scandalous and excessive news, but also *good* news (Luke 2:10). There is joy in heaven over one sinner that repents (Luke 15:7). Jesus opens a way that he calls blessed or happy. And the final test must be, does the preaching promote love? The preaching of Francis was certainly fresh, disturbing, breath-taking, bringing joy and producing love in those who responded.

Francis gives his friars an outline sermon in the *Rule of 1221*.

> Whenever they see fit, my friars may exhort the people to praise God with words like these: "Fear him and honour him, praise him and bless him, thank and adore him, the Lord Almighty, in Trinity and unity, Father, Son and Holy Spirit, Creator of all. Repent, for the kingdom of heaven is at hand [Matthew 3:2]; remember we must soon die. Forgive and you shall be forgiven; give and it shall be given to you [Luke 6:38]; if you do not forgive, neither will your Father in heaven forgive you your offences [Mark 11:26]. Confess all your sins. It is well for those who die repentant; they shall have a place in the kingdom of heaven. Woe to those who die unrepentant; they shall be children of the devil whose work they do and they shall go into everlasting fire. Be on your guard and keep clear of all evil, standing firm to the last."[11]

Why is it that, in our day, talk of hell-fire is totally unacceptable? After all, it is prominent in the teaching of Christ in the Gospels and in the New Testament generally (Matthew 5:22 etc.). But people of our time (guilty as we all feel ourselves to be, when we dare to go a bit under the surface) completely turn off when hell is spoken of. Indeed, most people would go further and say it is very wrong to frighten people and to caricature the God of love as vindictive and punishing.

I put the matter this way: the God we worship is always love. He made all that is, in love; creation reflects his love and goodness. He left us free to make a voluntary response of love, for love by its nature must be freely given. What can he do if we refuse to give it? He sees the consequences which follow for us – the sense of alienation, animosity towards others (for we project our faults on to them), the loss of freedom as evil habits dominate us. He sees, and comes to deliver. He comes in Jesus, he shows us what human life is capable of and what God is like – tackling the consequences of sin and helping men and women back to wholeness. He takes the consequences of rejection on the cross, he prays there for our forgiveness and, in trust, gives up his spirit to the Father (Luke 23:46). His death is for all (2 Corinthians 5:15). His resurrection inaugurates the new humanity, which includes all who choose it. His love continually works (and he is round every corner to which our wrong choices take us) to bring us back to our true self. If we choose not to accept it, not to co-operate, he has no choice but to leave us out. To be left out is hell. "To turn aside from thee is hell, to walk with thee is heaven."[12] If we won't forgive others, we suffer in ourselves the consequences of bitterness and hatred; if we practise deceit we shall pay by not being trusted; if we grab and cheat and possess and defraud, people will find it hard to share with us and we shall be denied the joy of receiving. All this means we suffer and, ultimately, we could destroy ourselves. And in that process God's love will seem absent, his presence will seem hostile – not because he has changed, but because we have put ourselves out of relationship with him. His love seems like wrath. So, to be with him seems terrible: heaven seems like hell. If we can't or won't turn back to him, we might prefer being away from him. He does not reject us; we reject him.

The reason so much of our preaching is effete is that we don't know how to say this to the people of our time. Is it because people today have so little theological background that God seems an irrelevance? Perhaps they did have more in Francis' time. In any case, the visiting preacher was a great attraction then. Yet many people in our culture believe in God and say that they pray. It is a very personal, individual thing which they say the Church doesn't help them with. What is it that we lack? What would help us communicate Christian faith today?

I worked for ten years in East London, where the people generously responded in lots of ways – churchgoing rarely being one of them. I can remember getting on like a house on fire until I tried to speak about God. Then, all of a sudden, a steel shutter came down and I had to decide how far to push the relationship and how far to hope that there would be another, more favourable opportunity. Was it that I was middle class, too sophisticated, saying it wrong? I wondered. Was it social conditioning that made it impossible for people to know what I was trying to tell them? Anyway, I couldn't, and can't, believe that God consigned them all to hell. I suppose if I did think that, I should take every opportunity to warn them; I should beg them to repent before it was too late and I should find myself with the sandwich-board men saying, "Prepare to meet thy God", or in a wayside pulpit intoning, "The wages of sin is death" (Romans 6:23). But not choosing that way (which in any case doesn't seem any more effective), I wonder if I am like the watchman in Ezekiel (3:17–21; 33:2–7) who, because he doesn't sound the warning trumpet, is responsible for the death of those who are destroyed.

I go back to the positive side of Francis – his trust in the positive nature of God in his universe – and to Francis' sermon to the birds at Bevagna:

My brothers, birds, you should praise your Creator very much and always love him. He gave you feathers to clothe you, wings so that you can fly and whatever else was necessary for you. God made you noble among his creatures and gave you a home in the purity of the air though you neither sow nor reap. He nevertheless protects and governs you without any solicitude on your part.[13]

The purpose of our preaching is to bring people into the knowledge of God's love, into glad, thankful co-operation with him. We celebrate all signs of God's life in all that is. He is in our fellow men and women, and we seek to affirm with them all that is good and to learn from them how to celebrate and appreciate it all more. If we can thus enter a rapport and friendship based on mutual appreciation and trust, it will not be long before we are also sharing our wounds, our hurts and our failures. In that context, God's mercy and forgiveness – his wounds – wjll speak. Our faith in the one who loved us and gave himself for us (Galatians 2:20) can be shared, as he shared himself with us. "Not a God has wounds, but thou alone."[14]

Perhaps it is because people in our culture are so unsure of themselves and so guilty in their little knowledge of God, that the approach can only be one of assurance and affirmation. Anything else would be too frightening and would lead to further hardening and distancing. In any case, God's goodness and purpose of love came before any misusing or distorting of it. God's goodness in creation, the coming of his kingdom, has to precede "repent, and believe in the Gospel" (cf. Mark 1:15; Romans 5:8; 2 Timothy 1:9). Christians who discover how to share that message and bring it alive to others are the true evangelists, of which we have woefully few.

Of course, only a small percentage of people ever listen to sermons. Though radio and television reach much wider audiences than those who are already church attenders, people can turn off in more ways than one. Preaching, then, cannot be the only or primary way of communicating. Though Francis was a great preacher, we recall that doing was more important for him than talking.[15] He says that it is a "worldly religious" who *talks* a lot[16] and that people seek glory from *reciting* great deeds rather than *doing them*.[17] The first part of Francis' *Testament* tells how he began to be converted by living among lepers. He is more remembered for what he did than for what he said. For all of us, what we do speaks louder than what we say.

We are more conscious today of the "us" and "them" in our secular Western societies, for Christians are increasingly a small minority. One response is to step up evangelism and fill stadiums with churchgoers hoping to bring some of their friends to Christ; another is to find ways of crossing over the gap between "us" and "them". It seems to me that the choice between the two will be a matter partly of temperament, partly of theology and partly of discerning the real situation and signs of the times.

All this has very practical consequences in our community. Local churches, finding themselves stuck in the "us" and "them" syndrome, yet hearing all that the Gospels say about mission, look to our community (among others, of course) to come in and lead "parish missions". These have been a feature of our life since the early days and I recently came across a picture of Brother Douglas on a "beach mission" in the 1930s. Techniques have changed since parish missions meant fourteen days of continuous evening services designed to teach the faith, challenge and convert. Today, the emphasis is on house meetings – to which churchgoers are urged to invite non-churchgoers in greater proportion than themselves, for open sharing – and on workshops, theme group discussions, demonstrations and the like. The quality of presentation on TV, now available in almost every home,

can make the more homespun efforts of churches seem third
rate. But I've learnt two things: one is that people learn by
doing and experiencing, and the second, which was put to me
by a former director of religious broadcasting, is that "there is
no better communication than someone who really believes
something saying it".

In housegroups (which usually terrify people beforehand –
it is still barely acceptable in this country for people to share
openly what matters to them most) I have found that some
people's words carry weight – however simple and inexpert
they are – because they express the experience of the one
using them. "Let the redeemed of the Lord say so" might be
the slogan for Christian evangelism today, but that would
involve helping Christians to discover and really *know* that
they are redeemed. It is this task which makes parish mission
for me worth the time and effort. It may be that, among other
things, putting Christians in a position where they have to try
to articulate what they believe, helps them not only to
discover what they do know, but also opens them up to learn
more. The Christian education and catechetical programmes
of dioceses provide opportunity for learning and are increasingly used. Some of the schemes, "open-door retreats" and
the like, help people to know with more than their heads. The
Christian knowledge that counts comes from reflection on
life in the light of Christ's revelation. The training of
prospective clergy away from colleges and seminaries may
also help this process, for we need clergy well enough in
touch with how life is for most people and clear how Gospel
perspectives affect it, so that they are not only pastors but
also trainers of the laity in mission.

The danger with parish missions and other evangelistic
efforts is that they widen the gap between churchgoers and
others. At worst, they increase the volume and insensitivity
of Christian slogans hurled around to unlistening ears. This
may be one reason that we sometimes have difficulty in

making up our mission teams of brothers and sisters (drawn often from both First and Third Orders). Many of our brothers and sisters see their daily life among ordinary people as their "mission". Rather, after the example of the Little Brothers and Sisters of Jesus, they see that the sharing in the daily experience (as far as possible) of those around them, and the bringing of it to God in prayer, is what they are called and sent to do. If articulation of their faith occurs naturally in the process, that's fine, but the emphasis is on sharing and praying and "being little".

In 1984 we asked all our houses to look at their activities in terms of mission and to invite people from around them to help in the evaluation. The result shows a great variety of availability and activity. From one place the four brothers write of their life in a very rough housing estate in one of the big cities where (unusually for us) they have, among other things, responsibility for a Christian congregation and its activities towards the district around them. Another brother lives in a flat in such a district, without organizational responsibility, seeking just to be part of, and of service to, the people. In another house, one brother works with a housing association trying to make some terrible tenement buildings more habitable for the largely immigrant families who use them, while another is concerned with a "step-by-step" Christian education programme in the local churches. In the same house, one sister is a homehelp with needy families, while another is a teacher in a local school. In other places, a brother works largely with young people in industry, another in the healing ministry, a sister with a day-care centre for homeless men. Another researches the Christian-Marxist dialogue, another is a university teacher in biblical theology, while another is engaged in stimulating and enabling a local self-help group. Several others are active in peace and justice issues, the feminist debate, lifestyles questions and the like. Some, too, offer hospitality for people in need, a place for meeting across social divides, a common ground for dialogue, a place to learn about prayer, a place for Christian instruction and conference. Some have more independent chaplaincies to seamen, to the deaf, to the dying, for instance, or activities in prisons, the armed forces, hospitals, schools or colleges, and some work at our school for maladjusted boys. Overall there was a great variety, all within the mission and the Franciscan tradition; the survey explained why it was not easy to find teams to go for a week or a fortnight on parish missions.

This is one small instance of the divergence between the local church congregation and the wide variety of other Christian groups and individual activities which go on alongside it with more or less independence. I hope our Society will keep a foot in both camps, as, in fact, most ordinary Christians do anyway. Similarly, those parts of our Society which are more "conventual" – that is, in houses apart – need the Third Order and the more informal houses and itinerant individuals to remind them of the fullness of the Franciscan way. The push and pull between the various ingredients – the caring ministry, the itinerant ministry, worship and prayer, hospitality, teaching the faith, personal counselling and spiritual direction, reflection and intellectual effort – make our Society what it is. There is plenty of scope for the wide variety of personalities called to it. As one who chose not to work in a family business, I hope our Society will avoid the temptation to feel that it is up to those coming behind to maintain and build up established "community works", for there is much fun (as well as torment) in pioneering new ones. But whatever we do, I hope it will speak to others of salvation.

New light about *saying by doing* is coming from Franciscan initiatives in Third World countries. Increasingly, we realize that the Christian mission is taking place in a post- or anti-colonial period of history. By the year 2000, the majority of Christians will be living in what are variously called the "Third World", the "Southern Hemisphere" or "developing countries" – even exceeding those in our "developed" world by as much as 40 per cent, so reversing the proportions almost exactly in the last hundred years.[18] How this will affect the central councils of the Church remains to be seen, but meetings of the World Council of Churches give an indication. The word "liberation" is increasingly heard, describing personal, social and political salvation.

Words of a Franciscan sister from Brazil at the 1982 Mattli Conference in Morschach, Switzerland, are included in the book from that conference.[19] Sister Benvenuta M. Silva of the Capuchin Missionary Sisters said that in her remote region of Brazil there were now some 110 small groups of religious living very simply among, and as, the people. She describes the apprehension with which she and others left more formal religious houses; she tells too of a similar difficulty in leaving old attitudes. "Besides our own personal difficulties, arising from our training, which had not been directed to this kind of commitment, we also had to struggle with the opposition of the institutional structures, which generally feared the challenges of the new, the unknown, the uncertain." Whether it meant urban slums, or rural remoteness, they decided to live among "the most distressed people, the weakest and those pushed furthest towards the brink". They discovered that their assumptions about "the people" were actually caricatures, coming from prejudice and their middle-class orientation towards "helpfulness". "Faced with this situation, we felt that there was but one way out, a way actually in conformity with the Gospel; so, like schoolgirls, we began to listen and learn . . . discovering the richness and wisdom in the daily life of the people. We observed how the people lived and thus gradually learned the difficult art of waiting . . . listening to the people in order to understand their needs and to give a response in conformity with the Gospel and permeated with the Franciscan spirit."[20]

Here is a response like that of Francis in the *Testament*. Her definition of today's lepers is: ". . . [those] who now suffer not so much from the leprosy of the flesh, as from the social leprosy of unjust poverty; from hunger, from unemployment or under-employment; from the most diverse forms of discrimination, in their marginal existence in society; from sickness caused by hunger; from miserable conditions of life, work and housing; and who suffer violence and all which our so-called civilized world has called into being over the course of centuries."[21] The sisters moved into their mission by discovering "step by step the mystery of God which is present in their midst" and by "taking an active part in their struggles and difficulties, their victories and defeats, their desires and anxieties, their joys and sorrows – and that means we must walk the way to liberation and redemption with them. The people expect of us that we be the sign of a new life, a symbol of resurrection and of hope. Therefore we must constantly renew our readiness to follow Christ."[22]

The sisters' witness puts them in the way of fulfilling the hopes of the encyclical *Gaudium et Spes* (1965) which says, "Religious life should be a permanent prophecy in the structure of the Church."[23] The whole prophetic tradition (cf. Jeremiah 20:7–18) comes from deep wrestling with God, resulting in speaking and acting in a way which pulls down and builds up (Jeremiah 1:10). From it, new creativity gives life to the institutional; but its message is often rejected and the prophet persecuted (Matthew 5:12; 23:30, 34, 37). Jesus, too, was in that line and fared no better (Matthew 21:33–41; 23:32). Francis was a prophet, as much and more by what he did than by what he said: there was in him a non-conforming streak. It remains to be seen how readily the established Church can accept new and non-conforming attitudes in its religious.

There is a confusion of language in Sister Benvenuta's article: she follows the common use of "man" for "mankind" or "humanity". In the United States and other "developed countries" we are being alerted to use inclusive, non-discriminatory language so that women are not put down by implication. The Mattli Inter-Franciscan Message[24] in the very next section after "In Favour of the Poor – Against Poverty" speaks of women's liberation in a section headed "For the Woman – Against Discrimination". It begins, "We are dismayed by the situation of the woman in the Third World. She is the poorest of the poor . . . treated as an object . . . merchandise, often exploited sexually . . . used as cheap labour and kept illiterate." It goes on to say:

> Francis discovered and highly esteemed the feminine in creation. He had a special love and devotion for the Mother of God, who gave Christ to the world.[25] He saw himself as a mother, conceiving life and protecting it.[26] He also tried to interpret inter-human relations in terms of motherhood.[27] In his wider love of God, friendship flowered with St Clare of Assisi[28] and Jacoba of Rome.[29] In his *Canticle of Brother Sun*, he called everything "sister" and "brother" thus bringing them into a harmonious unity . . . we must make a special option for the oppressed woman.[30]

The other headings in this remarkable document might well provide an agenda for a renewal of Franciscan attitudes and action: "The Rights of the Poor as the Rights of God", "Striving for Justice and Peace", "Instruments of Reconciliation", "A Liberating Solidarity", "Dialogue with Other Religions", "The Word Must Become Flesh: Inculturation", "Overcoming Clericalism through Fraternity", "To Learn by Living and Doing: Formation", "Reaching Out to the Transcendent: Prayer and Contemplation". The document came from a conference organized in the eight hundredth celebration year of the birth of St Francis by the General Secretaries for Mission of the four Franciscan Orders – Order of Friars Minor, Order of Friars Minor (Capuchin), Order of Friars Minor (Conventual), and Third Order Regular. Fifty participants from twenty-eight countries attended, of which ten were sisters and five were representatives of the Secular Franciscan Order.[31] At that time the total number of men in the four Orders was approximately 37,000;[32] in addition, there are about five times as many women in Franciscan congregations and then too the Secular Franciscans (Tertiaries). I often think that our tiny Anglican Franciscan group (which incidentally gets a mention in the follow-up proposals of the congress) has much greater freedom and flexibility than the great Orders. I only hope that we use it: we have a remarkable opportunity, not least among our fellow Anglicans.

One of the other items in the Mattli statement, "Dialogue with Other Religions", takes us to the heart of the current debate among Christians on "mission through proclamation" or "mission through dialogue". Francis can be claimed as the champion of both. He was the first of the religious founders to include a section in his Rule about mission and in it he describes the two modes.[33]

In his day, the Islamic hordes were the big bogey (as in some places they still are) at the walls of European Christendom. They had virtually taken over the Byzantine Empire, were in the holy places of Palestine, along the North African coast and into bits of Spain and were called, by most Western Christians, the "infidel", the "unbelievers". From time to time crusades were called for to stave off the menace and to free the holy places.

Francis had another way. He called for mission, and in these terms:

Our Lord told his apostles: "Behold I am sending you

forth like sheep in the midst of wolves. Be therefore wise as serpents and guileless as doves" [Matthew 10:16]. And so the friars who are inspired by God to work as missionaries among the Saracens and other unbelievers, must get permission to go from their Minister, who is their servant . . . The brothers who go can conduct themselves among them spiritually in two ways. One way is to avoid quarrels or disputes and "be subject to every human creature for God's sake" [1 Peter 2:13], so bearing witness to the fact that they are Christians. Another way is to proclaim the Word of God openly when they see that is God's will, calling on their hearers to believe in God Almighty . . . that they may be baptized and become Christians . . . They may tell them all that, and more, as God inspires them . . . [34]

Francis warns that this second way will expose them to persecution and possibly death and, indeed, the five brothers who chose it and preached against the Prophet in Morocco, were martyred in 1220. Francis celebrated their fidelity and poverty of spirit, saying, "Now I have real friars minor!"[35] The criterion about which way to choose, he gives as "When they see that is God's will"; the martyrs believed this was what they were doing. Francis, too, seems to have had a real desire to give himself with the totality of a martyr, but his attempts to get to the Saracens were thwarted in 1212 and 1215.[36] However, he was present at the great siege of Damietta (at which 6,000 Crusaders lost their lives).[37] He was appalled at the behaviour of the Christians and preached penance to them; then, amazingly, he set out across no man's land to the enemy's lines. Whether his intention was martyrdom or to preach penance or reconciliation, his audacity and simplicity alone can account for his safe passage to the Sultan Melek-al-Kamil (1217–38). Various accounts of what happened are preserved.[38] Certainly he was heard. He

explained himself as a messenger of the Most High God; the
Sultan was impressed and gave him safe conduct back and
permission for the brothers to travel in the Holy Land.[39] And
there is some evidence that Francis was impressed and
changed by the experience:[40] his humble, respectful
approach made it all possible.

Openness to the insights of others and the humility of
listening are the strategy most favoured in the world mission
of our time. One of the most surprising documents of Vatican
II in 1965 was the *Declaration on the Relationship of the
Church to Non-Christian Religions*. It speaks of the Church's
task of "fostering unity and love among men and even among
nations . . . For all peoples comprise a single community and
have a single origin since God made the whole race of men
dwell over the entire face of the earth (Acts 17:26). One also
is their final goal, God. His providence, his manifestations of
goodness and his saving designs extend to all men (Wisdom
8:1; Acts 14:17; Romans 2:6–7; 1 Timothy 2:4).[41]

These words are in sharp contrast with those of St Francis
Xavier, the great sixteenth-century missionary: "The native
Indians have no culture whatsoever . . . It is difficult to live
amongst a people which does not know God, and which does
not live according to its reasoning because it is so steeped in
sin."[42]

What are Christians actually doing today in relation to
those of other faiths? Apart from direct evangelism, there are
at least four other approaches.

1. Some follow Charles de Foucauld (1858–1916)[43] who
went to Tamanrasset in the Sahara, praying especially for the
Tuareg and for the whole of humanity. Silent, as a hermit, he
prayed especially to Jesus who was present with him in the
Blessed Sacrament. His followers, the Little Brothers and
Sisters of Jesus, see theirs as a contemplative vocation, but
they live it in the deserts of this world – in industrial cities,

among the Boat People of Hong Kong, for instance – always
with and like the poorest. Their manual work, like that of
those around them, is essential for their survival. They don't
see their vocation as including evangelization or practical
helping (except in immediate human necessity). It is interesting that some have moved over to the Little Brothers of the
Gospel, who, while living simply among the poor, seek to
include evangelization.

2. Another Christian approach is that of a life of service
among the poor. Mother Teresa of Calcutta and her sisters
are the best known example. Mother Teresa left her established community for Christ's sake, to work for the poor, sick
and dying on the streets of Calcutta. She says of St Francis:

> Rather than a master, Francis is for me and my sisters an
> example of total dedication to God through Christ and his
> poor. Francis' teaching consists of being in love with Jesus
> Christ, his example lies in his having continually put his
> teaching into practice. There is no doubt if Francis were to
> return (a pure hypothesis) he would serve the poor as I am
> trying to do. He would do it not just with words, but
> especially by throwing his heart into it and doing what the
> Spirit of the Lord told him to do. His example is still valid.
> Love is always new, just as the poor are always new, as are
> the lepers, the excluded, those without bread or hope. He
> has always stimulated and comforted me. My sisters and I
> chose the poor completely freely: it was the same choice
> that Francis made.[44]

In many parts of the world, through hospitals, village clinics,
agricultural projects, drilling for water, relief of the hungry,
care of refugees, literacy programmes and the like, Christians
of all traditions express the Gospel. Sometimes their labours
lead to converts, and sometimes to the local indigenous
people learning similar ways to express care. Mother Teresa's
success in attracting Indian women and men to such service is

a remarkable feature of her charism. When asked what her community can give that State benefit (if it existed) can't, she said simply, "love".[45]

3. Some think this approach lacks political edge and that its paternalism helps to maintain the status quo. Helder Camara says: "When I give the poor bread they call me a saint, when I ask why the poor have no bread they call me a Communist."[46] Many South American Christians work for political change. One such is a former Superior of the Little Brothers in South America, Arturo Paoli, who now spends six months of the year in Venezuela in "a radical Franciscan Carmel" – largely in the solitary prayer that Francis loved so much – and six months moving among the poorest families and communities in the Brazilian Mato Grosso. He wrote:

> Francis is our most congenial model, the one we must try most to imitate. Because, he did not proclaim poverty in the abstract, he proposed and lived in total identification with the world of the poor, the people, "the minores" and the lowliest of his time. He made a *choice of class* even though he would never have accepted a *class struggle*. Francis, as Charles de Foucauld said, lived "like them", he never wanted to share the power of the clergy, the priests. He did not want the girdle of the nobility, the shoes and purse of the bourgeoisie and merchants, the lawyer's inkpot, the sword of the violent, or even the sword of justice. I think that the Order of Friars Minor of the future should and could be a lay order.[47]

Like many churchmen in South America, Paoli is deeply committed to the liberation of the people from oppressive government and economic forces, translating the Gospel and its struggle, with its risk and cost, into political terms.

4. A fourth contemporary response is illustrated in the life of Father Placid Tempels OFM, described in Father Arnulf Camps' chapter in *Build Up My Church* on "Franciscan

Dialogue with Other Religions".[48] He served most of his life in Zaire. Beginning there in 1933, he spent the first ten years (as he describes himself) as a priest who "acted like a boss, lord and master of his church, who knew all, said all, while the faithful had only to listen and keep quiet . . . For ten years . . . my eyes fixed always on my manual, I tried all methods, all possible clichés to make the Christian religion understood, accepted and practised . . . in spite of everything the engine didn't start up." From 1943 he decided to sit down with the Bantu people and listen to their deepest aspirations and dialogue. " 'What we think,' they said to me, 'what we want, what we're looking for, is life, full, total life . . . fecundity . . . vital union with other beings visible and invisible . . . a communion of life, a union of life between all beings.' "[49] Tempels was back in Belgium from 1946 to 1949, but returned to Zaire in 1949 for a further phase which he called "encounter", from which the Jamaa Movement began.[50]

Another and only slightly less controversial figure in such a dialogue approach to mission is Father Vincent Donovan, whose story is more accessible in *Christianity Rediscovered: An Epistle from the Masai*.[51] He tells in detail of his dialogues with an East African tribe and the outcome in tribal baptisms and an indigenous Church, very different from the Church of the mission compound and colonialist style.

In quite a different context, the priest-worker movement, for instance in France in the sixties, and the work of bodies like the Sheffield Industrial Mission in England,[52] illustrate the attempt through dialogue to reach across what divides the proletarian bulk of the population of Western Europe from the Christian Church. Such attempts sometimes created groups of Christian workers, but were rarely able to integrate them with local congregations. Perhaps the greatest lesson of those who saw dialogue as the first step in evangelism – Donovan's experience bears this out – is that many cultures put solidarity with their tribe or class above individual con-version. Because they think in group terms, the approach has to be towards group change rather than snatching brands from the burning (Zechariah 3:2). Some see conversion of any sort as incidental. Living in openness and dialogue among those of other religions or none, is what they are about.

Is this, as some claim, an end in itself? Christ is present in all men, he is "the true light, which lighteth every man that cometh into the world" (John 1:9) and the Holy Spirit is alive not only in every person but in their religion too. Others ques-tion this theology – most radically "Catholic Traditionalists" who abhor Vatican II's aberrations and who are quoted by Walbert Bühlmann in his *All Have the Same God*.

> Original sin, the source of all other sins, is thus the source also of all pagan "religions", as schismatic, heretical, apostate distortions, mutilations, abbreviations and counterfeits of the one true religion. Hence they are all symptoms of opposition to God, of untruthfulness, stupi-dity and helplessness, they are under the dominion of Satan, the father of sin . . . [53]

Clearly, from this theological standpoint, dialogue with other religions would be apostasy. Another point of view is expressed, however, by Pope John Paul II in *Familiaris Con-sortio* (1981):

> In conformity with her constant tradition, the Church receives from various cultures everything that is able to express better the unsearchable riches of Christ. Only with the help of all cultures will it be possible for those riches to be made manifest even more clearly, and for the Church to progress daily towards a more complete and profound awareness of truth which has already been given to her in its entirety by the Lord.[54]

Certainly, men like Father William Johnston SJ,[55] who lived in Japan and went through the full Soto Zen training, have helped me to drop some of the blinkers which prevent me seeing increasingly the whole Christ. Likewise, those who have lived closely to Indian peoples bring a Catholic understanding greatly different from Western Catholicism.[56] We live in a Church spanning six continents (some say five, but most prefer to separate South from North America) of very different cultures. Francis didn't hesitate to address his message to every nation, tribe and people. We wait in hope for the gathering of the nations into Christ – but we can believe in the meantime that for those who do not know the name of Christ, or who cannot distinguish him from the Western presentation, or who cannot see him in the Church's message of life but who follow truth, beauty and goodness in whatever form, not rejecting that which is of God, will find themselves eventually at home in his kingdom. Such a hope does not mean that all religions are equally valuable – there is darkness and light in all – but it does mean that God is not confined to the Christian or any other religious expression. I believe Christians are very lucky to know God in Christ, with all the graces and blessing which come from life in the Church. They have something to share and I long that we shall so live what we know (and partly know) in Christian faith in such a way that others will want to share it. Francis, I believe, knew that sharing was a mutual activity.

Francis recommended either humble co-existence with the Saracens (an option that many Christians in minority situations today under fundamentalist Moslem governments or, for that matter, under atheist Marxist governments, have little choice but to follow) or fearless proclamation at whatever cost (and Christians in today's world under both rightist and leftist oppressions show the cost – confinement, torture and martyrdom). Which option Christians choose today will vary. Our choice will be partly determined by how

much we have in us of Francis, the clear-cut Western
Catholic, and how much of Francis, the lover of all mankind
and all that God has made. I believe that it is by deep
commitment to God in one religion that we come to
appreciate people of other religions and none, and so move
towards the universal brotherhood (or sisterhood) which was
Francis' message to the world and which should be ours too.

Chapter 8
Dying

We live at a time when death is fought off as an enemy – at least, that is, till very old age when many people long for it as a friend. When death approaches we deny it and try to "cheer up" the gravely ill by false reassurances. We are afraid of our own fears and of theirs too. When death comes we try to insulate ourselves from its impact by not going near the body and by sanitizing every aspect of its disposal. More serious, we often repress our grief and try to dodge the mourning. I wonder where all this denial of death comes from: I'm sure it does us no good.

Francis died at forty-four. When he knew death was approaching he said simply "welcome Sister Death".[1] He asked to be laid naked on the bare earth.[2] He sang aloud in his last days, so much so that Brother Elias was afraid he would cause a scandal.[3] He wrote a new stanza for his *Canticle*:

> Praised be my Lord, by our Sister the death of the body
> From which no man escapeth.[4]

"I have done what it was mine to do," he said to the brothers, "may Christ teach you what is yours",[5] and he blessed them. When the time came on Saturday evening, 3 October 1226, he asked for the beginning of Chapter 13 of the Gospel of John to be read.[6] "Jesus knew that his hour had come and he must leave this world and go to the Father. He had always loved his own who were in the world, and now he was to show the full extent of his love." Saying Psalm 142 with the brothers, he gently "fell asleep" in the Lord.[7] As though it was broad daylight a flight of skylarks trilled and thrilled above his cell, celebrating his entry into glory.[8]

I suppose Francis yielded to death with such apparent ease because he was used to letting go. He had exercised the muscles of trust and readiness throughout his life. In a way, his real death had happened long before when he had "handed himself over, soul and body, to our Lord Jesus Christ."[9] Each day, "dying to self", "dying to sin", "being crucified with Christ", the life he now lived, he lived by faith in the Son of God – as St Paul says, "who loved me and gave himself for me" (Galatians 2:20). That death with Christ, that burial with him in baptism (Romans 6:3–4) was lived out daily: "Every day I die" (1 Corinthians 15:31). He daily chose God, going his way. And so he could gently allow one more death to happen at the end.

In his Narnia tale, *The Last Battle*, C. S. Lewis catches for us both the fear of death and its promise.[10] All the animals and humans are forced to go into a little wooden shed which contains an unknown terror. Once inside, however, they find it amazingly spacious. They come eventually to the lion, Aslan, the ruler of heaven and earth, and each must approach him and look into his eyes.[11] As they look, the expression of some of them turns to hatred and fear and they depart to one side. But others look with recognition, relief and love, and they go to the other. There is fear for all of us in the unknown. But we can come to know one who will never leave us nor forsake us (1 Kings 8:57; Matthew 28:20; Hebrews 13:5–6). Looking into his eyes we are safe.

We all live out the mystery of death and life at varying levels of consciousness. I believe, too, that all of us know, or partly know, God, whether we can name him or not. I see parents working for their children, and people voluntarily putting themselves out for others, giving themselves to the care of the elderly or handicapped or ill. Most of us admire this. We call it being human, humane. There are extreme examples of it: a soldier in war may heroically risk his life to save his comrades. Father Maximilian Kolbe (a Polish Franciscan, canonized in 1984) took the place of Sergeant Francis Gajowniczek, a family man, in the death chamber at Auschwitz.[12] But there are plenty of more homely examples. Self-preservation is natural to us, but so is self-giving. People will "die to self" in support of a cause they believe in. The women of Ireland, Catholic and Protestant together, took great risks in their peace movement. The women of Greenham Common put up with great hardships to make their protest against nuclear weapons. Fighters for justice and peace risk prison, torture and worse, for what they believe in. Indeed, Martin Luther King said, "You have no right to live till you've got something worth dying for."[13] Francis was ready to die for the cause of our Lord Jesus Christ. He wanted with his whole being to co-operate in the work of redemption. He was ready to put aside all that stood in his way: "forgetting what is behind me . . . I press towards the goal to win the prize which is God's call to the life above, in Christ Jesus" (Philippians 3:13–14). The drive is not just for a future prize in heaven, but to share life with Christ in the here and now, counting all things as loss to take hold of that for which Christ has taken hold of me, "to experience the power of his resurrection, and to share his sufferings, in growing conformity with his death" (Philippians 3:7–12). Francis had the same single-minded purposefulness as these passages from St Paul indicate. "So fervent were the love and compassion of blessed Francis", says the writer of the *Mirror of Perfection*, "for the sorrows and sufferings of Christ, and so deep was his inward and outward grief over the Passion day by day that he never considered his own infirmities."[14]

Three more accessible illustrations may bring this kind of heroism nearer to our daily experience.

1. *Most of us will leave one thing, however good, if we see something better.* The reaching out for it may take courage. When we are afraid to let go, we cling to what we have. Yet if we are convinced of the value of the next thing, most of us will move on. In fact, throughout our human development this has been the pattern. It may seem lovely to be a passive, admired baby and have everything done for us, but at a certain stage it seems more desirable to fend for ourselves a bit, to move around, to crawl, to stand up, to toddle – even taking the risk of sitting down again suddenly with people laughing at us. Again, most of us manage the trauma of going to school and submitting to all the new demands on us, even though home seems so much safer. We left, too, the security of childhood for the storms of adolescence and the struggle to become ourselves, to come to terms with our new sexual development and to find a peer group of our own choosing. Extraordinarily, too, most people give up that hard-won mixture of independence and group solidarity for a one-to-one relationship, moving towards interdependence and all the demands of marriage and family. So we go on through many more stages, leaving one thing, with its appropriate attitude and behaviours, to find another. And at the end of our life, laden with all this experience (and with the things we have collected in the process), we come like overloaded camels to the eye of a needle (Mark 10:25), to let things go and to enter into the most spacious life of all. Death is the gate of life eternal.

2. *Most of us recognize the experience of letting go into something bigger than ourselves.* We may discover it in music, in physical exercise, sport or manual work; we may be taken out of ourselves by a good book, a good friend, the experience of love; we might experience an inrush of creativity and new life and do things we never dreamt we could. I have spoken already about this mysterious Tao. Part of the skill of life is letting it happen, putting ourselves into its

flow. But, of course, the way to such habitual freedom is through hard effort, failure, humiliation and maybe pain. When things seem to be going all right we think we can manage by ourselves. Paul discovered that there was a power of God "made perfect in weakness" (2 Corinthians 12:9) and came to be glad even for the weaknesses which reminded him of it. People of all religions train themselves by the self-discipline of fasting and prayer, for instance, to become habitually open to this power. They are willing to lose life to find a life so much fuller. The whole universe is alive with God's energy and there is an invitation to us to become part of it.

3. *The true value of something is seen more clearly when we stand back from it.* If we really want to find it we have to lose it. It is strange how a drowning man sees his whole life in a flash. Only after someone has died do we see the quality of their lives. A friend of mine in the Order of Friars Minor, Father Eric Doyle,[15] died in 1984 in his early forties. I had always enjoyed his "gadfly" Franciscan spirit and was impressed by his learning, but, brought up short by his death, I came to appreciate even more the quality of his life. I came across a talk he gave at St George's, Windsor, in 1976:

If we stop short at the beauty of creatures, we will never know their intrinsic value, nor their real significance. The poverty of total renunciation means to go to God in total nakedness, to stand before him with nothing between him and ourselves, to gaze at him before whom the mountains skip and the rivers clap their hands, in our finitude and creaturehood stripped of everything, including self, and thus to wait upon his holy will. With no conditions, no obstacles, no distractions as we stand before God, his love can come into us and pervade our entire being with light and warmth. By and in his love it is revealed to us that God loves the otter, the red campion and the sun; to know that

God loves them is of infinitely greater significance than our rejoicing in the playfulness of the otter, the loveliness of the red campion or the splendour of the sun.

Mystical death to the world in imitation of Christ's most free death is the indispensable condition for knowledge and love of it as the glory of God. To love the world, to love oneself in the world, one must first renounce everything, disinherit oneself totally, go out into the desert, flee the world. Then, in coming to know how God loves the world, one will love it in, through and with the love that he is. By God's most gracious love one grasps the intrinsic value of the world: it is a sacrament of the Love that remains forever.

St Francis renounced everything, yet he loved the world so passionately. Disinherited, the world was his.

There is, however, a resistance in all of us to this principle of "letting go". Francis is stern and challenging about it. His stanza on death in the *Canticle* concludes:

> Woe to those who die in mortal sin!
> Happy are those She (death) finds doing your will;
> The second death can do no harm to them.

Francis tells the preachers to warn people that they must die and that punishments await those who have misused themselves and others and this world's goods, trying thus to cheat God and dodge the consequences. The very vivid deathbed scene in *The Letter to All the Faithful*, for instance, finishes up with:

> We should all realize that no matter where or how a man dies, if he is in a state of mortal sin and does not repent when he could have done so and did not, the devil tears his soul from his body with such anguish and distress that only a person who has experienced it can appreciate it. All the talent and ability, all the learning and wisdom which he

thought his own, are taken away from him . . . relatives
and friends bear off his property . . . worms feast on his
body . . . So he loses both body and soul in this short life
and goes to hell, where he will be tormented without end.

Before we write this off as "medievalism" we may recall the
words of Jesus, who said that he who sneers at his brother will
"answer for it in the fires of hell" (Matthew 5:22), and that we
must forgive our brother from the heart (Matthew 18:34,35)
lest we go to torment and prison. It is a torment which we
experience now when we will not let go of a past wrong or
hurt or grievance. If we won't let the thing go, we shall
continue to take the consequences. And the consequences are
deadly, separating us from others, alienating us, embittering
us, breeding hatred in us, even causing us to do others harm.
In our dissatisfaction we can come to blame God, projecting
on to him our angry, hurt feelings, refusing to forgive him for
what he has not given to us or for what we don't like about our
life, or the life of the world. We set him up in a nature other
than his, building up barriers to his grace, cutting ourselves
off from him and eventually denying his existence. If we
deny not only his existence but also his attributes, like love,
beauty, truth, when the time comes to look our Aslan in the
eyes, we shan't want to know and shall prefer to depart into
the darkness away from him, however tormenting it is. "Hell
is God's final compliment"[16] – he never removes our right to
choose.

Francis points to a better way than hell, finishing the same
letter:

In that love which is God, I, Brother Francis, the least of
your servants and worthy only to kiss your feet, beg and
implore all those to whom this letter comes to hear these
words of our Lord Jesus Christ in a spirit of humility and
love, putting them into practice with all gentleness and
observing them perfectly.

This better way is made possible by the Holy Spirit. In the prayer which ends his *Letter to a General Chapter*, Francis says: "Being cleansed, enlightened and enflamed by the ardour of the Holy Spirit we may follow in the footsteps of our Lord Jesus Christ, and so make our way to you, Most High, by your grace alone." "Enflamed by the Holy Spirit" we exchange one fire for another, as T. S. Eliot says:

> The only hope or else despair,
> Lies in the choice of pyre or pyre –
> To be redeemed from fire by fire.[17]

A good deal of Francis' teaching is in the well-established form of virtues and vices, with corresponding blessings and woes. "We give you thanks because your Son is to come a second time in the glory of his majesty and cast the damned who refused to do penance and acknowledge you into everlasting fire; while to all those who acknowledged you, adored you and served you by a life of penance, he will say 'Come, blessed of my Father, take possession of the kingdom prepared for you from the foundation of the world'" [Matthew 25:34].[18]

There is advice too about how to deal with sin.

Try to realize the dignity God has conferred on you. He created and formed your body in the image of his beloved Son, and your soul in his own likeness [Genesis 1:26]. And yet every creature under heaven serves and acknowledges and obeys its Creator better than you do. Even the devils were not solely responsible for crucifying him: it was you who crucified him with them and you continue to crucify him by taking pleasure in your vices and sins. What have you to be proud of? . . . But there is one thing of which we can all boast: we can boast of our humiliations [2 Corinthians 12:9] and in taking up daily the holy cross of our Lord Jesus Christ.[19] . . . Look at the Good Shepherd, my brothers. To save his sheep he endured the agony of the cross.[20]

Likewise, in *The Praises of the Virtues*:

All holy virtues, God keep you, God from whom you proceed and come. In all the world there is not a man who can possess any of you without first dying to himself . . . Each and every one of you puts vice and sin to shame . . . holy obedience puts to shame all natural and selfish desires. It mortifies our lower nature, and makes it obey the Spirit and our fellow men . . .

Francis is both practical and detailed in spelling out in ethical terms how to put aside sin and follow our Lord Jesus Christ.

Have we in our time swung too far to the other extreme? We are right to present the positive and the good first and to assure people of God's essential good will, for I believe that, just under the surface, men and women in our culture are so guilt-ridden that only by coming to such assurance of faith can they look at sin at all. Sin is best overcome by "the expulsive power of a new affection", the discovery of a better path to pursue. The heightening of fear is counter-productive: the emphasis on rights and wrongs, unless expressed in relationship terms, deadens people further. There is a new emphasis in Ignatian spirituality away from the old "examen of conscience" (What have I done wrong today?) to an "examination of consciousness" (How far have I kept in touch with the Lord and his will today?) For all that Francis says about sin and punishment, it is his relationship to Christ that comes through.

How glorious, how holy and wonderful it is to have a Father in heaven. How holy it is, how beautiful and lovable, to have in heaven a Bridegroom. How holy and beloved, how pleasing and lowly, how peaceful, delight-

ful, lovable and desirable above all things it is to have a
Brother like this, who laid down his life for the sheep and
prayed to his Father for us . . . [21]

The work of Brother Jesus who "redeems us", "sets us free",
"cleanses us by his precious blood", comes time and again in
Francis' writings. "He has brought us peace", "he has
reconciled us to Almighty God". He is "the Son of the Most
High God", "the glorious Word of the Father", and "he is
present with us always" and "every day" and "he will live in
us to save us".

And it was the Father's will that his blessed and glorious
Son, whom he gave to us and who was born for our sake,
should offer himself by his own blood as a sacrifice and
victim on the altar of the cross, and this not for himself,
through whom all things were made, but for our sins,
leaving us an example that we may follow in his steps [1
Peter 2:21]. It is the Father's will that we should be saved
by his Son and that we should receive him with a pure
heart and chaste body. [22]

Celano says, "Francis was always thinking of Jesus, Jesus was
in his mouth, in his ears, in his eyes, in his hands, Jesus was
in his whole being.[23] He sees him in the lamb[24], in the rock,
and in every tree his cross."[25] In almost every paragraph of
the *Rule of 1221*, phrases occur like "our Lord Jesus Christ
says", or "he says in the Gospel", or "as he himself puts it", or
"remember the words of our Lord Jesus Christ". Francis'
spirituality is very Jesus-centred, for in him he finds
salvation.

There is a dilemma for those who earnestly pursue moral
perfection. Either they fail and feel bad, or they think they've
succeeded and become prigs. But if we know, as Francis
does, that all goodness comes from God, we can open
ourselves to receive it as a gift and get our eyes off ourselves to

praise God. We can know that despite failure we are accepted in the Beloved. In the acceptance of that is our salvation. Seeing ourselves at the foot of the cross, accepted and forgiven, we might in our imagination bring there also our enemies and those from whom we are alienated; they too are accepted and forgiven. And if we look across at them we may be able to forgive them too and (even more difficult) let them forgive us. If there is rage and spite and hurt still in our system, it is to God we had best express it. He can take it (and has already). When we have got it all out and are open and vulnerable we may hear him say, "Yes, but I still love you", "Father, forgive them; for they know not what they do" (Luke 23:34). With the sting taken out of sin we can better work out how to get things right. There will still be consequences to work through, but purgatory is much better than hell.

This Christian theology of grace underlies the quest for perfection in Christ. Any training we undertake to grow towards it needs to be appropriate to the end for which we aim. Leonardo Boff says, "Mortification . . . lies in the activity of putting to death the overflowing of the passions so that their creative power may be directed towards holiness and humanization",[26] and "penances, apparently so inhuman, which Francis undertook were the price he had to pay for his profound humanity".[27]

Certainly Francis was very tough on himself. Bonaventure says:

When Francis saw that great numbers of lay-people were being inspired by his example to embrace Christ's cross fervently, he took heart; and like a brave leader in Christ's army, he determined to carry off the prize of victory by preaching virtue to a heroic degree. Recalling the words of St Paul, "those who belong to Christ have mortified nature with all its passions and its impulses" (Galatians 5:24), he mortified his lower appetites so strictly that he scarcely took enough food or drink to stay alive.[28]

If Francis was sometimes extreme with himself, he was always gentle with others. He spoke approvingly of the way his body had co-operated: "It was obedient in all things," he told a novice, "spared itself in nothing but rushed almost headlong to obey all my commands . . . In this, I and it agreed that we would serve the Lord Christ, without any reluctance."[29] When reproved for his severity, he would reply that he had been given to the Order as an example that "as an eagle he might encourage his young ones to fly".[30] In the Rule,[31] the brothers are enjoined to eat what is set before them and not to be ashamed (when it is necessary) to beg. They are to fast in Lent and in Advent and on Fridays. With the fasting goes prayer.

Francis had a fiery temperament which he directed to following Christ, but the story of his making a snow family and saying, "There, Francis, there is your wife, your sons, your children" and rolling around in the snow shows something of the cost.[32] The famous story of perfect joy points to a confidence in God that can even patiently endure not being recognized, as was shown when he got home exhausted to his friary and was beaten up and driven away as a scoundrel.[33] It is perfect joy when nothing can separate a man from the love of God in Christ Jesus (Romans 8:38–39).

There is a good deal of caution about ascetical practices in our time. Father Anselm Romb (OFM Conv.), in his *Franciscan Charism*, says: "A great deal of mortification unrelated to practical ministry does more to destroy the psychic energy necessary for human growth than to retard the sin which is corrosive of human growth." And again, "Suffering in its own right has no meaning in Jewish and Christian thought." "Asceticism grows out of ministry, not the reverse."[34] We usually link fasting today with a particular purpose. A Christian might stop eating meat because such a high proportion of cereal in our hungry world goes to producing meat for the rich. Another might refuse to buy food from certain countries, the political regimes of which are unjust. Fasting in solidarity with the starving and sending them money through relief agencies, or adopting a lifestyle which recognizes the unfair distribution of world resources, are further examples of Christians making a commitment to a new world. And again, with prayer, not having a lie-in on a Sunday morning, or going to bed early enough to get up for a morning prayer-time are ways of asceticism. Our aim is to move towards integration and wholeness, with the body an honoured partner in the whole person, the whole person integrated with society and its destiny. Such disciplines and deprivals as this quest entails can be taken in our stride. Margaret Wiles in the *Dictionary of Christian Spirituality* says, "Mortification . . . the activity of dying to one's compulsive pursuits of lesser goods in order to pursue, with undiluted energy and affection, relationship to God, the ultimate good of the whole human being."[35] "The ultimate Christian asceticism", someone has said, "is to live one's life in obedience to Christ as he reveals himself in the present moment." The purpose of all asceticism is to be open.

Two years before his death (the same year incidentally, 1224, that he sent Agnellus of Pisa and seven other friars to England[36]) Francis had a remarkable experience of Christ which, though well attested in all the sources, I speak of with a certain reticence. His body was marked in hands and feet and side with the marks of Christ crucified. Though he tried to conceal them, there were gnarled black lumps like nails, their heads on the top of his feet and the outside of his hands, and in his right side a wound that sometimes bled. The story of how this happened is as follows.[37] Francis loved solitude and sometimes went to Mount La Verna where there was a small hermitage. The mountain had several rocky crags and Francis, for his retreat from 15 August to 29 September in 1224, chose a remote ledge accessible only by a tree trunk laid across a ravine. Brother Leo was to come each day with food and call from the far side, only crossing if Francis responded. Leo saw a strange bright light from heaven resting on Francis praying, and on another occasion, on 17 September, "a seraph, containing the form of a man" rested on him, leaving there the prints of the Crucified. Francis had prayed for two graces: "That during my life I may feel in my soul and in my body, as much as possible that pain which you, dear Jesus, sustained in the hour of your most bitter Passion", and "that I may feel in my heart, as much as possible that excessive love with which you, O Son of God, were inflamed in, willingly enduring such suffering for us sinners."[38] The gift of the first is what is known as the "stigmata"; the second is the burning, joyful love which stayed with Francis through his two final years.

There are modern examples of this phenomenon (Padre Pio of San Giovanni Rotondo, Foggia, Italy, who died in 1968, for instance[39]). No doubt psychological explanations can be postulated. For myself, because I don't doubt the reality of what happened, any explanations of how it happened are secondary. I ask rather, what does it mean? Francis had a specially close awareness of Jesus and shared with him in his sufferings for the world. He bore in his body "the marks of the Lord Jesus" (Galatians 6:17), as Paul did through the rigours and persecution of his missionary labours (2 Corinthians 11:23–28). These marks, literal in Francis, were a gift congruous with all which preceded them. It was a very intimate gift expressing outwardly an inward relationship.

Franciscan spirituality, as we have seen, is this-worldly, bodily, practical, because God took our flesh and blood in

Jesus and is present to us in material bread and wine. It is nourished by an affective intimacy with the poor human Jesus, with Mary his Mother, with Jesus crucified, with his wounds and his sacred heart of love. Francis had long meditated on Christ's Passion, imitated his Lord, kept company with him faithfully and had been thrown into ecstasy by the love between them. He had externalized this in his way of life; now Christ branded his body with the very wounds of love.

The writer of the last book in the New Testament has a vision of all the redeemed in heaven offering to God "who sits upon the throne and to the Lamb" . . . "Blessing and glory and wisdom and thanksgiving and honour and power and might" (Revelation 7:10,12). They have come out of the great tribulation, being cleansed in this blood (Revelation 7:14). On their foreheads they bear the name of their God (Revelation 7:3; 14:1; 22:4). The name of God in the Old Testament was signified by the last letter of the Hebrew alphabet – T.[40] The prophet Ezekiel was told to mark the foreheads of God's people with it (Ezekiel 9:4,6). Francis loved T because it meant God's name and nature now disclosed more fully in Jesus who died on a T. The tau cross has become a Franciscan symbol.[41]

At baptism, the cross is marked on our foreheads. Every Christian has the obligation to live out its meaning. Francis lived it out so fully that the T was marked not only on his forehead but on his whole body. He carried about with him the death of Jesus, so that the life of Jesus might be seen in him (2 Corinthians 4:10–11; cf. Galatians 6:17).

Chapter 9
Choosing

He was just over thirty, becoming a full-time student late. He wore glasses and looked very serious as he sat in my room that evening. "It's a matter of life or death", he said, and began to explore the "ultimate existential choice". Not having much of a head for philosophical heights and in any case listening more to what he was saying behind the words, I responded with what I hoped were knowing and reassuring grunts, and so the conversation continued for nearly an hour. Suddenly he said, "What do you think?" It rather bowled me out. "Hang on a minute", I said and rushed upstairs. I came back with a little picture of Francis, looking a bit like Pan playing an imaginary fiddle, two sticks drawn across each other. I put it on his lap. "That's what I think", I said. He looked at it for a long time. Then he said slowly, "I suppose you mean I take myself too seriously." "Oh, not only that", I replied. "I was trying to point you to the 'belly laugh behind all that is'."

I don't know where the phrase came from or quite why I said it, but it did the trick. He had been sent by his college because he was so seized up that, although he was an excellent student (who eventually got a First), he couldn't write his exam papers: anxiety had taken over. Looking at Francis dancing and clowning, something happened, and he smiled. He told me the next day that after he left me he went into the chapel next door and laughed for an hour.

What is "the belly laugh behind all that is"? I was really

talking about God. I was actually saying that "it's all right" or, with Mother Julian, "all will be well, all things will be well, all manner of things will be well".[1] I was saying, "You really can trust, you really can 'let go', it is all right." And so the muscles relaxed, both in his face and in his guts and in his head. He stopped being afraid and his system began to work again. Some of the walks in our lovely Dorset countryside that in later months and years we went together, opened my eyes to the glory all around and in all that is, as few other things have. His pure delight and attentive interest in it all was a dance in itself and I got caught up into it. His exuberance showed itself too in poetry and literature and also in a fierce anger against the ecological damage of our times. He was in touch with a whole reality, the reality to which Francis points.

But to my disappointment he hasn't yet quite entered those areas of Francis which we have been looking at from his writings. I mean the things about sin, faith, penance, the Lord Jesus Christ, his life in poverty, his death in nakedness, about the brotherhood he started and its complexity in our developed and complicated world and about the life-and-death choices with which he confronts us. Perhaps one day my friend will see it and enter new fields of delight and salvation. For if we try to limit Francis to his empathy with all things and his gentle yielding to the flow of the Tao of life, we miss out on what he thought most worth writing about. He assumed the Most High Lord God's presence in all things. He knew that that same God had become a Brother to us in our spoilt humanity. He believed too that the same God comes to us continually as we enter with our fellow Christians through the Word and Eucharist into the Communion of his body and blood. The Holy Spirit, alive in all things, alive in all humans, in all religions, is alive in Jesus and in his Church to bring us to salvation. Were this not to be so there would be nothing to laugh about. For there is much in the world, in our lives, for which we can only weep, as Francis wept for the suffering of Christ, which includes all our lesser sufferings. He wept for lepers, for the poor, for the impenitent, the hard-hearted, the unforgiving, the terrorized and the terrorizing, the Crusader and the Saracen, the oppressed and the oppressors. In Christ he had found his own liberation "from the life of sin" and he met others with an attitude and message of liberation, reconciliation, new life. This message was not strident but winsomely little and gentle, yet all the stronger for that and subtly more confronting. Francis somehow gets under our skin. Even if he'd said or written nothing, Francis' life would have attracted and challenged. But he did speak and write because he knew there was a knowledge more than intuition alone, though dead unless the Spirit gives it life.

Francis spoke in the name of the one who had entered our human travail, yearning that our humanity should come back home to its source in God and find there the Father who makes all "brother" and "sister" again. That speaking involved entering the travail, coming into the agony, feeling in his soul and body the pain which only love makes possible. And so the one who died at forty-four lives on like his Master before him, and speaks across the centuries to each of us however "the existential angst" takes us. And his word gently puts to us a choice. We can either trust and come to the richness of that forgiving grace which sets us free to love, serve, obey and choose the little and poor; or else we can go on in the poverty of this-worldly power with its riches and knowledge, which tries to wrench out of life what it wants for itself. Yes, it is a life-and-death choice, fortunately not made all at once, but in our every decision. Most of us are slow learners and fear a final exam, so it is not more fear we need, but more confidence in the "belly laugh". "It is a fearful thing to fall into the hands of the living God" (Hebrews 10:31). To look our Aslan in the eyes we need courage from his grace.

I remember that on my last night in the parish (and the next day, weeping behind *The Times* on the train all the way from Lincolnshire to London, and then walking across to Waterloo, looking at the City as though I would never see it again, and catching my train to begin my noviciate at the Friary in Dorset), we sang a hymn which caught my aspiration completely:

> Fill thou my life, O Lord my God,
> In every part with praise,
> That my whole being may proclaim
> Thy being and thy ways.
>
> Not for the lip of praise alone,
> Nor e'en the praising heart,
> I ask, but for a life made up
> Of praise in every part:
>
> Praise in the common things of life,
> Its goings out and in;
> Praise in each duty and each deed,
> However small and mean.
>
> So shall no part of day or night
> Unblest or common be;
> But all my life, in every step,
> Be fellowship with thee.[2]

Tremulously I came to our Society hoping to bring my life together in God. I'm still working at it, or rather working hard to let go into what he is doing in me. People help me, both spiritual directors, religious Superiors, peers and the people in many places that I have been given opportunity to serve. The daily disciplines of prayer – prayer so much more catered for and safeguarded than most people's – put me in the way of learning to "pray without ceasing" (1 Thessalonians 5:17). But I suppose that what gets in the way is the struggle within myself to trust, to put aside anxiety and worldly considerations, the "free-floating" anger, the desire. to possess, the irrational sense of being "hard done by" or of it "not being fair". It is the struggle with all these things so that I can be open to God, ready for his will and not dominated by the unresolved in myself or by the powers of evil – this makes up my daily life. And it's such a relief when I choose with God and it "happens"!

Many people have much less choice about the big things in life than I have had: sheer survival, getting something for themselves and their families to eat occupies most of their attention. Or in our more affluent world, the struggle to find any job makes it a luxury to ask the great questions like "Is this what I'm called to?"; I must take any job that "brings in the bread" and helps a bit with the boredom and worthlessness feelings which marginalize and dispirit. In this world, how I get on with people at home and work and at the pub or club occupies most of my inner attention with little opportunity to discover that all these relationships are grounded in the one who loves us all beyond our imagining. So I cannot but consider myself a very lucky person to have such a range of opportunities, variety of work and interest, the chance to go to other parts of the world and to cross many culture lines, to have deep intimacy in loving relationships with people of all ages and both sexes, and to have all this grounded in God who alone gives it purpose and life. Not always actually to feel lucky is just part of how we are, but deep down I am thankful.

I am glad I'm not God, having to deal in such exquisite delicacy with so many millions of people in so many settings – let alone counting the very hairs of their heads and knowing every sparrow that falls to the ground (Matthew 10:29–30; Luke 12:6–7). But I'm glad to know (and partly know) such a God and to have some little share in what he is all about. For I don't know much about what life would be for otherwise.

And for those who can't name him (yet) and only know him through all the other things, I want to do all I can to put them in the way of being lucky too, for the best luck of all is to know God and have fellowship with him.

The world has changed a lot since my father worked so hard at his business and had such clear ideas about patriotism, war, self-reliance, enterprise and the rest. All kinds of technology have dethroned the god of Work. And this will be great if it sets us free for new work, the work of loving, serving, growing. Francis had to choose between Pietro Bernadone and "our Father": there is no choice if that's where we get to. It set him free to discover the loving and serving which were the proper way of his growth. Let's hope that he and Pietro are friends now, understanding each other in the communion of saints. Let's hope, too, that with the god of Work dethroned, the living God will take his place and enable everyone to find a meaning and purpose for their lives, so that together we can tackle the questions that threaten our world: the nuclear issue, poverty – and affluence – justice and peace, and the range of other things briefly referred to in these pages. For whether the choices are big or small, they are all part of the same process by which we make (or mar) our lives.

But all this can seem a bit airy-fairy. Someone could say, "If you reckon you became a friar because you were impressed by Francis of Assisi kissing and serving a leper, how have you got on with doing the same yourself?" I wish I had a simpler answer than "option for the poor", "the various opportunities I've had to be with marginalized people", "dealing with the leper in myself and others", "the rich and the clever have souls too", "being part of a team which helps others do this or that", and the rest, which sound like self-justification. Perhaps on the Last Day the question won't be in quite that form. But in that form, Franciscans today need to ask themselves whether their choice to follow Christ in the way of blessed Francis does actually mean they are available to God and to his poor. It is easy enough to end up serving one's own needs and the needs of those of like mind. If the wider Church capitulates to that, there is no hope of it having any real contribution to make to the tasks of our century – nor of the one not far ahead. Maybe all of us will have to discover our vocation again by some rude awakening. The dying Francis said to his followers: "Let us begin, brothers, to serve the Lord our God, for up to now we have made little or no progress."[3]

The process of making up one's mind about anything can be so complicated that we easily give up. Actually, giving up might not be such a bad thing, because when we stop concentrating too hard on a decision we often find we make it without noticing. Much deciding is in the timing anyway. Anxiety and self-importance are its greatest enemies.

So if you are a young woman or man – or a person of any age – with any real choice about your vocation, what can help you? I offer seven suggestions. Recognize that the vocation is the same for all of us, to know and serve God. See that, as Christians, our vocation is to become living cells in the Body of Christ, fulfilling the function God wants for it. Know that he wants us to discover what that is: we can reasonably ask him to show us. Discover through the circumstances of your life, and yourself as you have come to accept yourself, what your options are and evaluate the pros and cons as far as you can. Seek out someone else you can trust to discuss it all with. Be prepared to hang on and let things unfold, without trying to force or to hurry them. In the end, take a gamble and ask God to stop you if it's wrong, or to teach you something through it if you've made a mistake. I think these are some of the ways we hear his belly laugh.

But it may be that our major life-choices are now about other things than "vocation"; about questions of marriage, jobs, churches, lifestyle, politics, or something else again. I think the same rules apply. And it's best if you can avoid the kind of confrontation with the choice which paralyses you. Consistency in our choices, so that we live integrated and congruous lives, is still a long way down the road for most of us and this can discourage us from moving on. But better if one part of us moves on and the rest has to catch up, than if the whole system gets stuck.

Francis had much more consistency, congruity and integration than most of us and it is not easy to say how much of this came from natural gifts and how much from grace. But though he soars as an eagle it doesn't let us off learning to fly. If we can't fly, maybe we can run or walk (Isaiah 40:31). None of us ever learnt to walk except by taking the first toddling step and risking the humiliation of sitting down hard and being laughed at. Best to ask God, "What first step can I take today?" than to do nothing, and it is remarkable what can happen when we get moving.

For Francis, the first question came by the river near Spoleto: "Francis, which is better to serve, the Lord or the servant?" May we with him reply, "Lord, what will you have me to do?"

Appendix

Appendix

The following list includes only those *writings* generally agreed to be by St Francis. The *Lives* (called *Legenda* – but without pejorative undertones) are those written within a hundred years of his death. The stories (and much of the Franciscan ethos is contained in stories) are often retold in varying styles. A good deal of critical work has been done on them (like the work on the stories about Jesus): the conclusions I give below are in the mainstream of modern opinion.

THE WRITINGS: these are in three groups

I   *The Rule and Life of the Friars Minor*
   1 *Rule of 1221*: (*regula non Bullata*, i.e., it was never given Papal approval.) It is the fullest of the Rules, giving a lot of general teaching and exhortation.
   2 *Rule of 1223*: Still the official Rule of the Order.
   3 *The Testament of St Francis* (1226): His mind in the last few weeks of his life.
   4 *Religious Life in Hermitages*: A short practical guide.
   5 *Form of Life* and *Last Will of St Clare*: A fragment of their intimacy.
   6 *The Admonitions*: Probably written at various times and collected. They are practical advice for the brothers on what attitudes to cultivate and how to behave.
   (Some would add the *Rule for the Third Order*.)

II   *The Letters*
   1 *To All the Faithful*: A long letter covering the range of Francis' teaching about the Father's love for us, and about the Lord Jesus and his Passion, about worship and praise,

repentance, the Gospel way, the joys of heaven, the pains of hell.

2 *To All Clerics*: This exhorts care of all to do with the Word and the Eucharist.

3 *To a General Chapter*: Quite a long letter surveying his teaching with praise, penitence and obedience at its core.

4 *To a Minister*: A tender letter (quite short) encouraging the Minister to be merciful to friars in sin.

5 *To All Superiors*: A short exhortation on Word and Eucharist.

6 *To the Rulers of the People*: Various teaching, including a warning that death comes to all and an exhortation to receive the Eucharist with penitence and obedience.

7 *To Brother Leo*: A short affectionate letter about following God's leading.

Some would add the *Letter to Brother Anthony*.

III *Writings on Prayer and Devotion*
  1 *The Praises of God*
  2 *The Canticle of Brother Sun*
  3 *The Praises of the Virtues*
  4 *Salutation of the Blessed Virgin Mary*
  5 *Praises before the Office*
  6 *The Office of the Passion*
(Some would add the paraphrases of the Lord's Prayer and the prayer "Absorbeat".)

All these (apart from the *Canticle*) were written in Latin ("bad Latin", Thomas of Eccleston calls it) most often by dictation, but occasionally in Francis' own handwriting (for instance, *The Praises of God* for Brother Leo) with a directness and simplicity in God which also authenticates them.

THE LIVES

1 *The First Life of St Francis* by Thomas of Celano (1229):

Written quickly to support and illustrate the life of the newly canonized saint, by a friar who had known him and who gathered information about him. He has an elegant (if somewhat sententious) style. It is an official, slightly colourless, non-controversial work.

2 *The Legend of the Three Companions* (Leo, Angelo and Rufino) (1246?):

Many believe that a close disciple (Angelo?) wrote or compiled Chapters 1–16 of it, possibly early on, and sent it in response to the Chapter's request of 1244. It has a primitive simplicity of style, it doesn't reflect the controversies that divided the Order, it does not appear to know Celano's *Second Life*; it ends at the year 1221 (the remaining years seem subsequently to be added from Bonaventure's 1263 Life). But we have no manuscripts dated before the fourteenth century, so some reject the above theory, saying that the work was not compiled until the fourteenth century, even though earlier material was used.

3 The Writings of Brother Leo (1246?), including *The Legend of Perugia*:

We only had fragments of these writings (by the closest companion of Francis) until in 1922 a manuscript known as Perugia 1046 was brought to light. It gives a moving portrait of Francis, in simple style, reflecting views congruous with Leo's; this document is known as *The Legend of Perugia*. Its relations to (2) above and (6) below is much disputed.

4 *The Second Life of St Francis* by Thomas of Celano (1247):

This incorporates much of the material from (2) and (3) above, or from a document known to them. It is much fuller, and a more intimate life than the *First Life* and shows Thomas sympathetic with the stricter party.

5 *The Major Life* by St Bonaventure (1263):

85 per cent of this is a remodelling of Celano but with an important new section (IX.7) on Francis and the Sultan. It is a

statesmanlike attempt by the Minister General to provide a Life satisfactory for the different groups of friars. It was followed in 1266 by a Chapter decision that all other Lives should be destroyed. An abbreviated form (*The Minor Life*) was also made for use in chapels.

6 *The Mirror of Perfection* (1317?):

Ninety chapters of this are the same as (3) above and 29 as (4) above, and there are only a few others. Many think that it is a fourteenth-century compilation of older material drawn up to witness to primitive and spiritual values. At times it has been seen as the earliest, most authentic account; and certainly it brings the reader a vivid impression of Francis.

7 *The Little Flowers of St Francis* (1327):

These delightful tales, collected by Brother Ugolino di Monte Santa Maria in the fourteenth century, come from the tradition of the Marches of Ancona, where the "primitive" and "spiritual" wing of the movement flourished. *The Little Flowers* (Fioretti) is the name given to the Italian version written fifty years after the Latin original; it is the first writing on Francis in the vernacular. It has done much to popularize Francis in our time, though the heightened miraculous and occasionally sentimental tone does not appeal to all.

References

References

Franciscan source references follow those given in *St Francis of Assisi: Writing and Early Biographies: English Omnibus of the Sources for the Life of St Francis*, edited by Marion A. Habig (Chicago: Franciscan Herald Press, 1973).

Abbreviations

1 Cel	Thomas of Celano's 1229 *Life*
2 Cel	Thomas of Celano's 1247 *Life*
Leg Comp	*The Legend of the Three Companions*
Leg Per	*The Legend of Perugia*
Bon	The 1263 *Major Life* of St Bonaventure
Mirror	*The Mirror of Perfection*
Flowers	*The Little Flowers of St Francis*
1221	The 1221 Rule (*non Bullata*)
1223	The 1223 Rule
Test	*The Testament of St Francis*
Admon	*The Admonitions of St Francis*

Chapter 1

1 *1 Cel* 17; *2 Cel* 9; *Leg Comp* 11; *Bon* I.5; II.6.
2 *Test*; cf. K. Esser OFM, *The Testament of St Francis*, trans. M. Karecki (Wisconsin: Franciscan Publishers, 1982).
3 *2 Cel* 3; *Leg Comp* 2.
4 *2 Cel* 4; *Leg Comp* 4.
5 *2 Cel* 5; *Leg Comp* 6; *Bon* I.2.
6 *2 Cel* 6; *Leg Comp* 6; *Bon* I.3.
7 *Leg Comp* 2.
8 *2 Cel* 8; *Leg Comp* 10; *Bon* I.6.

9 *Leg Comp* 7.
10 Strictly Romanesque; cf. A. Fortini, *Francis of Assisi* (New York: Crossroad, 1981), p. 215 with note. The style is transitional, moving from the strict Byzantine symbolism into a more human Christ. It reflects the devotion to the human Christ which grew from the end of the eleventh century and was greatly fostered by St Bernard of Clairvaux (1090–1153). Also see, amongst others, G. L. Prestige, *Fathers and Heretics* (SPCK, 1948), esp. the Epilogue; and R. W. Southern, *The Making of the Middle Ages* (Hutchinson, 1953), esp. p. 240.
11 Now in the Basilica of Santa Chiara, Assisi.
12 *2 Cel* 10; *Leg Comp* 13; *Bon* II.1.
13 *2 Cel* 11; *Leg Comp* 13.
14 *1 Cel* 8; *Leg Comp* 16; *Bon* II.1.
15 *1 Cel* 14–15; *2 Cel* 12; *Leg Comp* 19; *Bon* II.4.
16 *1 Cel* 16–17.
17 *Bon* II.7; *1 Cel* 18; *2 Cel* 11.
18 *1 Cel* 22; *Leg Comp* 25; *Bon* III.1.
19 *1 Cel* 22.
20 Anthony Bloom, *Living Prayer* (Darton Longman & Todd, 1966), p. 11.
21 H. Twells (1823–1900), *English Hymnal*, no. 266, v.6.
22 *1221* ch. 22; *Admon* XII.
23 *Bon* V.6.
24 *2 Cel* 129; *Leg Per* 96; *Mirror* 97.
25 Kathleen Burne, *The Life and Letters of Father Andrew, SDC* (Mowbrays, 1948).

Chapter 2
1 *1 Cel* 24; *2 Cel* 15; *Leg Comp* 27; *Bon* III.3; *Flowers* 2.
2 *Leg Comp* 28.
3 cf. *1 Cel* 25; *Leg Comp* 32; *Bon* III.4.
4 *Leg Comp* 33.
5 *1 Cel* 32; *Bon* III.8.
6 *1 Cel* 26.
7 *1 Cel* 27; *Leg Comp* 36; *Bon* III.6.
8 *Test.*

9   John R. H. Moorman, *St Francis of Assisi* (SCM, 1950; SPCK, 1963, 1976), pp. 50–54.

10 *1 Cel* 14; *2 Cel* 15.

11 *Bon* III.3; *Leg Comp* 28; *Flowers* 2.

12 *1 Cel* 32–33; *Leg Comp* 47–53; *Bon* III.9.

13 *1221*, esp. chs. 4, 6; *Mirror* 13.

14 *2 Cel* 17; *Leg Comp* 49–52.

15 cf. John R. H. Moorman, *A History of the Franciscan Order* (from its origins to the year 1517) (Oxford University Press, 1968), p. 71.

16 *1 Cel* 55–57; *2 Cel* 30; *Bon* IX.5–6.

17 cf. Moorman, *A History*, op. cit., pp. 67–68; Original source: *Chronicle of Fra Giordano di Giano*, 5, English trans., *XIIIth Century Chronicles*, trans. Placid Hermann OFM (Chicago: Franciscan Herald Press, 1961); also, A. Mockler, *Francis of Assisi: The Wandering Years* (Phaidon, 1976), p. 223.

18 *1 Cel* 38.

19 Prologue to *Mirror*; *Bon* IV.11.

20 *Bull: Solet annuere* (The 1220 "Noviciate" Bull was *Cum secundum consilium*.)

21 cf. esp. *1223*, chs. 1, 8, 10.

22 *1 Cel* 18.

23 Although the title Minister General is used in the Rule (*1221*, ch. 5; *1223*, chs. 8, 9) it does not seem to have been given to anyone until after Francis' death. When Francis resigned in 1220, Peter Catanii was named Vicar, followed by Elias in 1221. Elias was Vicar until the death of Francis. In 1227 he was appointed by Pope Gregory IX to supervise the building of the Basilica of St Francis in Assisi. He was appointed Minister General in 1232 and remained so until 1239 when he was deposed for abusing the office and later excommunicated. He died in 1253.

23a Appointed Protector of the Order 1220, later Pope Gregory IX (1227–41). cf. *1 Cel* 99 (on his character and Francis' wishes concerning him).

24 *Leg Comp* 14; *Leg Per* 37; *Mirror* 92.

25 *Test*; *1 Cel* 45; *Leg Comp* 37; *Bon* IV.3.

26 *Leg Per* 44; *Mirror* 101.

27   *2 Cel* 108; *Leg Per* 81.

28   *2 Cel* 37.

29   *1 Cel* 57; *Bon* IX.7.

30   *1221*, ch. 15.

31   *2 Cel* 166; *Leg Per* 48; *Mirror* 115; *Bon* V.9.

32   *1 Cel* 107.

33   *1 Cel* 88, 109–110; *2 Cel* 214–217; *Leg Comp* 68; *Bon* XIV.6.

34   C. S. Lewis, *The Great Divorce* (Collins, Fount Paperbacks, 1977), esp. p. 43.

35   Barrie Williams, *The Franciscan Revival in the Anglican Communion* (DLT, 1982).

36   cf. Father Francis SSF, *Life of Brother Douglas* (Mowbrays, 1959, 1974); George Seaver and Coleman Jennings, *Tales of Brother Douglas* (Mowbrays, 1960). The provisional Rule of 1927 (quoted in Williams, op. cit., p. 108) stated: "The Community consists of 1. Homeless Wayfarers who are able and willing to work, and 2. Religious brothers living under a simple Rule of Life."

37   Father Francis, op. cit., pp. 49–50.

38   Ibid., ch. 14.

39   Father Dennis, *The Life of Father Algy* (Hodder & Stoughton, 1964).

40   *The Franciscan* (the Society of St Francis publication issued three times a year), vol. XXIII, no. 3, Sept. 1981, p. 129.

41   See ch. 6 for the ecclesiastical position of the Society.

42   The prayer known as the St Francis prayer, though expressing much of his spirit, dates from the nineteenth century.

43   *Letter to All the Faithful*.

Chapter 3

1   *2 Cel* 102; also, *Bon* XI. 1–2.

2   *Bon* III.3; *1 Cel* 24; etc.

3   Duane V. Lapsanski, *Evangelical Perfection* (New York: St Bonaventure University, 1977), examines the teachings of such groups. Also, cf. E. A. Armstrong, *St Francis, Nature Mystic* (1973); Mockler, op. cit.; K. Esser OFM, *The Origins of the Franciscan Order* (Chicago: Franciscan Herald Press, 1970).

4 Dom David Knowles, *The Religious Orders in England* (Cambridge University Press, 1950), pp. 121–122.

5 Some have suggested that Brother Caesar of Speyer helped him with Scripture references. cf. article in *Concilium* (see ch. 7, note 38, for full reference); Théophile Desbonnets, *The Franciscan Reading of the Scriptures*, esp. p. 43.

6 See Standard Edition (DLT, 1966).

7 Collect for Advent II (*Book of Common Prayer* and *Alternative Service Book*).

8 *The Spiritual Exercises of St Ignatius*, trans. T. Corbishley SJ (Anthony Clarke, 1963), and the translation with modern paraphrase by David Fleming SJ (New York: Doubleday, 1983). In our time, Ignatian spirituality has been revived in a new form. In the British Isles, St Beuno's in North Wales is the centre.

9 Archimandrite Sofrony, *The Undistorted Image* (Faith Press, 1958), Part II (the Staretz's writings), ch. 1, pp. 115–118.

10 *2 Cel* 62, 105; *Leg Per* 96; *Mirror* 3, 5.

11 *Leg Per* 72–73; cf. also *2 Cel* 195; *Mirror* 4.

12 cf. *2 Cel* 163; *Leg Per* 70.

13 *Admon* V.

14 *Test* – "*Idiotae et subditi onmibus*"; cf. also, *2 Cel* 145; *Bon* VI.5.

15 San Georgio: *1 Cel* 23. For all Francis' early life and background see esp. Fortini, op. cit.

16 cf. *1 Cel* 93; *Leg Per* 115; *Mirror* 50, for importance of example (deeds) rather than words.

17 Moorman, *A History* op. cit., p. 246 (with echo by Jacopone da Todi); full reference – Quaracchi, *Analecta Franciscana*, 10 vols., 1885–1926, vol. III, p. 86.

18 Quaracchi, *St Bonaventurae Opera Omnia*, 1898, vol. III, p. 336. Also quoted in R. B. Brooke, *Early Franciscan Government* (CUP, 1959), p. 273.

19 Moorman, *A History* op. cit., ch. 17 et al.

20 See the Appendix for description of the various writings.

21 *Mirror* 4.

22 Gustavo Gutiérrez, *A Theology of Liberation* (USA: Maryknoll, 1973; SCM Press, 1974).

23 Celano has many stories of Francis and animals: cf. *1 Cel* 60–1; 77–9; *2 Cel* 165–171.

24 *1 Cel* 80; *2 Cel* 165.

25 Leonardo Boff, *Saint Francis: A Model for Human Liberation* (New York: Crossroad, 1982; SCM, 1985), pp. 3–4.

Chapter 4

1 References to the psalms are given in the Hebrew numbering (as in most versions of the Old Testament and Anglican Prayer Books). The Greek numbering which follows the Vulgate Bible is used in most Catholic liturgical forms (cf. also *The Grail Psalter*, published as *The Psalms*, trans. J. Gelineau (Collins, 1966), esp. p. 15.

2 Full title: *Morning and Evening with Night Prayer from the Divine Office* (Collins, 1976).

3 Faith Press, 1976.

4 cf. *1223*, ch. 3, but with the Gallican Psalter – Innocent III developed this new Office.

5 *Praises before the Office*.

6 *1221*, ch. 3; *1223*, ch. 3.

7 cf. The paraphrase of the "Our Father".

8 *Leg Per* 95; *Mirror* 94; *Bon* X.6; *2 Cel* 96.

9 Though Eucharistic theology was thus expressed in Francis' day, today the emphasis is more on the action of the whole liturgy and in all the people rather than on the *moment* of consecration and the words of the priest.

10 cf. esp. *Letter to All Clerics*, *Letter to All the Faithful* and *1 Cel* 62, *Bon* IV.3.

11 *Admon* I.

12 *Letter to a General Chapter*.

13 *2 Cel* 10; *Bon* II.1.

14 *Leg Comp* 14; *Leg Per* 37; *Mirror* 92; *2 Cel* 11.

15 *1 Cel* 45; *Mirror* 118.

16 *Admon* VI.

17 *1221*, ch. 23.

18 cf. *Letter to a General Chapter*: "If the tomb where he lay for only a short time . . . "

19 *1 Cel* 84–87; *Bon* X.7.

20   *1 Cel* 6; *Leg Comp* 12.

21   Santa Maria degli Angeli.

22   cf. *1 Cel* 63, 91–2; *2 Cel* 46, 168.

23   But note that Mary is taken to be Mary Magdalene. The Magdalene was the penitent and contemplative *par excellence* in Western tradition. Penitence becomes part of the adoration.

24   *2 Cel* 94–95.

25   *2 Cel* 95.

26   *Bon* X.4.

27   *1 Cel* 26.

28   *Flowers* 2.

29   *Bon* X.6.

30   cf. *1223*, ch. 10.

31   Lao-Tzu, *Tao te Ching*, trans. D. C. Lau (Penguin, 1963), LVI.128.

32   *1221*, ch. 23.

33   After Dionysius the Areopagite (Acts 17), but writings are generally agreed to have been written by a Syrian monk of the 6th century. Though he wrote positively (cf. *The Divine Names*), his writings are best known for the incomprehensibility of God (cf. *Mystical Theology*).

34   cf. *The Cloud of Unknowing*, trans. C. Wolters (Penguin, 1961).

35   St Bonaventure, *The Soul's Journey into God* (Classics of Western Spirituality) (New York: Paulist Press, and SPCK, 1978), esp. pp. 60, 95, 114.

36   *1 Cel* 80, 109; *2 Cel* 213, 217; *Mirror* 100–1, 120; *Leg Per* 43–44. Also, E. Leclerc OFM, *The Canticle of the Creatures* (Chicago: Franciscan Herald Press, 1970).

37   *Leg Per* 44; *Mirror* 101.

38   *The Oxford Dictionary of the Christian Church*, ed. F. L. Cross (OUP, 1957), Article on Duns Scotus, pp. 426–427.

Chapter 5

1   *2 Cel* 172.

2   *1221*, ch. 4.

3   Bloom, op. cit., esp. ch. 8; also, *School of Prayer* (DLT, 1970).

4 Bernard of Clairvaux, *On the Love of God* (Mowbrays, 1950).

5 *1221*, ch. 23.

6 Julian of Norwich, *Revelations of Divine Love*, trans. C. Wolters (Penguin, 1966), ch. 5, pp. 68–69.

7 cf. amongst others, *Faith and Contemplation* (DLT, 1974); *The Truth will make you Free* (DLT, 1976); *The Living God* (DLT, 1980).

8 W. Langland, *Piers the Plowman*, trans. J. F. Goodridge (Penguin, 1959), bk XI, p. 133 (also, p. 87).

9 *1 Cel* 42; *Bon* IV.3; *Leg Comp* 55.

10 *1 Cel* 21; *2 Cel* 18; *Leg Per* 8; *Leg Comp* 56; *Mirror* 55; *Bon* II.8.

11 eg. *Letter to a General Chapter*.

12 *2 Cel* 137.

13 cf. *Letter to Brother Leo* and *Blessing for Brother Leo*; also, *2 Cel* 49.

14 *1 Cel* 44; *Leg Comp* 55.

15 *Mirror* 9; *Leg Per* 13; *2 Cel* 59.

16 *1221*, ch. 9; *1223* ch. 6.

17 *2 Cel* 176; *Leg Per* 5; *Mirror* 28.

18 *2 Cel* 22; *Bon* V.7; *Mirror* 27; *Leg Per* 1.

19 *1 Cel* 2.

20 *1 Cel* 17.

21 *1 Cel* 83.

22 *1223*, ch. 6.

23 *1221*, ch. 7.

24 cf. H. Chadwick, *The Early Church* (Penguin, 1967), p. 56.

25 *1221*, ch. 13 (but contrast *1223*, ch. 11, together with ch. 7).

26 Boff, op. cit., esp. ch. 1, pp. 5–41.

27 *Legend of St Clare* 14, and his *Form of Life* and *Last Will of St Clare*.

28 *Bon* XII.2; *Flowers* 16.

29 *1221*, ch. 17, 22; *Admon* IX; *Letter to a Minister*.

30 *Admon* IX.

31 *Leg Per* 90; *Mirror* 66; *Flowers* 26.

32 *Flowers* 21.

33 *Bon* IX.8; also, *1 Cel* 57; *Flowers* 24. (for further details and references cf. ch. 7.)

34   *Test*; *1 Cel* 23; *Bon* III.2; *Leg Per* 67; *Leg Comp* 26.

35   *2 Cel* 37; *Mirror* 101.

36   *2 Cel* 85; *Leg Per* 89; *Mirror* 37; *Bon* VIII.5; *1 Cel* 76.

37   Amongst others, *Revolution through Peace* (New York: Harper & Row, 1972); *A Thousand Reasons for Living* (DLT, 1981).

38   For the name "Friars Minor", cf. *Leg Per* 67; *Mirror* 26; *1 Cel* 38; *1221*, ch. 6, 7; *1223*, ch. 1.

39   Bishop Desmond Tutu, *Hope and Suffering* (Collins, Fount Paperbacks, 1983); cf. ch. 6 for more on the Third Order.

40   Quoted from a speech made to the Anglo-Catholic Conference in 1923. Printed as the tract, *Our Present Duty* (Church Literature Association, 1973); cf. also, H. Maynard Smith, *Frank, Bishop of Zanzibar (1871–1924)* (SPCK, 1926), esp. p. 302.

41   *Admon* XXVII.

Chapter 6

1   Boff, op. cit., ch. 1.

2   Prue Wilson, *My Father took me to the Circus* (DLT, 1984).

3   *Letter to Brother Leo*.

4   *Admon* III.

5   *Admon* III.

6   *1221*, ch. 5. See also in a *Letter to All the Faithful*: "However no one can be bound to obey another in anything that is sinful or criminal."

7   *1223*, ch. 4.

8   *1223*, ch. 10.

9   *Letter to a Minister*.

10   *1223*, ch. 7.

11   *1223*, ch. 10.

12   *Admon* IV; XX.

13   "Minister" was the name given to Superiors: cf. *1 Cel* 184–188; *1221*, ch. 2.

14   *1221*, ch. 4, 5; *1223*, esp. ch. 8, 10.

15   *2 Cel* 193.

16   cf. esp. *Leg Comp* 57–61; also, *1221*, ch. 18; *1223*, ch. 8; and *Flowers* 18; *Mirror* 68; *Leg Per* 114.

17 *Admon* VII.

18 cf. also, ending to *1221*, ch. 23.

19 *Admon* XVII.

20 *1 Cel* 71; *2 Cel* 9, 94, et al.

21 *The Praises of the Virtues*.

22 *1221*, ch. 7.

23 Eugen Herrigel, *Zen in the Art of Archery* (Routledge & Kegan Paul, 1972).

24 Ibid., p. 46.

25 *1221*, ch. 23.

26 David Clark, *Basic Communities* (SPCK, 1977), and *The Liberation of the Church* (The National Centre for Christian Communities and Networks, 1984).

27 cf. heading of *1221* and *1223*, ch. 1.

Chapter 7

1 *1221*, ch. 23.

2 *1 Cel* 23, and for "The Lord give you Peace" cf. *Leg Per* 67; *Leg Comp* 26; *Bon* III.2.

3 *1 Cel* 36.

4 *1 Cel* 37.

5 This whole section closely resembles the Bull of Francis' canonization, July 1228.

6 *1 Cel* 72.

7 *1 Cel* 73 and cf. *Bon* XII.7.

8 Brother Kenneth was one of the first three to take vows (on 14 February 1931).

9 Quoted in a pamphlet on Intercession and taken from a card in the Julian Cell, St Julian's Church, Norwich; cf. also, R. Llewelyn, *With Pity Not With Blame* (DLT, 1982), and *Love Bade Me Welcome* (DLT, 1984).

10 John Fenton and Michael Hare Duke, *Good News* (SCM, 1976).

11 *1221*, ch. 21.

12 J. G. Whittier (1807–92), *English Hymnal*, no. 408, v.7.

13 *1 Cel* 58; cf. also, *Bon* XII.3.

14 From "God's Wounds" – a poem by Edward Shillito (published just after the First World War).

15 *1 Cel* 93; *Leg Per* 74, 115.

16 *1221*, ch. 17.

17 *Mirror* 4.

18 cf. *Build Up My Church* (see next note for full reference), ch. 4, esp. p. 56.

19 *Build Up My Church: Franciscan Inspirations for and from the Third World*, ed. Leonardo Boff OFM and Walbert Bühlmann OFM (Cap.) (Chicago: Interprovincial Secretariat for Missions of the English-Speaking Conference of the Order of Friars Minor, 1984).

20 Ibid., ch. 11, esp. p. 169.

21 Ibid., pp. 165–166.

22 Ibid., p. 171.

23 cf. *Documents of Vatican II*, ed. Walter M. Abbott SJ (Geoffrey Chapman, 1966), pp. 199–309; and *Build Up My Church*, ch. 11, p. 172.

24 *Build Up My Church*, ch. 15, pp. 215–223.

25 *Salutation of the Blessed Virgin*; also, *2 Cel* 198; *Bon* IX.3.

26 *2 Cel* 16.

27 *1221*, ch. 9; *1223*, ch. 6; *Religious Life in Hermitages*.

28 *Leg Per* 109; *Flowers* 15, 16.

29 *Leg Per* 101; *Mirror* 112. Brother Jacoba, as Francis called her, was a rich Roman widow whom Francis often stayed with in Rome. Summoned only by her intuition she came to his deathbed bringing some of his favourite honey-cakes. Her remains lie today in the Basilica of St Francis, Assisi.

30 *Build Up My Church*, ch. 15, p. 217.

31 Ibid., Preface, p. vii.

32 cf. 1985 *Catholic Almanac*, numbers as at 1 January 1983 were OFM 20, 262, OFM (Cap.) 11, 849, OFM (Conv.) 4,065, TOR 891.

33 *1221*, ch. 16; *1223* ch. 12.

34 *1221*, ch. 16. Note which mode was put first – the second one was by far the most accepted in his day. The Rule, of course, was written after Francis' visit to the Holy Land and his meeting with the Sultan.

35 cf. Moorman, *A History*, op. cit., p. 229. Full account in *Passio Sanctorum Martyrium*, pp. 15–21.

36 *Bon* IX 5–9; *1 Cel* 55–57.

37 Francis had predicted the defeat: cf. *2 Cel* 30; *Bon* XI.3.

38 *1 Cel* 57; *Bon* IX.7; *Flowers* 24. Also, Francis de Beer, "St Francis and Islam" in *Concilium*; *Francis of Assisi Today*, ed. Christian Duqnoc and Casiano Floristán (New York: Seabury Press and T. & T. Clark, 1981).

39 *Flowers* 24.

40 Mockler, op. cit., makes much of the importance to Francis of "the crusade" and the effect on him of this incident. cf. also, Fortini, op. cit., esp. ch. 11. Francis' meeting with Islam also pervades much of the work of the Italian Franciscan scholar, G. Bassetti Sani OFM. In English, see his biography of *Louis Massignon*, trans. A. Cutler (Chicago: Franciscan Herald Press, 1974), and the references to Francis there.

41 *Documents of Vatican II*, pp. 660–668, para. 1.

42 Quoted in Walbert Bühlmann OFM (Cap.), *All Have the Same God: An Encounter with the Peoples and Religions of Asia* (St Paul's Publications, 1979), p. 20.

43 *Meditations of a Hermit* (Burns & Oates, 1981); *Letters from the Desert* (Burns & Oates, 1977); also, R. Voillaume, *Seeds of the Desert* (Burns & Oates, 1955), and others cited in ch. 5, note 7.

44 "Francis of Assisi Today" and "Francis, Evangelism and Popular Communities", Nazareno Fabbretti in *Concilium*, p. 35.

45 Mother Teresa's books include *Love of Christ* (Collins, Fount Paperbacks, 1982); *A Gift for God* (Collins, Fount Paperbacks, 1981).

46 cf. ch. 5, note 36.

47 Fabbretti, op. cit., p. 34.

48 *Build Up My Church*, ch. 9, pp. 131–148.

49 Ibid., p. 143, with further references.

50 Ibid., p. 144.

51 Vincent J. Donovan, *Christianity Rediscovered: An Epistle from the Masai* (SCM, 1982).

52 cf. E. R. Wickham, *Church People in an Industrial Society* (Lutterworth, 1957); *Encounter with Modern Society* (Lutterworth, 1964).

53 A. Holzer, *Vaticanum II*, Basel 1977 (Union of Loyal Catholics in Switzerland), pp. 179 ff, quoted by W. Bühlmann, p. 205.

54 Published by The Catholic Truth Society, 1981, para. 10, p. 17. (See also, *Gaudium et Spes*, para. 44, p. 946.)

55 *Christian Zen* (New York: Harper & Row, 1974); *Silent Music* (Collins, 1974); *The Still Point* (USA: Fordham University Press, 1980); *The Inner Eye of Love* (Collins, 1978); *The Mirror Mind* (Collins, 1981).

56 cf. Writings of Henri le Saux OSB (Abhishiktānanda): *Prayer* (SPCK, 1972); *Saccidānanda: A Christian Approach to Advaitic Experience* (Indian SPCK, 1974). Also, Father Bede Griffiths, *The Golden String* (Collins, Harvill Press, 1964); *Marriage of East and West* (Collins, 1982); Jules Monchanin, *In Quest of the Absolute*, ed. J. G. Weber, Cistercian Studies Series no. 51 (Mowbrays, 1977); and Raimundo Panikkar; *The Trinity and the Religious Experience of Man* (DLT, 1973); *The Unknown Christ of Hinduism* (DLT, 1981).

Chapter 8

1   *2 Cel* 217; *Mirror* 122.

2   *2 Cel* 214, 217; *Bon* XIV.3.

3   *Mirror* 121; *Leg Per* 64.

4   *Mirror* 123; *Leg Per* 100.

5   *2 Cel* 214.

6   *1 Cel* 110; *2 Cel* 217; *Bon* XIV.5. It is interesting that in the Eucharistic context of John, ch. 13, Francis meditates on the footwashing (see his reference to it in *Admon* IV) and in an "agape" meal with his disciples recalls the Last Supper (esp. *Leg Per* 117, and *2 Cel* 217).

7   *1 Cel* 109.

8   *Bon* XIV.6; also, *Leg Per* 110.

9   *1221*, ch. 16.

10 C. S. Lewis, *The Last Battle* (Collins, Fontana Lions, 1980).

11 Ibid., p. 146.

12 Desmond Forristal, *Maximilian of Auschwitz* (Ward River Press, 1982), pp. 173–175.

13 Originally in a speech given in Detroit, 23 June 1963; cf. also,

M. Luther King, *Strength to Love* (Collins, 1969); *The Trumpet of Conscience* (Hodder & Stoughton, 1968).

14   *Mirror* 91.

15   cf. E. Doyle OFM, *St Francis and the Song of Brotherhood* (Allen & Unwin, 1980).

16   This aphorism is sometimes attributed to G. K. Chesterton: see his famous short biography, *Francis of Assisi* (Hodder & Stoughton, 1924, revised 1957).

17   "Little Gidding" from T. S. Eliot's *Four Quartets* (Faber & Faber, 1944), lines 204–206.

18   *1221*, ch. 23.

19   *Admon* V.

20   *Admon* VI.

21   *Letter to All the Faithful*.

22   Ibid.

23   *1 Cel* 115.

24   *1 Cel* 77.

25   *Mirror* 118.

26   Boff, op. cit., p. 21.

27   Ibid., p. 22.

28   *Bon* V.1.

29   *2 Cel* 211.

30   *2 Cel* 173.

31   *1221*, ch. 3; *1223*, ch.3.

32   *2 Cel* 117; *Bon* V.4.

33   *Flowers* 8; also, cf. Appendix 1 to *Flowers* for a variation on this story.

34   Anselm W. Romb OFM (Conv.), *The Franciscan Charism* (New Jersey: St Anthony Guild Press, 1969), p. 87.

35   *Dictionary of Christian Spirituality*, ed. Gordon Wakefield (SCM, 1983), p. 270.

36   cf. J. R. H. Moorman, *The Franciscans in England* (Mowbrays, 1974), pp. 1–11.

37   cf. *1 Cel* 94–95; *Bon* XIII.1–3; *Leg Comp* 69, and esp. *Flowers* – "The Considerations on the Holy Stigmata", chs. 1–5. (The "Considerations" are a special section of *Flowers* devoted to this incident.)

38   3rd "Consideration on the Holy Stigmata"; cf. also, 5th

"Consideration".

39 cf. J. McCaffery, *The Friar of San Giovanni* (DLT, 1978), and Mary Ingoldsby, *Padre Pio: His Life and Mission* (Veritas Publications, 1978).

40 cf. Brown, Driver and Briggs, *A Hebrew and English Lexicon of the Old Testament* (Clarendon Press, 1906, and subsequent editions), p. 1063. (In ancient script this letter was cruciform.)

41 cf. *2 Cel* 106; *Bon* IV.9.

Chapter 9

1 Julian of Norwich, op. cit., ch. 27, p. 103.

2 H. Bonar (1808–89), *Hymns Ancient and Modern Revised*, no. 373; (*Ancient and Modern* version, no. 705, reads "from sacredness be free" in v.7, line 2).

3 *1 Cel* 103; *Bon* XIV.1.

Also available in Fount Paperbacks

The Sacrament of the Present Moment
JEAN-PIERRE DE CAUSSADE

'It is good to have this classic from the days of the Quietist tensions with its thesis that we can and must find God in the totality of our immediate situation . . .'

The Expository Times

The Poems of St John of the Cross
TRANSLATED BY ROY CAMPBELL

'Mr Campbell has recreated the extraordinary subtlety of the music of the original in an English verse worthy of it and that climbs from aspiration to ecstasy as if it were itself the poem.'

The Guardian

Thérèse of Lisieux
MICHAEL HOLLINGS

A superb portrait of one of the most popular of all saints.

'This book is well worth recommending . . . presents a simple factual outline of Thérèse's life and teaching . . . (with) incidents . . . applied to our own everyday lives.'

Review for Contemplatives of all Traditions

I, Francis
CARLO CARRETTO

This unusual and compelling book is a sustained meditation on the spirituality of St Francis of Assisi, bringing the meaning of his message to our time.

'A book one will not forget.'

Eric Doyle, The Tablet

Also available in Fount Paperbacks

Journey for a Soul
GEORGE APPLETON

'Wherever you turn in this inexpensive but extraordinarily valuable paperback you will benefit from sharing this man's pilgrimage of the soul.'

Methodist Recorder

The Imitation of Christ
THOMAS A KEMPIS

After the Bible, this is perhaps the most widely read book in the world. It describes the way of the follower of Christ – an intensely practical book, which faces the temptations and difficulties of daily life, but also describes the joys and helps which are found on the way.

Autobiography of a Saint: Thérèse of Lisieux
RONALD KNOX

'Ronald Knox has bequeathed us a wholly lucid, natural and enchanting version . . . the actual process of translating seems to have vanished, and a miracle wrought, as though St Teresa were speaking to us in English . . . his triumphant gift to posterity.'

G. B. Stern, The Sunday Times

The Way of a Disciple
GEORGE APPLETON

'. . . a lovely book and an immensely rewarding one . . . his prayers have proved of help to many.'

Donald Coggan

Also available in Fount Paperbacks

BOOKS BY C. S. LEWIS

Reflections on the Psalms

'Absolutely packed with wisdom. It is clearly the fruit of very much
reflection . . . upon one's own darkness of spirit, one's own fumbling
and grasping in the shadows of prayer or of penitence.'

Trevor Huddleston

Miracles

'This is a brilliant book, abounding in lucid exposition and
illuminating metaphor.'

Charles Davey, The Observer

The Problem of Pain

'Written with clarity and force, and out of much knowledge and
experience.'

Times Literary Supplement

Surprised by Joy

'His outstanding gift is clarity. You can take it at two levels, as
straight autobiography, or as a kind of spiritual thriller, a
detective's probing of clue and motive . . .'

Isabel Quigley, Sunday Times

Fount Paperbacks

Fount is one of the leading paperback publishers of religious books and below are some of its recent titles.

- [ ] THE WAY OF ST FRANCIS Murray Bodo £2.50
- [ ] GATEWAY TO HOPE Maria Boulding £1.95
- [ ] LET PEACE DISTURB YOU Michael Buckley £1.95
- [ ] DEAR GOD, MOST OF THE TIME YOU'RE QUITE NICE Maggie Durran £1.95
- [ ] CHRISTIAN ENGLAND VOL 3 David L Edwards £4.95
- [ ] A DAZZLING DARKNESS Patrick Grant £3.95
- [ ] PRAYER AND THE PURSUIT OF HAPPINESS Richard Harries £1.95
- [ ] THE WAY OF THE CROSS Richard Holloway £1.95
- [ ] THE WOUNDED STAG William Johnston £2.50
- [ ] YES, LORD I BELIEVE Edmund Jones £1.75
- [ ] THE WORDS OF MARTIN LUTHER KING Coretta Scott King (Ed) £1.75
- [ ] BOXEN C S Lewis £4.95
- [ ] THE CASE AGAINST GOD Gerald Priestland £2.75
- [ ] A MARTYR FOR THE TRUTH Grazyna Sikorska £1.95
- [ ] PRAYERS IN LARGE PRINT Rita Snowden £2.50
- [ ] AN IMPOSSIBLE GOD Frank Topping £1.95
- [ ] WATER INTO WINE Stephen Verney £2.50

All Fount paperbacks are available at your bookshop or newsagent, or they can be ordered by post from Fount Paperbacks, Cash Sales Department, G.P.O. Box 29, Douglas, Isle of Man, British Isles. Please send purchase price, plus 15p per book, maximum postage £3. Customers outside the U.K. send purchase price, plus 15p per book. Cheque, postal or money order. No currency.

NAME (Block letters) _____

ADDRESS _____

_____

SHILLINGBURY TALES

SHILLINGBURY
TALES
Francis Essex

NEW ENGLISH LIBRARY/TIMES MIRROR

This book is dedicated to my wife
Jeanne

'If you would be known, and not
know, vegetate in a village;
if you would know, and not be
known, live in a city.'

SHILLINGBURY TALES

AUTHOR'S NOTE

I HAVE wondered sometimes why it is that authors, having completed some seventy-five thousand words, then find it necessary to write five hundred more by way of introduction. It has taken but one book of my own to provide an answer so far as I am concerned. *Shillingbury Tales* has not emerged as a novel simply resultant on my own work but, rather, because an extraordinary number of friends and professional colleagues contributed their expertise to a series of events in which no single person was the sole arbiter. I would like to express gratitude to some of them.

'The Shillingbury Blowers' was written as a short story in March 1974 during a flight to New York where I was meeting an Australian named Bruce Gyngell. I pushed the penned manuscript into his hand when he was going to bed and at six-thirty the next morning he telephoned down to my room urging me to write it as a screenplay. This was written whilst on holiday that summer, whereafter it lay in a drawer until September 1978. Jack Gill read the script because he was looking for exclusively English film subjects, and agreed to put up the production money. There have to *be* people like Jack if show-business is to survive, but I never cease to marvel at the unhesitating trust which caused him to back an insubstantial concept with very real money.

Greg Smith produced the TV movie the following year, Val Guest directed it with his own unrivalled distinction, and Trevor Howard starred in the role of Old Saltie; Robin Nedwell, Diane Keen, and Jack Douglas created the parts of Peter, Sally, and Jake. It is their interpretation of the written word which now returns to print within descriptive passages on the following pages. As also does the work of Lionel Jeffries, Bernard Cribbins, Jean-Pierre Cassel, John Standing, Gwen Watford, Nigel Lambert, Diana King, Helen Gelzer, Linda Hayden, Eric Francis, and Joe Black, all of whom transformed stage directions into living characters with the careful artistry which so typifies their work, and underlines the uncanny casting ability of Greg Smith.

The series was written during the winter and spring of

1980 during daily early morning and late night sessions. By June I was two scripts behind schedule and beginning to worry. One Saturday afternoon the front doorbell chimed and my close friend Bob Monkhouse stood there. He gave me, actually *gave* me, three typewritten pages outlining the basic story of Cuffy the Tinker. 'I thought it might come in handy,' was all he said. Come in *handy* . . . !

Then there was Jeanne, my wife, who spent hours in public libraries, on the telephone, or calling on various authorities, researching answers to questions thrown across the breakfast table. There was Ed Welch who underscored my scenes with inspired music. There were the people of Aldbury who allowed us to invade their magical village and turn it into Shillingbury. Finally, there was Paula Burdon, who types faster than I can read, who alone ensured that the publisher's deadline would be met.

When I finished *Shillingbury Tales* last night I thought I had written it all by myself.

This morning I realised I hadn't.

Francis Essex
December 1980

CHAPTER ONE

IT STOPPED raining on the Wednesday.

By four o'clock that afternoon a watery sun was casting weak shadows across the Green. The evening turned out to be quite pleasant but of course it was too late for anything to dry, and even as the Oddfellows Arms closed its doors for the night a sudden light breeze caused the sycamore trees to drop a thousand drips on homeward bound drinkers.

Then, with an inconsistency typical of English summers, the sun rose on Thursday morning with a confidence such that the miserable dampness of three preceding weeks might never have happened. It was one of those days when the texture of dawn air promised heat to come, where the sureness of a blue sky forbade the intrusion of anything more than a few high-flying fluffy clouds placed for effect, and where a dozen pockets of sleepy mist looked forward to being chased away by breakfast time.

The village was an early riser, but the cows were already gathered at the gate by the time Jake's daughter Mandy arrived to lead them to the milking parlour. Their progress up Long Lane blocked the passage of a couple of cars headed towards the station, but both drivers waited, relaxed and smiling – it was that kind of morning. The newspaper boy ignored his mackintosh hanging by the front door as he left the house, without his mind consciously registering it was the first occasion he had done so for twenty-one days, and Harvey the Post adopted his heatwave delivery pace even before the sun began to shine in earnest.

Sixty miles away Sally noticed the change in the weather. She'd woken shortly after five and crept from the bed to look out of the window. As a bubble of excitement exploded inside her she decided to wake Peter.

'Darling,' she whispered.

A grunt. Followed by, 'What is it?'

'It's a lovely day, that's what it is.'

'What's time?'

'Quarter-past five.'

'Good God!'

He turned over heavily and lay absolutely still for several seconds. Then with a monumental effort he raised his head and opened one eye towards the window. 'Great,' he commented. And went back to sleep.

Sally climbed back into bed and lay beside her husband. The moving van wasn't due until eight-thirty at the earliest and everything that could possibly be packed, was. She rested on her back, hands behind the head, and looked around their bedroom. A packing case standing incongruously by her dressing table, the window bare with its curtains neatly folded on a chair, an oblong patch on the wall where the Peter Scott picture of flying geese normally hung. A bright yellow blotch of sunlight appeared on the ceiling above her head and for several minutes she watched it, trying to observe its movement down the wall.

Impulsively she rolled on to her side and put her arms around Peter. She squeezed him tightly, pressing herself into his back. Nothing happened.

Today was Thursday; the day they were moving to Shillingbury. It was too exciting to stay in bed. Whilst washing herself, Sally thought for the hundredth time about how she would arrange the furniture in their cottage. She grinned at herself in the mirror.

She was enormously attractive although not even Peter called her beautiful. He said she was at her loveliest when she was asleep and had photographed her once to prove it, but the picture came out under-exposed and slightly soft focus. She had great eyes, a wonderful smile, and a good figure. So the legs weren't so hot and she didn't fill a sweater like some girls, but then Peter wasn't exactly an Adonis either.

He used to look his best when he played piano with the group, but since they changed the combo and he took up music arranging full-time, he hardly played at all. Not seriously anyway – occasionally a few chord sequences played standing up with a pencil protruding from his mouth. But he was tall. And dark. And that was about it.

Her reflection in the mirror grinned back.

The weekend came and the *Sunday Express* carried a front-page headline: 'Sizzling in the Seventies', illustrated by a bikini-clad model basking near the Serpentine. It reported long queues of traffic facing frustration on all roads to the coast, and one learned commentator succeeded in becoming the first to worry about the danger of drought.

Peter and Sally exchanged hardly a word throughout the Sunday, so totally absorbed were they in the adventure of getting straight. The heavy work was more or less complete and she was engrossed in the task of turning a cottage into a home by correctly placing their personal ornaments. He was bold enough to have emerged into the tiny plot of a front garden. His first garden – his own bit of land. He walked round it first, carefully studying every plant. Then he leaned against the fence and simply looked. On the whole it was fairly untidy, but what should be removed? He found a bent fork left behind by the previous owner and prodded uncertainly for half-an-hour before admitting to himself that he had absolutely no idea what he was doing.

Around teatime he noticed the climbing rose was coming away from the wall. Here was a job he could tackle, for it was clear to the rawest recruit among amateur gardeners that the rose needed tying back to rusted iron hooks in the brickwork. Peter fetched the kitchen steps and set to with a will.

It was then the church bells started. It wasn't too bad at first but as the minutes passed it slowly degenerated into a cacophony of sound which, even as he listened, became indescribably worse. For five minutes the bell-tower crashed out a jumble of doubles, triples, caters and cinques mixed together in a great conflict of sound. Suddenly they stopped. Quite abruptly in the middle of a phrase. As if the Lord could stand only so much and had struck down the bellringers. 'Thank God for that,' Peter muttered to himself.

Below him and to his right the living room window was opened from within. 'Pete.'

'Hi.'

'Cup of tea?'

'Great.'

He descended the steps and took the mug of tea from his wife, sucking his thumb at the same time. 'How's it going?' she enquired.

'Half-time score: Old Established Rose, three; Proud New Owner, nil.'

'You can't expect green fingers the first weekend.'

11

'I've got red ones the first ten minutes.'

Sally threw him a sympathetic grin and, reaching inside, brought out a mug for herself. She sipped from it, both elbows resting on the window frame. 'I'm going to love living here.'

He leaned against the wall and, with his head almost alongside hers, stared across their garden to the church grounds beyond. 'I could do without being intimate neighbours of those bells.'

'Yes, how about that? They weren't ringing when the house agent showed us round.'

'You bet they weren't. He'd know better.'

'Never mind,' she said. 'It'll only be on Sundays.'

'Better be. I couldn't write a note while they're clanging that lot.'

She responded dreamily. 'Darling, you're going to live in absolute peace and compose magnificent symphonies, no less!'

He pushed himself away from the wall and wandered back towards the steps. 'We have yet to see how the pop scene fits into the Village scene.'

She experienced a small flutter of insecurity. She hated it when any part of their relationship seemed to be on trial. She looked away and her eyes fell on the hideous statuette Peter's aunt had presented to them as a wedding present. She picked it up and leaned out of the window again. 'Remember this?'

Peter glanced at the brilliantly shiny china portrayal of a nude maiden emptying what looked like a bucket of water. 'I thought we'd managed to lose that. Couldn't Pickfords have broken it?'

'No such luck. Still, she might have made it to Shilling-bury but come the first Bring-and-Buy sale and she's anybody's.' He laughed at her, drained his mug, and returned it. She knew she'd been over-sensitive. 'How long will you be?' she asked, indicating the rose.

'One more tie, then to hell with it – I'm beat!'

'Me too. I've cleared the packing cases.'

'Clever girl.'

Peter reached into the window, pulled himself to her, and kissed her gently.

'What was that for?' she wanted to know.

'For putting up with me. And for finding this cottage.'

'You do like it?'

'Would I be up a ladder getting lacerated?'

She rested her head against his and looked over his shoulder towards the church. 'I'll tell you what, though,' she whispered.

'What?'

'I'll lay you odds that this old boy is one way or another connected with those bells.'

Peter turned his head to follow her gaze and saw the distant figure of an elderly man emerging through a side door of the church.

Old Saltie felt the heat of the sun as he stepped out of the church. He took the longer path through the cemetery so that he might pass beneath the copper beech which had stood there all his life and his father's before him. Saltie loved this ground, the way the trees seemed to protect the old church, the sweep of grass leading to a shady bank which defied the mower and demanded a scythe. He passed Mother Colcridge's grave where, inexplicably, the headstone had canted to a forty-five degree angle thirteen years ago in the middle of a thunderstorm, causing a number of superstitious souls to renew their lapsed attendance at Evensong.

He paused by his wife's grave. 'Bit late today, dear', he explained. 'Band rehearsal should have started five minutes gone but the Reverend was held up by a tea-party and we had to ring a few extra changes. Gave a special pull for you – hope you noticed.'

He missed Mary, missed her badly. It was worse in winter when the long nights afforded too much opportunity for remembering. Sundays were better. He could wear his best suit, part the grey hair with a comb dipped in water, polish up the shoes and pop a clean handkerchief into the breast pocket. Everybody loved Old Saltie. For half a century he'd been the most respected man in the village, although nowadays he seemed less able to tackle the things he used to. He still rang the bells of course, undertook a spot of gardening here and there, and took part in the annual charity walk which he never failed to complete despite the blisters.

Most of all he had The Band.

He was nearly abreast of the Breams' cottage before he noticed the young couple watching him. He remembered; it wasn't the Breams' cottage any longer, was it? It had been purchased by a young fellow and his lady – London they came from. What was his name, now? Higgins. Couldn't say he took to it, it didn't roll off the tongue like a Warwickshire name. 'Lovely evening,' he offered as he drew near. 'Settling in then?' He took in the steps by the climbing rose. 'You're having her off, I see.'

Peter curbed a lift of his eyebrow. 'I'm trying to tie it up.'

'No strength in all that whippy growth.'

'No?' responded Peter uncertainly.

'You want to cut it back to those new shoots starting up from the root, see?' The old man entered the garden unbidden.

'Where's your secateurs?'

'My –? Oh, clippers – over here.'

'We'll have her romping over the wall in no time. Comes from being ignored.'

As he headed straight for the lower regions of the rose Sally spoke up. 'Darling –!' From the inflection of her voice Peter knew she meant: What's the old fool *doing?* He picked up her cue.

'We quite like it as it is, I'm afraid.' As the old man drew back he added lamely, 'She is having a gentle romp.'

'You don't want her down?'

'We'd rather not.'

'Suit yourself.' Then a warning: 'Only she'll never come to anything left to herself.'

Sally said, brightly and firmly, 'We'll think about it Mr –'

'Wicklow. Dan Wicklow. Everybody calls me Saltie.'

She gave him her best smile. 'Thanks awfully for the advice.'

'Advice given is nothing. It's advice taken as counts.' Saltie looked at the girl, his eyes softening as he took in her friendly, open smile. 'Good evening to you.'

As he went on his way Peter looked at the rose. 'Ignore him, Rose. I think you're fantastic. Besides, you can't live in Rose Cottage without a bloody rose.'

That was about five minutes before the band began to play.

St George's Church of England was built in 1475 but it was three hundred years before someone decided a church hall would look well adjoined to it. When the new structure was finished the natural name to choose for it was St George's Church Hall. However, a hundred and fifty years after *that* Saltie's father, Herbert Wicklow, who was a carpenter by trade, persuaded the parish council to put up a village hall as well. Presumably because he had an eye on the joinery contract. So in 1925 they put up a fine building and nobody seemed in the least surprised when it was named St George's Hall. In fact all three buildings were referred to as 'St George's' and nobody ever seemed confused.

Over the years St George's Hall had taken on a distinctive character. It was never anything but spotlessly clean, the glass shone in the tall windows, the wood block floor glowed, and the chairs were neatly stacked against the back wall. The hall also betrayed signs of needing repair in odd spots. The stage was definitely uneven and Mrs Tipping, who gave ballet classes to the primary schoolgirls, swore it was a loose floorboard which caused her to break an ankle whilst performing a *pas seul* from *The Sleeping Beauty*. In 1950 the stage curtains had disintigrated during cleaning and had never been re-placed.

In the light of the low evening sunshine seventeen members of the Shillingbury Brass Band awaited the arrival of their founder-conductor. Music stands and chairs were set for the weekly practice session. Saltie's podium had been placed reverently in position – it was the last thing his father had made.

The Shillingbury Blowers were secure, peaceable men, happy and contented. There was Jake on lead cornet. A bit devious was Jake. An elderly farmer, something of an organiser, with a touch of union background when he was a younger man. Not one to make snap decisions, he liked time to *think*. But once he'd *thought* no power on earth would shift him.

On the other hand no power on earth would *start* Sam on tuba. A little hard of hearing, slow on the uptake, but loyally willing. Musically speaking his part was relatively simple; bar after bar of 'Pom-pom-pom-pom-pom-pom' into which the old chap happily lost himself in his little world of bass notes.

Reggie, with his trombone, was patient, ruddy, rotund, and bald. A born follower of everything except the conductor's beat, he looked to Jake for a lead. Sitting alongside Sam he was able to keep the deaf tuba player abreast of anything of importance – like when the band had reached the end of a piece.

Harvey was a jolly man, blessed with a loud laugh, a ready sense of humour, and a big drum. He was invariably five minutes late for any appointment and apologised only if he delayed his colleagues beyond that period. He strutted through the door, shoulders back and stomach thrust forward as if in anticipation of the weight of his drum. 'Bells has stopped,' he announced.

Reggie removed his lips from the mouthpiece just sufficiently to enable speech. 'Aye. He'll be along in a minute.'

Harvey asked Jake if his Bess was in the family way. The farmer nodded and the band offered congratulations.

'So you was successful, then?' somebody commented.

'Course I was.'

'Never thought you would be,' grinned Harvey, with a wink towards Reggie. 'Bess were that embarrassed. Doing it in public for all to see. You could have taken her back shed!'

Jake smiled quietly. He'd heard all this before. 'I'll tell you what, though,' he said, 'I'll have trouble with that cow before spring. She'll not calve easy, I know it.'

The band continued to emit the odd 'Tweet' and 'Pom' of tuning-up noises. Matthew, Basil and Alan tried a few scales with Jake in the cornet section, Eddie blew breathily into his trombone as he sat beside Reggie; Phil and Sydney cradled their saxophones as they sat apart from the rest discussing football. Suddenly, and without warning, Sam let fly with the loud tuba passage from Wagner's *Lohengrin* Overture.

Reggie said, 'Hold it a second, Sam.' But he had to pull the instrument away from his neighbour's face. 'Give it a rest.'

'I like that bit,' objected Sam belligerently. 'It's the only time we get a tune to play.'

'But not now. We're talking.'

'We come here for band practice. And I'm going to practise.' Sam continued to sulk into his tuba, but quietly, until Old Saltie came in through the main door. He walked towards the band with a slight hint of swagger and an air of authority. 'Good evening, gentlemen.' There came an assortment of 'Good evening, Saltie' from the men. 'We'll take the Elgar,' said Saltie as he stepped up on to the podium and took a stumpy baton from his inside pocket.

Chair legs squeaked as the players leaned forward to select the appropriate sheet of music. Sam knocked his music stand over but Reggie put it right for him. Saltie tapped his baton and the band settled.

Sam asked, 'Are we going to get a story, Saltie?' Every week the same. A tradition harking back into the mists of time. Old Saltie's story. The men looked up at him expectantly. When a slight smile softened his features and he lowered his arms to his sides, they sat back comfortably.

Saltie told them, 'It is an evening in high summer, here in the heart of Warwickshire. On such a night as this, in just such a place as Shillingbury, there came a stirring in the breast of Sir Edward when he was Master of the King's Musick. A great Englishman – perhaps the greatest of them all. He bequeathed our nation many a fine and noble melody and we will pay tribute to him now by playing his patriotic march, *Pomp and Circumstance* Number One.'

The conductor paused. Then he raised his arms. Jake muttered, *sotto voce,* so as not to break the atmosphere: 'Give it all you've got, lads.'

And Old Saltie began to conduct.

People reacted in a number of varied ways when first they heard the Shillingbury Blowers. All were startled, but some conveyed this with little more than a wince whereas other tenderer subjects jumped violently. Not many among the jump-violently category found themselves at full stretch from the top of a ladder when the sound assailed them, and Peter was unlucky in this respect. Neither ladder nor climbing rose could do much to help him. Peter and the ladder hit the ground simultaneously whilst the rose, a more experienced listener, pondered a moment before parting company from the wall and covering the new gardener like a thorny duvet. 'God Almighty!' said Peter.

Wrenching himself free of clutching branches, he stood up, looked around in mild panic, and fled into the cottage. He pulled closed the windows with little effect – The Shillingbury Blowers could penetrate nine inches of concrete at two hundred yards range.

In St George's Hall the seventeen men were transported into their own special nostalgia. Each poured a personal emotion into every note and, as the music progressed, they became engulfed by a procession of feelings; of patriotism for their country, pride in their village, loyalty to their friends, love of their dear ones, surging warmth toward all mankind. As one mental tableau followed another it was greeted with additional effort – an extra twiddly-bit around the melody, a bonus triplet added to the steady beat of the big drum, a sudden crescendo on a sagging phrase from the trombone.

The Shillingbury Brass Band was without question the worst band anyone could remember hearing within living memory.

'And so we come to item five on the agenda: The Shillingbury Brass Band. I believe this is your motion, Mr Fennel.'

In a main room of the modest town hall members of the parish council sat round a long table. Mr Charles, the chairman, silver-haired, quietly spoken, and indestructibly polite, looked towards the forceful and ambitious young builder. Fennel, however, was looking nervously at Old Saltie, who sat ominously motionless, like an explosive charge ready to meet its detonator.

'Yes. Well – I mean, it's not good enough.' Fennel had not made an impressive start.

Saltie stirred slightly. 'Not good enough?'

'What I'm saying is, the band doesn't seem to – er – do very well.'

'Do very well?' asked Saltie.

Fennel swallowed and tried a new tack. 'After all, can the village afford a band?'

'Can the village –?' but Mr Charles interrupted Saltie smoothly and authoritatively. 'Ah. A positive question deserving a positive answer. Mrs Simpkins?'

Mrs Simpkins was the Hon. Treasurer and the chairman had discovered that by tossing a simple calculation in her direction almost as they took their places at the start of the meeting, they could rely on being disturbed by nothing noisier than subdued counting sounds for two hours.

'I'm afraid I – Mr Chairman – unexpected. I might need notice of that question.' She ploughed helplessly through sheaves of paper as if a sudden whirlwind had struck her end of the table.

Meadows spoke up in that blunt, forthright manner of his that so irritated the chairman. 'Not the point if I may say so. Young Fennel ducking the issue. Shirking from speaking his mind. "Not good enough," he says; "Not good enough for what?" asks Mr Wicklow; "Not good enough for the *village*", say I.' He sat back and folded his arms but, as Mr Charles opened his mouth to speak, he unfolded them and leant forward again. ' "Doesn't do well", states Mr Fennel; "Well enough for what?" demands Mr Wicklow; "Well enough for *anything*", say I.' For a second time the chairman narrowly missed getting a word in. 'Well enough to qualify for the All Counties Championship,' finished Meadows. 'To even qualify, let alone win it!'

Old Saltie listened in angry silence as the conversation rumbled back and forth with increasing waves of criticism. The moment of truth arrived when Fennel stared stolidly at the table in front of him and muttered in a voice strangulated by nerves, 'The lads can't play.'

'I didn't quite catch that,' began Saltie dangerously.

'He said the lads can't play, Mr Wicklow,' said Mrs Simpkins helpfully from her welter of accounts.

Saltie rose to his feet. 'Can't play –?' But Meadows waved him down again.

'Now, Saltie, it's no use starting that again. The boy's right.'

Mr Charles endeavoured to avert the impending disaster. 'My wife and I have always considered it to be a very good band. But then of course we can't hear it where we live. Nevertheless, the record shows fine work performed by Saltie here. Fine work over many years.'

'Hear, hear,' from Mrs Simpkins, peering severely over her glasses.

'He is a highly respected man in Shillingbury,' continued Mr Charles, 'and greatly loved by the players in the band.'

'Founder-conductor,' Saltie reminded him.

'Quite so,' agreed the chairman.

'Thirty-four years,' added Saltie.

'Indeed yes.'

'Formed in 1945 to commemorate the disbandment of the Shillingbury Home Guard.'

'There you are, you see.' Mr Charles rushed on hurriedly before Saltie could further assist. 'And whenever Saltie here raises his baton there's not one man-jack of them who does not give of his best. Each player pours his soul into the music. Every phrase is played with feeling. With emotion.'

'And with inaccuracy,' muttered Meadows.

He'd commented with realism rather than malice but his remark brought forth smiles. The meeting relaxed. Fennel leaned back and rested an arm along the adjoining chair. Meadows pushed away from the table and crossed his legs. Mr Charles crossed both hands behind his head. Mrs Simpkins removed her spectacles as they all reminisced comfortably on past musical misdemeanours. Saltie temporarily became forgotten amid genial memories.

'Reggie achieves a roundness of tone from his trombone even when he's a touch unsure as to the note itself.'

'Ma Cronin's their only fan and she's as deaf as a post.'

'When they play *Land of Hope and Glory* their love for Saltie is augmented by a surge of patriotic fervour which so improves the tune as to render it totally unrecognisable.'

'In the Christmas Draw, first prize was two tickets for the Carol Concert and second prize was *four* tickets.' Mr Charles had topped them all and they laughed with deep contentment. At last they became aware of Old Saltie as he rose slowly to his feet. The laughter stifled into embarrassed silence. The conductor surveyed his colleagues for several seconds before addressing them with considerable dignity. 'Chairman and gentlemen on the council. I'm sorry you do not find approval for my little band. We may not be the London Symphony Orchestra but we are a group bonded together by a common love of harmony. I say this to you; destroy The Shillingbury Brass Band and you destroy Shillingbury.' Saltie paused for a moment and seemed to reach a decision within himself. 'If you find no pleasure from our music perhaps it is the leadership at fault. We used to say there were no bad soldiers in an army, only bad officers. Maybe there are not bad musicians, only bad conductors. Show me a better man and I shall step down.'

The council members spoke all at once.

'Oh no –'

'But we can't have that –'

'You mustn't think –'

Old Saltie looked up, a last hope flickering. 'You mean, you do not wish me to resign?'

The council responded, again simultaneously.

'Well, I think we *do* –'

'Actually, it would be the best thing –'

'Oh yes, rather –'

'We feel perhaps you should –'

Mr Charles summed up. 'It's just that we don't want you to be *upset!*'

Completely crestfallen, Saltie looked from one face to another. None could meet his gaze. With his back inscrutably straight, Old Saltie turned from the table, and left the room.

There followed a silence during which nobody looked at anybody. Mrs Simpkins fumbled and found a sheet of paper. 'I think I've found a cost sheet that is relevant to the Band,' she began.

Meadows said, 'Shut up, Mrs Simpkins, for God's sake.'

CHAPTER TWO

THE SAXONS called Shillingbury old, which meant that parts of the village were very old indeed. For two thousand years or more men and women had lived, worked, and died there; through times of peace and war, prosperity and hardship. Inevitably their experiences echoed and re-echoed deep inside the timber-framed, brick-and-tile cottages, and it was almost possible to feel the past where it had indelibly marked the place where they had lived.

It was to one of these cottages bordering the green that Sally was invited for her first experience of a fund-raising coffee morning.

All the women were much older than she, and appeared at first to be remarkably unmemorable. They wore colourless clothes and little make-up, but they made her feel at home and seemed genuinely interested in her first reactions to village life. Her hostess accepted the shiny nude maiden as Sally's Bring-and-Buy offering with an exclaimed 'Oh, how absolutely er –' which expression was never completed. Then she poured her a cup of coffee and introduced Mrs Meadows.

Sally found Mrs Meadows to be an amusing woman with a dry sense of humour; an essential for survival, she was told, if one was married to Mr Meadows. He had a seat on the parish council, which forum appeared to spend more time discussing The Shillingbury Brass Band than the lack of amenities or the threatened road-widening scheme. She heard how the old conductor had resigned and that now the council couldn't decide whether to let the band fall by the wayside or appoint a new conductor.

It was a natural opportunity for Sally to tell her about Peter. She'd met him in the recording company where she worked and married him a year later. Mrs Meadows seemed to imagine that writers of pop music required less skill than exponents of the classics, and Sally became embroiled in a conversation about the musical education of orchestral arrangers.

The morning passed quickly but when it was time to leave she found herself staring at the shiny nude maiden standing on the sale table, embarrassingly unwanted. Suffering a moment of panic in case anyone asked which guest was guilty of bringing the tasteless statuette, Sally rushed over and purchased the wretched thing for two pounds.

That evening she sat with Peter in the private bar of the Oddfellows Arms. He interrupted her story of the coffee morning before it was half completed. 'I'm sorry, Sal. No way.'

'Well, I think that's pretty selfish.' She had said too much to Mrs Meadows and was entirely in the wrong. Her best defence was attack. 'All I'm saying –'

'It's a dreadful little band and I don't want any part of it.'

'Peter, I told you. I don't intend to do the housework and cooking to the exclusion of all else. I need mental stimulus and I plan to become a part of this village. I think that you conducting the band would be a good move. I am your wife and I do have some judgement.'

'Being married to a musician does not give perfect pitch to someone who is tone deaf.'

'That's not fair!'

She resented being the Little Woman in the wrong but, as she sipped her gin and tonic, decided to alter tactics. 'Besides, I've promised,' she confessed.

'You've what?'

'There was this woman at the coffee morning. She told me about a problem the council has with an old conductor who's past it, or something. They're looking for a younger man to pull the band into shape and make a go of it.'

'I don't believe I'm hearing this.' Peter looked at his wife as she affectedly studied her glass. 'So you promised on my behalf.'

'Sort of.'

'How much "sort of"?'

'Well –'

'Enough to be left with egg on your face if I turn it down?'

'Sort of.'

'That's great!' He took her glass and walked to the bar. As he ordered the same again he heard a heated discussion coming from the public bar. He glanced across and saw the group of elderly men; some were carrying cornet

23

or saxophone cases.

When he returned to the table Sally said, 'Being part of the place where you live isn't much to demand.'

'Demand?' he queried.

She amended it. 'Request, then.'

'Because if –'

'I said "request"!'

Peter spoke sharply. 'Sally, there's no point in arguing.' Then, timing it perfectly, 'I'll do it.'

The clouds cleared. She smiled and squeezed his arm.

'But for God's sake let's keep it out of the *Musical Express*,' he added.

In the public bar Jake was saying, 'Resigned? I've never heard so much nonsense in all my life. We're not having it. No more to be said.'

Harvey, who had broken the news, looked particularly concerned. 'It's what I heard.'

'What'll become of us?' asked Reggie. Then to Harvey, 'Where did you get it from anyway?'

It was a rhetorical question. Harvey's ability for uncovering titbits of news and gossip was known throughout Shillingbury. As the village postman he enjoyed reading, where possible, the mail he delivered. There was nothing underhand or secretive about it; he took pleasure in being the bearer of tidings good and bad, and invariably announced the text of a postcard to the recipient whilst still several yards from the front door.

'It makes no odds where he got it from,' said Jake. 'We plays for Saltie or we plays for nobody.'

Reggie agreed. 'Aside of aught else we should have been consulted before bringing in a man from outside. Internal Promotion.'

'Aye, but not you, Reggie,' said Harvey. 'You've not got the puff for it.'

'What'll we do, Jake?' asked Sam.

'I got to think a bit.'

Basil suggested they made their feelings known by blowing a few raspberries, but Jake shook his head. The band had its pride. Then he squared his shoulders.

'I'll tell you what we're going to do. We're going to turn up and meet this new conductor.'

'But you just said –'

'I know what I just said, Reggie. Now I'm saying

summat else, aren't I? We're going to turn up and meet this new fellow. Then we're going to play it a bit crafty.'

He touched the side of his nose and the band drew closer. Jake looked at them as they awaited his next words.

'Who's buying?' he enquired.

A full week elapsed before Jake outlined his plan to The Shillingbury Blowers. Then he stood before them in St George's Hall as they awaited the arrival of their new conductor. 'Give us your attention over here.' The old men looked up at him attentively. 'We'll give him *March of the Toreadors* and we'll go all out to impress. Afterwards, while he's congratulating us, I shall rise to my feet. I'll tell him, polite but firm, that Shillingbury has just heard the last note of music until Saltie's back in office. Then we'll pack away our instruments and walk out the door.'

The band was impressed. That was the thing about Jake – he always came up with the right course of action. Only Sam had a question. 'Will we get a story first?' he asked.

'No story tonight, Sam.'

'Saltie always told us a story. To get us in the mood.'

The farmer looked at the tuba player and allowed him a gentle smile. 'You'll just have to work yourself up on your own.' He sat down in the lead cornet chair and joined the rest as they tuned up and practised odd phrases. The main door opened and the band fell silent with surprise as Saltie came in followed by Peter and Sally. The old conductor marched straight to the podium and, taking care to fix his eyes on a point just above their heads, addressed them quietly. 'Gentlemen, I introduce you to Mr Peter Higgins. Some of you may have made his acquaintance, seeing he and his good lady recently moved into the village from London. He's done his time at the Guildhall School of Music and has letters after his name pertaining to a musical education which has culminated in him writing for a pop group, the – er – Close Encounters.'

'I've heard 'em,' muttered Jake with a wealth of expression.

'Mr Higgins has agreed to take over The Shillingbury Brass Band and I know you'll do your best for him as you always have for me.' There was a slight rustle from the band. After a pause Saltie continued with some emotion. 'Naturally, I am sad to hand over a baton I have cherished over many happy years, but if it will help towards harvesting the fruits of artistic endeavour, then my gesture will not have been in vain.' He stepped down and, before Peter could respond with a few suitable words, walked carefully to the door and disappeared.

Sam whispered to Reggie, 'We got a story after all.'

Peter found himself on the podium facing a band of suspicious old faces. He bade them Good evening, introduced Sally by telling them that she too played several musical instruments, namely the stereo, the radio, and a vacuum cleaner tuned to B flat. He laughed nervously but if he'd hoped for a response from the band he certainly didn't get one. Then he enquired as to which piece of music they would select by way of introduction to each other.

'*The March of the Toreadors,*' replied Jake, speaking clearly.

Must we?, thought Peter. But aloud he said, 'Okay. *March of the Toreadors* it shall be.'

Each man checked the part on the stand before him, Jake nodded significantly to his colleagues, and Peter raised his baton. 'I'll give you four in,' he advised. 'Nice brisk tempo. Here we go. One – two – three – four!'

The Shillingbury Blowers put everything they had into the piece, determined to impress him. Old Saltie's parting words had moved them to supreme effort, and all the extra phrases, nuances, lingering tones, and surprise beats were included in two minutes of raucous caterwauling. Eventually Peter had little option but to signal a halt, but by then the players were transported to higher plains and did not see him. 'Just a minute . . . Hold it, please . . . SHUT UP!' His desperate shout seemed to penetrate the din and a few eyes looked up at him. One by one the musicians tailed off until only Sam was left blindly engrossed in his Pom-pom-pom-pom. At last he too became aware that all was not as it should be and he peered round the side of his tuba. Then he stopped playing and there was blessed silence.

'Is he pleased?' he asked Reggie.

'No, I don't think he is.'

Peter realised he was in for a few unpleasant moments, and steeled himself to tell the old men he'd just heard the most horrendous sounds of his musical career. He'd hoped that on the first occasion of their meeting the band would have played its best.

'That was our best,' explained Sam naively.

The Shillingbury Blowers looked at their new conductor in stunned amazement as he complained that they played out of time and out of tune. It was clear they'd have to return to first principles, and, to this end, he requested the first chord. No more, just play the first chord. But they were too transfixed to play anything. 'Excuse me,' asked a shaken Jake, 'are you telling us we can't play?'

'Out of the shambles I heard I couldn't detect a meaningful note of music.'

The farmer wanted to get it quite clear. 'We can't play *The March of the Toreadors?*' he repeated. 'Is that what you're saying?'

'If you hadn't told me the title I'd never have guessed it,' replied Peter. He turned to the rest of the band and tried to speak encouragingly of working together through weeks of patient rehearsal until they got better.

'Got better?' Jake rose to his feet. 'That was IT!'

Peter remained patient. 'Would you take your seat, please?'

'We're not your Guildhall students, you know.'

'Would you please sit down?'

'*March of the Toreadors* has been the pride of our repertoire since you was in short trousers.'

'If you'll just sit down –'

Jake pointed a finger at him. 'Mr Wicklow never spoke to us like that. Not never once in all the years we was together.'

'I'm asking you to sit down,' said Peter, raising his voice.

Jake thundered his reply. 'And you're a YOUNG UPSTART!'

In the instant of its being spoken the description became another indelible mark on the history of Shillingbury. It was to be Peter's nickname for several decades, used in times of irritation or affection. He'd be Young Upstart on his ninetieth birthday; it would never change. For several seconds the accusation rang round his brain

27

and he was only dimly aware of Jake's command, 'Everybody out!'

The band left as a man; not the dignified exit they had planned but decisively effective for all that. A few moments later Peter and Sally were alone in the hall. She said, 'Somehow I don't get the impression they love you as much as they loved Old Saltie.'

As the band poured into the public bar, Sam asked, 'Was that how you intended, Jake?'

'No, it was not how I intended,' the farmer replied angrily. 'He's a Young Upstart.'

'What are we going to do now?' asked Reggie.

'I dunno for the moment. He's bested us, see. By saying as we can't play he's put *us* in the wrong.'

Harvey suggested, 'We could say he didn't conduct us proper.'

'*Didn't* he conduct us proper?'

'I don't know. I wasn't looking at him.'

'He's bested us,' repeated Jake bitterly. 'Took away the only means of getting Saltie back.'

'So what are we going to do?' demanded Reggie a second time.

Jake glared at him. 'Let me think a bit, will you? We got to make plans.'

Sally was all too aware she had enmeshed Peter and herself into a complication altogether out of proportion to the innocent conversation she'd had with Mrs Meadows. She was taken aback by the effect it seemed to have on the village and, from various remarks made either to her or in her hearing, it was clear that her plan to become a part of the place where she lived had misfired badly. More surprising was Peter's own reaction. She had prepared herself for a slightly pompous lecture, and was ready to admit being wrong, say that at least they'd given it a go, and forget the whole thing. Instead he said, 'I'm going to get music out of that stubborn group of geriatrics if it's the last thing I do.' It was a side of him she hadn't seen before.

Something good will emerge out of almost anything and in this case it was Jake's daughter, Mandy. She was an attractive, level-headed girl who helped him run the farm since her mother had died. She handled him well with an outspoken directness which defused his irascible temper and helped keep things in perspective. She was engaged to

David the Vet and it was anyone's guess how Jake would be kept under control when she married.

Mandy had little time for village gossip and, finding Sally nearer her age than anyone else around, chatted to her freely. She told her that Mr Charles felt that Saltie should somehow be reinstated, and Mr Meadows considered Peter's appointment to be an absolute flop – Sally could not help smiling at the girl's unthinking bluntness. 'The thing is that last week we had a band that couldn't play properly,' said Mandy. 'Now we've got one that won't play at all.'

'You mean they'd withdraw their invitation to Peter?' asked Sally.

'It seems like it.'

'I think we might have something to say about that.'

Mandy sighed. 'I was afraid you might.'

'Oh, what a mess.'

'I wouldn't worry for the time being. Mr Charles has called for an informal meeting at the council offices, but it might never take place.

'Why's that?'

'Saltie's refused to attend unless he can be accompanied by his shop steward!'

'His shop –?'

'Dad!' grinned Jake's daughter. 'That's how I know so much about it.'

Sally shook her head wonderingly. 'I never imagined union action in Shillingbury.'

'I know,' agreed Mandy. 'They seem such harmless old men. And the band's never been any trouble – except when they play, of course.'

The informal meeting did take place but served rather to confuse matters further instead of solving them. The chairman and Meadows sat on one side of the council-room table facing Saltie and Jake. Almost a confrontation.

'I am led to believe,' Mr Charles opened, 'that a difference of opinion arose at a recent rehearsal between members of the band and the new conductor appointed by council.' He'd hoped to adopt a friendly tone but, when he looked at the others, they avoided his eye. 'And that the lead cornet player – that's you, Jake – decided to terminate the rehearsal by marching your colleagues out.

Is that correct?'

'I'm not prepared to comment on what I did, nor apologise for it neither,' countered Jake. 'What we'd like to discuss is how it came about that the council appointed a new conductor without consulting my – er – members.'

'Ah, but we did. There was a full and frank discussion.'

Saltie looked up. 'There was no mention of a new man before I left.'

Jake leaned forward accusingly. 'It's our information that Mrs Meadows talked to Young Upstart's wife at a coffee morning.'

Mr Charles frowned slightly. 'Young – ?'

Meadows said, 'He means Higgins.'

'And that they fixed it up between them,' concluded Jake.

'Hardly likely, d'you think?' Meadows asked him.

The chairman waited a moment before giving a sharp little nod, as if to regain control of the meeting.

'In any event, I suggest it's water under the bridge. Mr Meadows and I have a proposal to put to you.'

'What sort of proposal?' enquired Jake suspiciously.

Mr Charles played his ace. 'That the council withdraws certain unfortunate remarks made at its last meeting and invites Saltie here to return to his position as conductor of The Shillingbury Brass Band.'

'Ah.' Jake leant back in his chair. He'd never imagined it would be so easy. It wasn't. When they looked at Saltie they saw a series of expressions that had not touched his face in a lifetime – sulky, angry, hurt, and unforgiving. 'No,' was all he said. The ace was trumped.

Jake looked at his friend, puzzled. Meadows was irritable. The chairman sighed and took one of his tablets. Saltie spoke, his voice shaking slightly. 'You said we couldn't play.'

'But I've explained that we wish to withdraw –'

'You laughed. You can't withdraw a laugh.'

'Surely an apology –'

'You *all* laughed!'

Saltie got up from the table, turned, and pointed a finger at them. 'I told you that to destroy the band was to destroy Shillingbury. Now you've found it out for yourselves you want things back as they were. Nice and simple, neat and tidy. Well, I'm not accepting.' He stumped away and looked out of the window.

'Oh dear!' said Mr Charles. He looked helplessly at Saltie's back, at Meadows frowning at the table, and at Jake studying the ceiling. 'Is there no form of compromise we could consider?'

'Maybe,' said Jake to the ceiling.

'Yes?'

'Seeing as Saltie won't conduct us, and we won't play without him, we need to give him more time to consider his position. In that case there could be an interim measure.'

'What's that, Jake?' asked the chairman.

It was the farmer's turn to play *his* card. The scheme he'd evolved through several long and sleepless nights of trying to apply union procedures to music-making. 'A process of non-cooperation.'

Meadows' jaw dropped in bewilderment. 'What the devil's a process of – ?'

'A Work-to-Rule. A Go-Slow.'

The chairman made a valiant attempt to understand. 'You mean you'd play the tunes more slowly.'

Meadows' jaw still dropped; he shook his head as well. 'You can't play "Abide with Me" any slower. You'd never finish.'

Jake was never long on patience at the best of times. 'I don't mean that at all,' he said, exasperation beginning to show. 'I mean we'd work to the book. No more, no less.'

'I'm afraid I don't understand,' said Mr Charles helplessly.

'We'll *play* the music, but we won't *interpret* it. Now do you see what I mean?'

The chairman and Meadows remained totally mystified. Only Saltie appreciated the sheer cunning of Jake's proposal and turned from the window with a knowing nod.

Jake explained carefully. 'Every piece of music has notes on it. Right? Notes of a certain value. Like you hold them for one beat, or two beats, or three. All according to what's written down. And there's other signs too – for loud and soft, faster or slower. Well, we'll play them just as they're on the music, but we won't help them on their way. You'll get the tunes straight, without any feeling to them.'

The chairman looked at him fairly blankly for several

seconds. 'It sounds an excellent arrangement to me,' he said, hoping he sounded convincing. 'What do you think, Mr Meadows?'

'I suppose so. How long will this musical go-slow last?'

'For as long as necessary,' replied Jake grimly.

'With no exceptions?' enquired Mr Charles hopefully. 'I was thinking of the Carol Concert and the Pensioners' Party.'

'Just two exceptions,' explained Meadows. 'A sort of Slow Slow Quick-Quick Slow!'

His joke went badly. 'No exceptions,' declared Jake.

The chairman summed up. 'Very well,' he said. 'We'll adopt your suggestion, Jake. And if Saltie sees things differently perhaps he'll let us know.'

'Never,' said Saltie.

Meadows turned to the chairman. 'It's going to be a long hard winter.'

The band was far quicker on the uptake than were the two members of the parish council. Even Sam got the point immediately when Jake explained the work-to-rule.

'Take your time from Young Upstart and give him the notes just as they're written,' he advised them.

News of the industrial action had spread round the village like a forest fire, so when Peter next met the band in St George's Hall, he was accompanied by Sally, Mr Charles, Fennel, Meadows, Mrs Simpkins, and some two dozen curious spectators. Peter mounted the podium and wasted no time on preliminaries. He asked them to take out the parts for *The Village Trot* and then, in crisp tones, he stated his requirements. 'Please follow the music carefully. Play the notes truly to their full value. No embellishments please. Take your time from me and give me the notes just as they're written.'

Sam whispered to Reggie, 'Is he in on the work-to-rule as well?'

'No, he's not,' said Reggie, suddenly worried that something might be about to go wrong.

'I'll give you three for nothing,' said Peter. 'Ready? One – two – three – AND . . . .'

So, working strictly to rule, The Shillingbury Blowers began to play. One eye on the music, the other on Peter, taking care to exceed in neither tempo nor notation.

It was as if Saint Cecilia, the patron of music, had laid a

gentle hand on the old men. It was a miracle. Mr Charles smiled at Mr Meadows, Mr Meadows winked at Mrs Simpkins, Fennel caught Sally's eye and gave a thumbs-up. The band was making the best sound of its existence. After two verses Peter signalled them to stop playing. They stopped. Together. Silence. Then everyone in the hall applauded. They smiled at the old men who stared back, dumbfounded. Jake scratched his head in sheer frustration. Sam stood up and took a bow before being pulled down violently by Reggie.

'But we're being clapped,' explained Sam.

'You've been clapped before, haven't you.'

Sam looked at him wide-eyed. 'No!' he said.

The curtain over the side exit door moved slightly. Saltie, who'd been standing in the dark, had heard enough. He left quietly – and nobody noticed him.

In the public bar, Terry the barmaid pulled their pints for them. Nobody had ordered; nobody felt like ordering, but Terry didn't need to be told – their order hadn't varied in fifty years.

Jake was angry. The rest were simply baffled.

'There's something funny going on here.'

'We did exactly what you said, Jake,' Harvey assured him.

'I know, I know.' Yet Young Upstart had seemed to like it. They'd all seemed to like it, even though they'd none of them given the music anything. No interpretation. Nothing.

'It was nice being clapped, Jake,' admitted Sam.

But Jake turned on him almost violently. 'We don't want any of that kind of talk, Brother. No blacklegging.'

'I only said it was nice being clapped.'

'I know. I heard you. If they think a quick round of applause is going to weaken our solidarity they've got another think coming.' A thought occurred to him. 'That's it. We must take a harder line, increase the pressure.'

'How do we do that, Jake?' asked Reggie.

'I'll tell you. We'll give it even less. Next time just tip the notes. Don't play them out. Just tip them.'

'Staccato,' said Harvey, who knew his musical terminology.

'Eh?' asked Jake, who didn't.

'That's the word for it. Staccato. You plays each note

33

short and sudden.'

Jake demolished him with a stare. 'That's what I said – tip 'em!'

'We can't give it anything by playing staccato,' said Sam. 'That's for certain sure.'

Jake drew himself up to his full height. 'I'll tell you something, Sam. We're never going to give it anything. Not while Young Upstart's there. Not while I've got a breath in my body.'

They all drank to that.

CHAPTER THREE

THE ENGLISH cottage garden was born more out of necessity than simple aesthetic pleasure.

As long ago as the ninth century villagers were able to call upon medieval monastery gardens for their simple medicinal requirements, such as a lotion from columbine leaves to cure sore throats, aromatic herbs to sweeten long-stored meat in winter, or to discourage flies in summer. The cloister gardens also grew flowers for church decoration, and the innocent snowdrop, madonna lily and rose date back to that time.

In 1530 Henry VIII was responsible for the Dissolution of the Monasteries and, in a few short months, the villagers' supply of useful plants and herbs was cut off. Thus was born the cottage garden. They were bad days for country folk, and many superstitions grew out of fear and poverty; seed potatoes should be planted only on Good Friday, granny bonnets would stave off the plague, golden rod indicated buried treasure.

Sally's voracious appetitite for things historical was matched only by an increasing interest in their little garden. Like Peter, she was totally ignorant about things horticultural, but she had good sense and a natural flair. Less than five miles away her parents' house sat within a sizeable plot, but she could not remember either of them even noticing the garden, let alone doing anything in it. So what she knew came from books and an ever-increasing fount of self-discovery.

Three or four weeks after the start of the work-to-rule she was easing out weeds from among the perennials with a border fork when she became aware of Old Saltie hovering uncertainly on the other side of the garden gate.

'Good morning, Mr Wicklow.'

'Ah. Yes. Good morning.' He shuffled awkwardly for a moment and Sally straightened up.

'Did you want something?' she asked encouragingly.

'Is your husband at home?'

'No. He's in London.'

'Oh. Well, in that case – I'll just be on my way.' But he didn't go. Leastways, not very far. Sally was puzzled by his strange hesitancy and, sticking her fork into the ground, she walked to the gate.

'Is there anything I can do?'

'No, no. It's all right, thank you.' Whatever the problem was it would have to be prised out of the stubborn old man. She leaned on the gate and set about it patiently. It wasn't until then she noticed he was carrying a large brown paper bag. She glanced back at her garden. 'Whilst you're here, Mr Wicklow, could you tell me the name of those spiky plants?'

The question brought him a few steps closer. 'Those there? They're shrubs really. Berberis.'

She grinned at him. 'I don't know the names of anything.'

'It comes out in the spring.'

She unlatched the gate and walked away causing him to follow. 'And this, over here?'

'Winter jasmine.' Out of the corner of her eye she saw him place the paper bag on a garden seat. 'It gives you a show of yellow at Christmas, if you're lucky.'

'We seem to have a mass of those grey things.'

Saltie smiled for the first time. 'That's always the way. They're weeds!'

Sally laughed. 'Shows how clever I am! Peter's been so busy there simply hasn't been time to tackle the garden.'

'Good tip for the first year is to let things be,' said Saltie. 'You never know what's hidden under there waiting to come up and delight you.'

'Yes, of course. What good sense.'

He was relaxing. 'Just keep things tidy, you know.' He led the way towards the corner of the lawn by the cottage. 'This garden's an absolute joy in March – there's hundreds of crocus all along there.'

'I was wondering –' ventured Sally.

'Aye?'

'I suppose you wouldn't be prepared to help us out a bit. With advice and, well – maybe a couple of mornings a week?'

He looked at her quietly. 'You don't want me here. It would be embarrassing for your husband. With the band and all that.'

'Nonsense. Peter's not like that.'

'Besides,' he said, 'I'm not a good enough gardener.

36

Not a good enough anything. I know a bit about a lot and a lot about nothing. That's why I never got anywhere in my life.'

Sally felt she was getting near the root of his problem. 'You're disappointed about the band.'

He smiled ruefully. 'Yes, I am. Oh, not only because of the conducting, but everything that went along with it. There was a friendship, you see. But now – even though Jake and the others are trying to get me back – there's an . . . awkwardness where it was easy before.'

They chatted for a few moments longer before he made to leave, promising he would think about the gardening and let her know. He reached the gate before Sally noticed the bag was still on the seat. 'Hey, don't forget this.' The moment she picked it up she knew what was inside and why he'd called at the cottage.

'Have a look.' Then, as she hesitated. 'Go, on, open it.' Sally felt inside and pulled out a silver trumpet. It had been presented to him when he left the Works. 'I thought it might be some sort of solution,' he explained. 'But now – I don't know –'

'You want to play to Peter.'

'Please don't say anything.'

'I know he'll want to hear you play.'

He shook his head. 'You don't understand. I've been walking up and down all morning worrying on it. I want to play to him but . . . he's an honest man, your husband, and he'll tell me straight.'

'Yes, he will,' she confirmed.

'Aye.' He gently took the trumpet from her. 'Well, I couldn't bear to discover this was something else I was second-best at.'

The Shillingbury Blowers were reeling from their third shock in a comparatively short space of time. Their tactic of playing every note staccato was proving less than successful because, inadvertently, they seemed to have stumbled across a sound that was gimmicky and trendy. A clipped rendition of 'While shepherds watched their flocks by night' gave the music a fresh new feel and the band a unique style.

Among the members of the parish council Mr Meadows

was the first to recommend that things be left to take their own course. The band was pursuing its policy of non-cooperation; so the players were happy. Young Upstart was making them sound a whole heap better; so he was happy. The council was taking more money from more engagements than ever before; so the councillors were happy. Where was the sense in changing anything?

Mrs Simpkins didn't agree and made one of her rare speeches. In all the years she'd lived in Shillingbury she'd never known such divisive hostility, and it was quite untrue that people were happy. If the council wanted a band that would go around winning festivals, that was one thing. But if they wanted something that would unite and bring together the people of their village, then that was something else.

However, members were unanimous in the view that the band had successfully developed an individual style which could quite easily catch on. Meadows added that Young Upstart had done a good job but the band was comprised of such obstinate old fools they couldn't see it.

Peter and Sally expressed much the same sentiments to each other one night in St George's Hall as they cleared up after a Thursday rehearsal. Most of the lights had been switched off, and Peter sat morosely on a stool watching his wife move in and out of pools of light as she collected music from the stands. He marvelled at the way in which goodwill had disappeared as talent had developed, and wondered how a simple farmer like Jake could have turned into a full-blown militant trouble-maker.

'Do you ever see Saltie?' she asked.

'No. Why? Is he behind it all?'

'Heavens no. He's as unhappy as we are.' She told him about Saltie's visit to the cottage, not for one moment worrying about betraying his secret – after all, a wife must confide in her husband. She described him as a nice old boy with a badly dented pride. Then she mentioned the silver trumpet in the brown paper bag.

Peter suddenly grinned and asked, 'Did you ever hear the story of the two trumpet players who auditioned for a vacancy in the London Symphony Orchestra?' She shook her head. 'The first one came in immaculately dressed. Dove grey suit, jewelled tie-pin. He took a brand new, golden trumpet from out of a velvet-lined case, shot his cuffs, raised the instrument to his lips, and started to play. He made the most terrible noise you ever heard. In came the other fellow. Shabby, down at heel, dirty old raincoat. Out of a brown paper bag he took a battered old brass cornet. He shot his tattered cuffs, raised it to his lips . . . and *he* started to play.' He paused, Sally looked at him enquiringly. 'And it was *worse*,' Peter finished, laughing at his own twist to the story.

Sally smile briefly, but then said seriously. 'Don't send up everything, Peter.'

'I'm not sending up everything.'

'Saltie wanted to play for you. He thought it might be a way of helping.'

Suddenly Peter became irritable. Partly because his joke had failed but more because he was totally frustrated by the entire situation.

'Shall I tell you something?' he said. 'I'm right up to there with people trying to help.'

'Does that include me?'

'You were the country bumpkin. Remember?' he accused. 'I doubted we'd fit into the village life in the first place.'

Her heart jolted. Once again she experienced the feeling of insecurity which came whenever Peter spoke wildly about their relationship. 'Let's not quarrel,' she pleaded. 'Everyone around here seems to be perpetually arguing.'

The weeks surrounding the annual Shillingbury Festival brought several engagements for the band. There was no doubt that the news of their unique style had spread abroad and large numbers of people were coming into the village from outside to hear them play. Only when it was rumoured that a spy from another famous local brass band had been seen listening intently did the parish council begin to express ambitions towards the county championships. One or two ventured to suggest that there was still an ingredient missing, difficult to put a finger on it, but the sound lacked something.

The band played on in utter bewilderment. Jake had ceased trying to keep abreast of events – the lads were working to rule and any talk about championships was not to be taken seriously. He worried about some of his colleagues seeming to enjoy the new arrangement, but when he tackled them about it they assured him that they were giving nothing to the music. Nothing.

There came another extraordinary incident on the evening of the Flower and Vegetable Show. The hall was full and the band, smartly dressed in uniform, was playing on the platform following the conclusion of the judging. Nobody left, they all listened attentively to the new sound.

Sally was watching Peter. His face showed a stubborn streak that matched the old men seated before him. It was a look she was beginning to know well but dislike deeply. He knew he was not really conducting the Blowers, that once they'd taken the tempo at the start of a piece they virtually ignored him, but he refused to give up. One or another of them would eventually have to give way.

On the far side of the hall a door opened a crack. Sally saw Old Saltie peer in, then half enter. He carried the brown paper bag. A sixth sense told her that this was it – the moment when one way or another the dispute would be resolved. The band finished the piece they were playing and the audience clapped. She looked back at the door – but it was closed again, with no sign of Saltie. She pushed her way through the crowd and quickly let herself out. An exit door was closing down the other end of a long corridor. She ran quickly and followed. She saw him just as he was disappearing into the darkness around the green. 'Mr Wicklow –' she called. He paused and allowed her to catch up with him. He didn't turn and she stopped several paces behind. She spoke again, this time quite softly. 'Come on, Saltie.'

He shook his head. 'Not now. I thought about it. Another time.'

'There won't *be* another time.'

'I'm too scared.'

He walked on. Sally moved after him, scrabbling around in her mind for something to make him stay. She was sure that if she lost him now the friction would continue for ever. 'You never called about the garden,' she said.

It made him stop. 'I'm sorry. No offence.'

She shook her head, meaning 'None taken.' Then she moved closer to him. 'But I was disappointed. That day – we shared a confidence. I felt privileged.'

40

'You didn't say anything to your husband?' he put in quickly.

Her eyes flickered briefly. 'No. Not a word,' she lied.

'Ah.' He moved off, 'Another time maybe.'

Sally followed again. 'We're letting things be in the garden – just like you advised. So we can see what comes up.'

'I'm glad.' He continued walking, with Sally tagging along behind wondering how she could prevent the situation slipping from her grasp.

'Saltie –' she pleaded. He stopped and slowly turned. 'Come on . . .'

'I'm frightened of failing. Can't you understand?'

'You're failing now, by creeping away.' She looked at him, directly, with a soft smile. 'If it's any help – I believe in you.'

They were the right words. A thousand memories stirred in his mind; incidents, loyalties, reliance, teamwork. He'd once described loyalty as the stuff of life and here was this young girl reminding him. If he'd had a daughter he'd have been proud for her to have the same gentle strength as this one. 'I'll play for you,' he said.

He received an ovation when they re-entered the hall. A few people clapped almost immediately, then, as Saltie strode towards the band stuffing his cap in a pocket and pulling the trumpet from its bag, others joined in until it spread to the whole audience. Sally remained at the back, suddenly nervous as she watched the whispered conversation with Peter. He shook his head at first, then seemed to reconsider.

The band was thrown into turmoil. They looked wildly to Jake for guidance but he needed time to *think* . . . and there wasn't any time. It had to be instant decision. They couldn't let Saltie down, but Jake suspected a trick. After all, Young Upstart was still there.

'*Oh Peaceful England*, gentlemen,' announced Peter.

Saltie took his place as the players took out the parts. 'Don't nobody give it nothing,' instructed Jake.

'Are you sure? Are you sure?' The band was desperately uncertain.

Jake sat white and tense. 'Nothing. Do you understand? Nothing!'

Peter had his arms raised, his baton steady, his eyes

challenging. They played the introduction and it was clear that Jake's command had carried – staccato, clipped, not at all as Edward German had written the music. It threw Saltie, and when it came to his entrance he stood paralysed, his lips dry, not a note of music in him. Sally watched Peter give a quick signal to the band; this time he was obeyed and the introduction was repeated. It was necessary to repeat it again and the audience began to fidget. Saltie caught her eye across all the heads. She smiled at him, confidently.

He raised his trumpet, licked his lips a couple of times. Peter brought down his left arm. The die was cast and Saltie began to play. He played the solo melody purely and sweetly. Clear as a bell. His old face became engrossed and the sound was as honest as he was. The patriotic theme, as English as the rolling Downs, was intensely moving as it seemed to summarise the emotions of the past weeks. There was something else. Sally heard it. So did Meadows, Fennel and Mr Charles. Saltie's legato trumpet playing sweetly against the staccato accompaniment, was a perfect blend of originality and tradition.

It was the missing ingredient.

They played *Oh Peaceful England* again three weeks later in the free-selection section of the preliminary auditions for the All Counties Brass Band Championships. Nothing was changed. Jake didn't know how to alter course without losing face so the sound remained as it was. In their private box the three adjudicators listened carefully. They nodded to each other, perhaps with a touch of surprise, and marked their papers.

When their decision was announced Sam was wide-eyed, ecstatic, baffled, and confused.

'We've qualified. We've qualified!'

'You mean *he's* qualified,' muttered Jake with a glare in Peter's direction.

It took a well developed sense of humour to work in concert with The Shillingbury Blowers. Peter had once told Sally that individually several of them didn't play too badly; some were, personally, reasonable enough fellows. But as a group of musicians and personalities they represented formidable opposition. Nevertheless, their insistence on playing the notes as written, but staccato, had the extraordinary effect of giving the band an individuality as well. The trouble was that, whilst their chances improved of winning an award at the county championships, morale sank to an all-time low. Sally bitterly regretted the role she had played in causing her husband to become involved. She felt embarrassed for him as he stood before the old men whose creased faces showed nothing but disapproval of both him and the sound they were producing. She tried to persuade him to give it up.

'I'll stand in front of those stubborn old fools for as long as it takes.' The obstinate look again.

'To do what?' Sally asked.

'To make them accept me.'

'Is it worth it?'

'Oh yes. It's worth it all right.' He tried to work it out aloud. 'They're fighting for something that means a great deal to them. I wish I knew what it is, but let's imagine it's not impossible that they're right and we're wrong.'

'So persuade Saltie back to conducting and let them get on with it.'

He shook his head. It was the first time he'd made any attempt to think the problem through logically. 'If they're right I want to be part of it. You see, that awful noise the first time we heard them. Suppose it wasn't just an awful noise . . .'

'It was. It was,' she said fervently.

'Suppose it was an expression of emotion in musical terms. Like jazz. Or native Zulu music which, let's face it, sounds pretty way-out to us. But it means something to those who understand it.'

Sally looked at him quizzically. 'You mean they're maybe more advanced than we are?'

'Different, anyway.'

'Oh boy!'

On the evening before the adjudications Peter made a final bid to win the friendship of his unwilling colleagues. He had called a rehearsal at St George's Hall but, at the last minute, he cancelled it and invited the band to join him in the bar of the Oddfellows Arms. The attempt could not be regarded as a success. As he placed the last brimming tankard on the table the players stared at him in complete silence.

'Cheers,' toasted Peter. 'Here's to us, and to tomorrow.' The men drank without uttering a word. Peter studied their faces and wondered how to cope with them. 'I decided against holding the rehearsal tonight because, frankly, there's no point.'

'Aye,' agreed Harvey into his beer.

'We'll meet tomorrow morning at the Green,' continued Peter. 'Half past nine. And the coach will take us to the County Hall.'

'What's the point of it, Mr Higgins?'

'The point of what, Sam?'

'Going to County Hall? To the championships? We're only going to make fools of ourselves.'

Peter assured him, 'We're going to win, Sam.'

The Band gurgled disparaging noises into their beers. It was Reggie's face which emerged first and voiced their thoughts. 'Some of us has always wanted to play in county championships,' he said. 'But not like this.'

'I wish I could make you understand,' tried Peter. 'The band sounds great. Really great.'

Harvey said, 'It's you as doesn't understand, Mr Higgins.'

It was Sam, of all people, who put his finger on it. He pointed out there'd been nothing but trouble since the band started sounding great. Reggie agreed they were better off when they'd played badly. And certainly happier. Peter was foundering. What could he say? It was Jake who was responsible for all this. He was about to say so when he became aware suddenly that it was Jake's voice which was missing from the conversation. 'Where's Jake?' he asked. 'He's never missed a rehearsal before. Is he all right?'

'Aye,' said Harvey. 'He's all right.'

Peter was worried. Despite his cantankerous personality the farmer was a good player and undoubtedly held the cornet section together. 'He's not planning to let us down tomorrow? We can't win without him.'

'We can't win any way up,' said Sam.

Reggie said, 'There's some of us had our differences with Jake. Some of us would like to see an end to the work-to-rule. But Jake says negotiations is at complete deadlock.'

'Jake talks too much,' declared Peter, reaching for his glass.

44

'We reckon it's become a feud between him and you,' went on Reggie.

'Why, for heaven's sake?'

'Jake reckons that making Saltie play trumpet were nothing more than a plot to cloud the issue.'

'Jake would rather be wrong than keep quiet.'

'Jake would rather be left alone,' said Sam with uncharacteristic firmness. 'Along with the rest of us. Like we've been for thirty years.'

Peter stopped dead, the glass halfway to his lips. He was beaten. The old men did not cloak their feelings with words. Slowly his glass went back on the table. Looking at them thoughtfully, he wiped his mouth with the back of his hand, and stood up. 'Well. It couldn't be said much clearer, could it.' He walked to the door and had reached it before a tinge of conscience caused Reggie to call after him. 'Jake's okay. He's in his cowshed with Bess. She's going to calve tonight and he's expecting trouble.'

Peter turned round and looked at the band, his face expressionless. Then with the tiniest of nods he left the pub.

The cowshed was one of several buildings bordering the cobbled yard which lay behind the farmhouse itself. It was dark by the time Peter arrived and he found Jake easily by the light filtering through gaps around the door. The farmer was lying comfortably on some bales of straw, sucking on an empty pipe. His eyes followed Peter as he came through the door and walked towards him. 'So it's Young Upstart come to see me.' He appeared less formidable amid his own surroundings. 'Missed the rehearsal, did I?'

'I was wondering –' began Peter.

'Worried about tomorrow, were you?' Jake interrupted.

'They told me about the cow. I came to see if I could help.'

Jake looked into the bowl of his pipe with a quiet smile. 'You? Help me?'

The younger man walked past the relaxed farmer towards the stalls and looked at the cow. 'She seems quiet enough at the moment.' He felt incongruous in the shed and Jake was indisputably superior in his own setting.

'She had a turn just before you came in,' said Jake. 'She's resting now.'

'What's the trouble exactly?'

'Exactly?' Jake looked up at him calmly. 'You want to know exactly. Her waters have broken, she's moaning and sweating. Walking round and round – won't lie down. My guess is that calf is wrong way round for presentation.'

'Oh.' Peter was at a loss. 'I don't know much about cows, I'm afraid.' He sat down as Jake replied evenly and equably, 'You don't know much about anything. Not about farmers, village life, nothing.'

'I know about music,' smiled Peter.

'Not our kind,' said Jake quickly. 'Nor why we play.'

'I realise the band used to treat rehearsals as some sort of social gathering.'

Jake looked at him quietly, his eyes expressionless, but no longer argumentative. 'You realise nothing.' He stuck the empty pipe in his mouth and sucked at it thoughtfully. 'There's some music that's there to be listened to; other music to be played.'

'It's the same thing.'

'It's not, you see. Take your chamber music. Quartets. Four men scraping away on fiddles. They're not playing for anyone but *themselves*. Nasty, thin little noise, but satisfying for them that makes it.'

'I can't agree with you,' objected Peter.

'Why else would they call it chamber music. It's so these four blokes can shut themselves in a room and scrape away to their heart's content.'

Peter smiled again. 'Is that what you do?'

'It's exactly what we do,' said Jake with no answering smile. 'Or *did*, before you came along.' He massaged his chin with the stem of his pipe. 'We got a pleasure out of it. A feeling.' His eyes softened as he allowed peaceful memories to permeate his mind. 'We'd think about England, our little village, our sons, daughters, loved ones. Saltie would tell us a story to get us all choked up. Then we'd *play*. I can hear it now.'

'So can I!' Peter was annoyed with himself for breaking the spell just as the older man was relaxing. But Jake gave him a level look and replied without heat.

'You won't rile me, Young Upstart. There's nothing

you can say will do that.'

'I didn't come here to rile you, Jake,' Peter said with a rueful smile. 'I came to . . . to try and understand, I suppose.'

A soft moan came from the direction of the stalls and Jake rose quickly to his feet. 'You *said* you came to help with Bess.'

'That too.'

The farmer was moving quickly to his cow. 'Then lend a hand over here. She's starting again.' He was a capable man and he handled the beast gently, assuredly, with soothing words and quiet competence. They worked together through the night, Peter assisting awkwardly but adequately. After Jake had scrubbed his hands and arms in a large sink Peter hung onto the cow's neck with all his weight as the farmer felt inside to establish the position of the calf. 'Its legs is tucked under its chest.' Then, 'Makes you feel a bit green, does it?'

'A bit,' admitted Peter.

'Takes getting used to.'

'You're so rough with her.'

'Not rough. Firm. That way she knows *I* know what I'm doing.' It was a long night. Jake had come prepared and, while they waited, he poured a mug of coffee from a Thermos flask and handed it to Peter.

'I dare say you can't allow for sentiment when it's your livelihood,' commented Peter as he took the coffee.

'You reckon?'

'Perhaps that's why you find a release from playing in the band.'

'Know all the answers, do you?'

Peter was stung into replying sharply. 'No. I was just asking. I was interested so I was asking.'

Jake looked at him again. A considering kind of look. As if trying to reach inside and fathom out the thinking of the younger man. Then the look focused past him as the farmer expressed his innermost thoughts. 'The trouble with this country is that two world wars has cut down all the tall poppies. In any field you get a few plants standing head and shoulders over the others. But when you've had them you're left with run-o'-the-mill. We'd used up the last of our best by 1945 and, since then, I dunno – we just

47

don't breed them any more. And if we do we hold them back until they're forced to leave the country if they're to grow.' He paused and sat silent for so long that Peter thought he'd drifted away into a dream. Then he continued quietly almost to himself. 'Saltie was a giant among men. Salt of the Earth – that's how he got his nickname. Now he's our last hope to keep alive some of the traditions that gave England a style of living not seen anywhere else in the world.' He heaved a deep sigh. 'Aye, all the tall poppies has been cut down and what's left would be better ploughed under.'

Peter spoke with a depth of honesty he'd not experienced in a long time. 'I have tried, Jake. With the band. I really have.'

'No point in playing music if you're so regimented you can't enjoy it,' explained Jake. Then, with regret rather than rancour, 'As for you and Saltie – you're just not in the same acreage.'

The cow did not die that night. Far from it. She was delivered of a fine calf just after dawn, following a period when the farmer thought they would lose them both. The two men spent another hour cleaning up and by five o'clock they were incredibly tired but well satisfied with the night's work. They'd seen more than the birth of a calf – a new understanding had come into the world as well.

'Jake –'

'Aye?'

'I feel we've done something really worthwhile.'

'We have, Young Upstart,' said Jake quite quietly. 'We have.'

'You will come?' Tomorrow, I mean. You will turn up?'

'It's today, son. Your precious brass band festival is today.'

Peter looked at the first rays of the sun shining into the cowshed. 'Yes. It's another day.'

Jake flopped back into the straw. Peter looked across at the newborn calf with its mother. Then a tentative look back to Jake. 'The coach leaves at nine, Jake.'

The farmer looked at his watch, his face betraying nothing. 'Then you've still time for a couple of hours kip,' he commented before shutting his eyes. Peter hesitated a moment, then stepped out of the door and into the morning sunshine.

After he'd gone Jake opened one eye and looked after him without expression.

Shillingbury was well populated with village historians, old folk who could remember the quality of life at the turn of the century, others who had created a romantically colourful and highly inaccurate history from legends and hearsay handed down from one generation to the next. The best known sources of information were the Reverend Arthur Norris, vicar of the thirteenth-century church; William Nicklin, landlord of the Oddfellows Arms, who invented superb snippets of past practices at the drop of a hat; and Marjorie Cavendish in The Corner Shop who had booklets on sale briefly describing the parish history.

Another lesser known authority was Cuffy, the Shillingbury tinker who lived in an old bus parked high above the village among the beechwoods which formed a backdrop to the old cottages and farms. Cuffy was more in touch with recent events of a day-to-day nature rather than anything which dated back to the manorial records. He would sit on the step of his broken-down vehicle and stare for hours on end at the incidents of life which unfolded constantly below him.

He could see Mrs Simpkins hanging out her washing, simple John Cronin glaring accusingly at his geranium plants which every year were so over-manured that they made massive leaves but no flowers, and the figure of Councillor Meadows bustling breathily along the High Street towards the Green. A bus waited there and already he'd seen several members of the brass band board and await departure to the county championships. Cuffy's eyes went back to Rose Cottage as Mr Higgins and his pretty young wife hurried out and walked quickly after Mr Meadows.

He enjoyed the solitude of his life above and beyond the village. He had no regrets, no envy, no sense of loss. His days had been empty for as many years as he could remember and there was no potential fulfillment holding out hope of any change in the future. But his waking hours were filled for all that. His simple requirements were met and he was contented – for the most part, that is.

He watched as Mr Higgins and his wife reached the bus and talked to Mr Meadows. They seemed to be having some kind of argument.

'Look,' said Peter, 'I've been with him all night. And I got through – I know I did.'

'Well, he hasn't turned up,' Sally pointed out. 'Face up to it, he's been against you all along.'

Meadows stepped in front of him. 'Are we or are we not going to the brass band contest?'

Peter pushed him aside and faced Sally. 'Sal, you don't understand. It's not the championship. Not any more. It's us. You want to be accepted here, be a part of the village. Me too.' He glanced at Meadows. 'After last night with Jake I was sure we'd made it and the feud was over.'

'Then more fool you,' was the councillor's reply.

Peter climbed aboard the bus. He was in time to hear Sam say, 'It makes no difference. It's hopeless anyway, with or without Jake.' Peter said, 'We'll drive past his place and pick him up.'

'You will. I won't.' Sally surprised herself at the abrupt way she'd spoken. Her husband turned back to her, amazement showing on his face. She went on, a touch uncertainly, 'Why should you chase after him? Make a stand, for heaven's sake. You'll have to one day.'

It was the first time they'd had a positive disagreement in public. For a moment he wrestled with his feelings, aware that all eyes were on him. He looked at Saltie who carefully smoothed the creases on the brown paper bag containing his trumpet. 'Okay. Let's go.'

The driver started the engine. 'To Jake's?' he asked.

'No,' said Peter. 'Take us straight to the County Hall.' As the bus gathered speed he opened his briefcase and pulled out a bundle of band parts. He skimmed through the sheets of manuscript, his mind working in overdrive. 'Saltie?' he called. The old man came out of a private reverie. 'Mmm?'

'You fill in lead cornet,' said Peter. The entire coach looked at him as though his mind had gone.

'Do *what*?' asked Saltie.

'Take over Jake's bits,' explained Peter.

'But I can't play cornet.'

'Take it on trumpet.'

'I'm already playing trumpet.'

50

'You'll have to transpose on sight, but you're a good enough musician.' He held up Saltie's solo part and the lead cornet part for him to see across the aisle. 'Look – like at section B – you're out in bar five, the tuba takes the next four, which gives you time to pick up the cornet part here.'

Meadows said, 'If you ask me you're hellbent on artistic suicide.'

Peter took a deep breath then, keeping his voice down, he asked, 'Mr Meadows. Do you believe in prayer?'

'Prayer?' repeated Meadows, taken aback. 'Yes, of course I do.'

'Then belt up and say one. There's a good chap.'

In the cow shed the calf stayed close to its mother. A chink of sunlight moved across the straw bales until it shone on the sleeping face of Jake. His eyes opened, he yawned, stretched, looked at his watch.

Then he panicked.

Backstage of the County Hall the Shillingbury Blowers huddled disconsolately in a small group as they listened to the band from Banley playing their showpiece for the adjudicators. Standing apart from them were Peter and Sally. Their emotions were running higher than their expressions of studied calm betrayed. Both were upset with each other, tense from their quarrel, and very angry with Jake.

Meadows hurried over. 'You're on next. After this lot has finished."

Peter nodded without enthusiasm and looked across towards his group of old men. Never had a band looked less like winning an award. Suddenly, he frowned. 'Where's Saltie, for God's sake?' To attempt a perform-ance without Jake was pushing their skill to the very limits; to try to play without a soloist would be plain dumb. 'Sal, find him – quick,' he asked despairingly.

She found him sitting on the bus, trumpet across his knees, apparently studying his reflection in the bowl. 'Saltie, you're on!'

He shook his head slowly. 'I can't do it.'

'Of course you can. Peter doesn't expect miracles.'

The old man dismissed this with a slight wave of the trumpet. 'It's not the music,' he said sadly.

'What then?'

He looked up at her, a perplexed old man who'd hopelessly lost his way. 'Everything,' he said. 'The band, Jake, everything. We've all grown apart. The whole purpose of the band was to keep us together after the Home Guard was disbanded. It's been my fault right from the off.'

She sat on a seat opposite him. 'If it's anyone's fault it's mine and Peter's.'

He carried on talking as if she hadn't spoken. 'First I didn't conduct them good enough; second, I behaved like a spoiled brat when they sacked me; third, I sulked when they offered me the job back. I've let them all down.'

'And what do you think you're doing now, mm?' she asked sharply. 'Sitting out here when they're waiting to go on.'

'The way I feel I'd only let them down worse. Even in the trumpet bits.'

Sally stood up with a glint of anger. 'Well, I'm glad you told me, Mr Wicklow. Because from anyone else I wouldn't have believed it.' She looked down at him and decided to spare nothing – there was no other way. 'I try very hard to see the person who commanded the Home Guard, who formed the band, and became a leading figure in Shillingbury for thirty-five years. But all I can see, Mr Wicklow, is a pig-headed old man filled with maudlin self-pity.' She stepped blindly off the bus and hurried away across the car park towards the stage door.

On stage the Banley band were finishing their piece. They'd played well, smart and assured in their bright jackets. By comparison the Shillingbury Blowers sat like sheep about to be led to the slaughter.

'Come on, Peter,' urged Meadows. 'You enter from the other side.' The young conductor looked at his depleted band, found himself unable to wish them 'good luck', and allowed Meadows to hurry him away.

It was after he'd crossed the stage behind the backing drapes, and reached the opposite wing, that Jake turned up. Jake with a wide grin. Jake with an embarrassed apology for falling asleep in the cowshed. Jake who'd used every imaginable form of transport from tractor to bicycle in order not to let the boys down. Jake who'd arrived in the nick of time. Saltie came in behind him, his eyes lighting up as he saw his old friend seize Young Upstart's hand and pump it up and down. Then the two old men hurried across to the band.

Jake took charge immediately and the band grouped round him with a sudden surge of renewed hope. Thank God he'd arrived in time. 'We was wrong,' he said urgently. 'We's been wrong all the time. About him, I mean.' He looked across at Peter. 'He's all right, I tell you. He's *all right*. Didn't he stay up all night helping me with Bess? Lads,' he continued earnestly, 'we've got a lot of things to *put right*. And we can start now. Help the boy along.'

The Banley band were leaving the stage and there were several minutes of confusion as the two groups exchanged places. Sam, in his hurry, knocked over three music stands which Reggie righted behind him. Harvey forgot his cymbal and had to rush off-stage to collect it, bumping heavily into Basil as he did so, Jake and Saltie looked at each other – a renewal of understanding between them.

When they were seated Peter entered to applause and mounted the podium. The seventeen old men looked up at him. They smiled. They nodded confidently. Peter, with a quiet swell of emotion, nodded and smiled back. They were friends at last. 'Give it all you've got,' Jake whispered to them. The work to rule was over.

Peter started to conduct and, for the first time in many months, the Shillingbury Blowers played their very best.

Young Upstart's face was a picture. First, amazement. Followed by abject horror.

Then he looked down at the warm, creased faces. He looked at the serenity of Sam 'Pom-pomming' away; he saw tears of happy emotion rolling from Reggie's eyes; he was aware of the devotion of Harvey as he popped in a quick triplet on the big drum; and he marvelled at the public declaration of friendship from Jake as he rose – actually rose to his feet – to help him out with an extra loud, extra protracted, twiddly-bit.

CHAPTER FOUR

SOME OF of the surnames by which Shillingbury identified its local inhabitants stretched back into history as far as the village itself. Before the Norman Conquest surnames, as they are known today, were rare. Individuals were described rather than named, sometimes by where they lived, often by their occupation, occasionally by physical appearance. Thus the Brooke family were so called because they could be found by the stream, whereas the Nash family lived near the ash trees. Mr Butcher's occupation was as obvious as Mr Baker's but, less apparent, the Middle English word for basket-maker was Bannister, or a harness-maker would be called Lorimer. On the other hand Abbott was almost certainly a nickname arising out of someone's dignified appearance rather than his calling. As the children grew older, and required separate identification, it was a simple matter to stick a 'son' on the end of their father's name as in Johnson, Williamson, or perhaps a possessive 's' on its own would do the trick, like in Richards. A few men must have been nice to know in those far off days for they were complimentarily described simply as Goodfellow, Fairweather or Wisdom.

Shillingbury was one of the villages of England which kept alive the tradition of descriptive names. There was Meadows the Butcher, David the Vet, Harvey the Post, Cuffy the Tinker, Madigan the Fish. Dan Wicklow had earned himself the nickname 'Old Saltie', Peter had rapidly picked up the title 'Young Upstart', Mandy was referred to most often as 'Jake's Girl'. The chairman, Mr Charles, was so called to distinguish him from his brothers Mr Harold, Mr John and Mr Leslie; another distinction was that the other three were all dead.

Cuffy the Tinker, re-nicknamed Winnie the Pooh when one was downwind of him, was a grumpy, surly, scruffy man. He was no village idiot and, despite his appearance, there was something likeable about him. National Assistance kept him alive, although he preferred to work rather than take charity. He undertook any job; mostly they turned out to be dirty ones because he'd tackle anything for a pound an hour. He accepted payment as if bestowing a favour and would take away cast-off clothing, mugs of tea, or anything else that was going, whilst voicing aloud the assumption it was because the donor didn't want it.

As he sat on the doorstep of his home the world he knew spread out below him like an animated panoramic painting. The church clock told him the time, the clouds gathering round the summit of Ashbury Hill forecast the weather, farm labourers in the fields offered a clue as to where small tasks to his liking might be worth seeking. It struck five and the tinker made a move. He could see Young Upstart's car parked in the station car park – and it was a good six-mile walk.

He arrived just over an hour later in time to see Mandy unloading a crate of chicks from Jake's Matra Rancho and hurry into the station. He concealed himself among the tall evergreen shrubs bordering the car park and, whilst waiting for her to come out, he scanned the parked cars until his eyes lit on Peter's MG Sports which, by then, had been joined by Mr Charles' elderly Rolls-Royce. As soon as Mandy had driven away Cuffy emerged from the bushes and approached them. His hand rested momentarily on the door handle of the Rolls, but he preferred the MG. A quick look round, eyes searching out hidden dangers, before he released the canvas cover and climbed into the driving seat.

An imaginary key in the ignition, a hand on the starter, his mouth uttered a Uhurg-uhurg-uhurg-BRUM! Brum-brum-brum-brum, and, with continued verbal sound effects, he play-acted reversing the car out of the space before accelerating through the gears up to a make-believe ninety miles an hour through winding country lanes. Several happy minutes were finally interrupted by the sound of the London train approaching and, bringing the car to a pretend skidding halt, the tinker scrambled out.

By the time Peter came out of the station carrying his briefcase Cuffy was innocently polishing the bonnet with the sleeve of his mackintosh.

'What are you doing?'

'Nothing.' There was indignation in the voice. 'Anyone can see I'm doing nothing.'

Peter raised a suspicious eyebrow at the scruffy figure and walked around the car unbuttoning the replaced canvas cover. 'How long have you been here?'

'Minutes only. Seconds almost. I walked in just as the train came in. Yes.' He feigned surprise as Peter picked up a large spotted handkerchief from the driving seat and handed it distastefully towards him. 'Ah, well now, that looks exactly like a handkerchief I used to own myself.'

'Take it!'

'Yes, sir.' Peter climbed into the car and Cuffy hovered hopefully. 'And you will have been busy conducting mighty business deals in the centre of world trade, I suppose.'

'I'm a musician, Cuffy.'

'You will have been conducting mighty symphony orchestras in the centre of the world's music, I suppose,' modified Cuffy without pause. Peter sighed.

'Get in,' he said.

'Me?'

'Get in! It's what you came for.' He reached into the back for an old newspaper which he spread on the front seat.

'If you'd care for me to join you in your motor car I'll be pleased to oblige,' said Cuffy generously.

'Do you really walk six miles to the station in the hope of getting a ride back?'

'Six miles,' scorned the tinker. 'What's six miles? A footstep in the journey of life.'

'You ought to write lyrics,' Peter commented as he drove out of the car park. He took the MG up to fifty miles an hour but Cuffy, emitting shouts of childlike enjoyment, urged him to drive even faster. When they screeched to a standstill outside Rose Cottage Peter was told he drove well despite being a bit slow on the corners. As they climbed out Cuffy added, 'I prefer an open car myself.'

'With you, yes,' agreed Peter. 'I hate to say this, Cuffy, but one needs plenty of fresh air swirling about when you're around.'

'So I've heard tell. Although I can't notice it myself, mind.' He followed Peter up the path and as far as the front door until he was asked if he was actually thinking of coming into the house as well. 'Ah. No. Thank you for inviting me but I haven't the time just now. I was walking with you not wanting to miss a word of what you were saying. About me smelling and that.'

'And that, Cuffy,' grinned Peter. 'And all that.'

In the living-room Sally stood on a pouffe trying on a dress while its creator, Mrs Simpkins, fussed around the hem on her knees, her mouth stuffed with pins. Peter kissed his wife, and Mrs Simpkins hummed a response to his cheery 'hullo'.

'How was London?' asked Sally.

'It's still there.' He went into the kitchen. 'Any beer in the fridge?'

'Should be. You didn't get another parking ticket?'

'No,' he called as he took out a bottle and looked for the opener. 'It's not as easy as that to get a parking ticket. You have to find a place to park first.' He came back into the room. 'What's the dress for?'

'Mandy's wedding. Don't you recognise it?'

'No. Why? Do you wear it every time Mandy gets married?'

'Take no notice of him,' Sally advised Mrs Simpkins. 'If it doesn't have crotchets and quavers, he's lost.'

Peter teased Mrs Simpkins that he'd just given her boyfriend a lift back from the station. Cuffy had a number of routine pastimes and one of these was his weekly proposal to the council's honorary treasurer. She greeted his advances with intense annoyance and often wished someone would put the cheeky devil in his place. When Peter pointed out that he simply wanted to be put in *her* place she was not amused, and seemed in some danger of swallowing the pins. 'Oh well. It's not going to be a double wedding then,' he said.

'Mr Higgins, I'd rather you didn't joke about such things,' she replied through the side of her mouth.

'It's Cuffy's idea, not mine. Him in his morning suit and you in your protective clothing.'

Another of Cuffy's pastimes was a daily visit to the Oddfellows Arms where, taking his pint to a corner table, he'd quietly watch the comings and goings of the locals, and once a week, laboriously fill in his football coupon. He could neither read nor write but he didn't need to know the names of the teams because his crosses went into the same places each time, as regular as clockwork. He'd learned how to write his name, he could copy Shilling-bury, the envelope was already printed, so he needed no more than that to become a rich man. Jake had asked him once if this was something he wanted.

'Never thought about it,' replied Cuffy. 'I could do with a bit more than I got now.'

'Inflation hit the begging bowl, has it?'

Cuffy had been greatly offended. 'I never begged. I'd rather work than take charity. You know that. Odd jobs. Mostly mucky ones.' Jake knew perfectly well. In fact it was he who provided more jobs for the tinker than anyone and, moreover, gave a fair performance of pretending the tasks genuinely needed doing. At a pound an hour Cuffy complained it was slave labour, but the surly, grudging relationship had lasted over many years.

When Terry the barmaid put his pint before him Cuffy drew out a tightly folded note. 'I seem to have only a five-pound note on me,' he said.

'Oh dear,' said Terry, true to form. 'And here's me clear out of change. You'll have to owe it till next time.'

'If that's what you want, I don't mind,' said Cuffy agreeably.

'How long have you had that fiver?' she asked.

'Not long.'

'When did you get rid of the big white note you had?'

'I sold it to an American for twelve pound fifty,' he said defensively.

'You're not as stupid as you look, are you?'

Over the years Harvey the Post had developed a remark-able talent for deducing with uncanny accuracy the con-tents of letters he delivered. Usually it was the postmark which triggered off a computer-like memory of the sen-der, sometimes it was the type of envelope, or even the stamp when it was of foreign origin. He offered a de luxe postal service by announcing personally the probable contents of any letter, whilst postcards he recited verba-tim. The only time he considered he'd done less than justice to the Queen's Mail was when he had to push it through the letter box without the pleasure of personal contact. The Postman's Knock in his case was nothing more than a delaying device for him to study the missives from every angle. By the time Sally opened the front door he was able to declare confidently, 'One for Mr Higgins from the London office, only it's not his pay cheque because the envelope's different.'

'Thank you, Harvey,' she sighed, trying to take it before he was ready to let go.

'And one for you from Liverpool. That'll be your uncle, I dare say.'

'It could be. Would you like me to let you know how he is?' Her attempted sarcasm bounced off him without leaving a mark.

When Peter came into the kitchen she was standing by the breakfast table reading her letter. He gave her a hug but she continued reading over his shoulder, so he released her and poured a cup of coffee instead. 'Uncle's going to America and taking Aunty with him. They want Cousin Cuthbert to come and stay with us for his half-term holiday.' Sally's cousin was a monster, a teenage Genghis Khan. The village had only recently forgiven them for his last visit when Peter had learned that love for a good woman did nothing to prevent an instant and intense dislike for her relations. Nevertheless he was nothing if not fairminded and treated the kid just as he would any other evil, obnoxious, snotty-nosed schoolboy.

He opened the envelope addressed to himself, glanced at the contents, and sagged visibly. Unlike her uncle and aunt, they would not be going to America. Following weeks of high pressure promotional work during the spring it had been arranged for The Close Encounters to tour several big cities in the States throughout the autumn. He had cancelled all commitments up to Christmas in order that he and Sally could join the Group, with him returning to his previous role on keyboard. Now the American musicians' union had refused entry, insisting that their own musicians accompany the Group. Peter had little complaint on that score; in the first place the accompaniments were pretty straightforward and, secondly, he'd made plenty of money in the past by accompanying American pop stars in this country as a result of the British union applying a similar ban. Nevertheless, with the arrival of this letter his entire autumn had gone out of the window.

'Something else will turn up,' Sally said philosophically.

'Yes,' muttered Peter. 'Your monster cousin!'

Along the back of the cowsheds at Jake's farm there ran a long ditch which carried away the surplus water and other things that cows leave behind them when they're waiting to be taken in for milking. It became clogged up with monotonous regularity and twice a year Cuffy would tackle the odorous job of digging it out. Rather than attempt to reach into the ditch from its banks, he would step deep into the squelching mud and wield his spade with such determination as to soak himself and anyone else who came near.

By eleven o'clock that morning he'd cleared some thirty feet and was well and truly sodden, when Mandy called out that tea was up in the kitchen. He deposited a final spadeful on the bank and struggled out of the ditch, generously splashing muddied water in all directions. He walked uncomfortably across the cobbled yard and arrived at the kitchen door.

'You're not bringing that lot in here,' declared Jake without feeling.

'Miss Mandy said about a cup of tea,' explained Cuffy.

Jake surveyed the drenched figure of the tinker. 'What have you been *doing*?' he demanded.

'You know what I've been doing.'

'I said clean it out not take a bath in it.'

'You can't clean it out from the top. You got to get in.'

The farmer's survey had reached his feet. 'You haven't even got any boots on.'

'I did have. They're in the ditch somewhere. Sucked off.'

'I beg your pardon?'

'My boots. They got sucked off.'

Mandy appeared at the kitchen window. 'How many sugars, Cuffy?' she called.

'Two,' he called back. Then, 'Er – one.' Then again, 'One-and-a-half!' Finally, getting it right, 'Largish ones.'

Jake took a final distasteful look at him. 'You can drink it out here.' He walked back into the house with a muttered, 'I never saw such a mess in all my life.'

Mandy gave her father a scolding look as she passed him; in some ways he was a bully and failed to appreciate the upset caused by his outspokenness. Cuffy waited grumpily for his tea and took the mug from her ungraciously. 'One-and-a-half largish ones,' she said cheerfully.

'People make it too sweet. Because I'm a tinker they think I like a lot of sugar. They never consider what it might do to my teeth.'

'Do you want a sandwich? Piece of cake?'

'Sandwich. Er – ' She waited, hand on hips. He changed his mind. 'Piece of cake.'

'Both?'

'Yes. I don't mind having both if you like.'

'I'm sure it's made my day,' she said without sarcasm as she went back into the kitchen.

Cuffy sipped at his tea and, alone, gave vent to his feelings about Jake's unfair criticism. 'Can't do a job like that and keep clean.' He said it several times and repeated it to Mandy when she reappeared carrying a doorstep sandwich and a thick slice of cake. 'Can't do a job like that and keep clean.'

'Take no notice of him.' She handed the food to him which presented a problem because he was already holding the mug. As he took a bite from the slice of cake a fair dollop of tea spilled down his front. With a mock sigh Mandy took the mug from him and, thus freed, he was able to munch away at cake and sandwich alternately.

'He knew it'd be a mucky job. That's why he give it to me.'

He sat on a feed sack and she joined him for a few moments. 'I said, take no notice. There are some things he can't do without you.'

'Of course there are,' Cuffy agreed belligerently. 'I'm a specialist.'

'Right. And I'm counting on you to keep specialising for him when I've gone.'

He looked at her, his mouth full of cake. 'You're not leaving, are you?'

She laughed. 'You don't think I'll carry on living here after I've married David the vet?' Cuffy hadn't thought about it – he'd imagined she was part of the farm, as permanent as the annual rotation of crops. 'We're going to Australia,' she continued. 'David's bought a veterinary practice outside Sydney and I'm going to help him.'

He was impressed. 'That's a fair long way, Australia. I

never been that far.' He was ready for another sup of tea and she handed him the mug.

'How far have you been, Cuffy?'

The tinker surveyed the horizon and half pointed with his sandwich, as if his world was contained within the limit of vision. 'Not very far. I'd have liked to go on a boat and sail the seven seas.'

'Do you know where they are?' asked the girl.

'Course I don't. But I'd have liked to sail them all the same. Or go up in an airy plane. I look up and see them like silver fish against the blue – and I wish . . .' His eyes clouded as a procession of undefined images passed through his mind. Then, more practically, 'But I wouldn't know where I was when I got there so what's the point?'

Mandy saw the tinker through a new perspective. She'd known him since she was a child but never before had she realised the true limitations of his ambition. So many things which for some were commonplace were, for him, out of reach. 'Cuffy,' she asked, 'what would you want to do most of all in the world?'

'Oh, I can answer you there.' He spoke without a moment's hesitation, innocently truthful. 'Most of all in the world – I'd want to be at your wedding.'

Mandy found herself at a loss. The idea was so preposterous she simply didn't know what to say. She laughed nervously, struggling to find words that would not offend. In the end she took his empty mug from him. 'I must wash up and clear away.' She rose and headed for the kitchen, saying over her shoulder, 'I'll see if I can find you a pair of boots.'

'If you got some you don't want I'd be willing to take them off you,' said Cuffy.

That afternoon Mandy told Sally about her conversation with Cuffy. She described how he was actually oozing mud when he asked if he could come to her wedding but, to her surprise, her friend didn't even smile. 'Presumably he wouldn't have oozed and dripped at the reception. Although, now I come to think of it, it's exactly what some of our guests did.'

'You're not suggesting I should have invited him?' asked Mandy. 'Dad would go mad. An out-of-work tramp at his daughter's wedding.'

Sally remembered that Peter was out of work as of that

morning. Of course, there was out of work and out of work, but, unless she worked hard on him, her husband was quite likely to turn up at the church in a torn rugby shirt and broken sandals. She couldn't laugh at an old man who wanted nothing more than to wish a bride happiness and feast his eyes on the sight of a village wedding.

'Now you've given me a conscience about it,' said Mandy. 'I'll miss you, Sally. You've been a good chum to me.'

'Sometimes I'm so good I make myself sick,' replied Sally.

At about the same time the subject of their conversation was cutting the tiny patch of front lawn before Mrs Simpkins' terraced bungalow. Cuffy, still in his damp clothes and reeking of things manural, pushed the old mower back and forth. 'Are you finished?' He looked up to see Mrs Simpkins standing in the open front door holding a freshly baked pie covered with tin foil.

'Nearly. A drop of oil here and there would make all the difference.'

'The lawn's not big enough to bother with oil.'

'It's not you that's pushing the mower,' he countered.

She was worried about him, catching a death of cold by wearing wet trousers but blanched at his outrageous suggestion of coming into the kitchen and taking them off to dry. 'You're not coming into my house. The very idea!'

'It'll be all right when we've made it legal.'

'In a minute I shall get very angry, you disgusting man.'

Cuffy gave a couple of vicious pushes at the mower. 'But I can *think* about it,' he threatened. 'There's nobody can stop me thinking about it.' Suddenly, he smiled at her. Not without effort because it was an unusual position for his mouth. She backed away in slight alarm, but he shouldered the mower and disappeared round the side of the bungalow. Mrs Simpkins was about to go indoors when she realised she still held the pie in her hand. When he returned she gave it to him – holding it at arm's length from his clothes. 'How will you get those things clean?'

'There's fresh running water up where I live.'

'You mean the river, I suppose,' she sniffed.

'I'll take off my trousers and sit on the bank eating your meat and potato pie while the stream washes them for me.'

She was easily shocked. 'You mean, you sit on the bank in your underpants?'

'Ain't got no underpants.'

Sally's cousin Cuthbert arrived at the weekend and, true to form, Peter left it until the last minute before driving to meet him at the station. He roared into the car park and found a scowling fourteen-year-old sitting on his suitcase. He uttered what he hoped sounded like a greeting and made welcoming noises around the theme of hoping the kid had had a good journey. This was largely ignored but the boy managed to slip a whoopie cushion on the driving seat just before Peter sat down and uttered a raucous, tuneless guffaw which Peter answered with a stiff smile.

As they drove through the lanes Cuthbert observed tactlessly that The Close Encounters didn't have a record in the charts and were slipping if, in fact, they hadn't gone out of fashion already. 'What's Shillingbury like?' he asked. 'Any better?'

'Worse,' replied Peter with a surge of annoyance. 'You'll hate it.'

'Still no action?'

'Not a movement.'

'No disco yet?'

'No disco. But the village band throws a dance every other Saturday.' Peter could manage to be fairly evil too when he put his mind to it.

Near a fork in the road he saw the distant figure of Cuffy hurrying towards them and applied the footbrake.

'Thought I'd missed you,' said an out-of-breath Cuffy before adopting his most mournful put-out face as he saw Cuthbert and realised there was no room in the car. He looked the boy over with an air of disapproval, and Cuthbert returned his look with one of hostile suspicion. The tinker set about walking back to the village with the attitude of a tragedian starting out on the death scene. 'All right,' said Peter. 'Cuthbert, into the back seat.'

'Me? In the back seat?'

'Unless you'd rather walk,' offered Peter curtly. At that moment he preferred the tinker to his wife's cousin. 'Jump in, Cuffy. It's not far but we'll make the most of it.'

As the car drove off Cuthbert caught the full polluted

slipstream from the man in front of him and buried his face in the whoopie cushion. It responded with its usual noise which fairly accurately summed up the boy's opinion.

Sally was working in the garden, when the MG arrived, and moved over to greet them. The weekend didn't start well. Peter said, 'He's had a bad journey, the group's out of the charts, there's no action here, and don't sit on any cushions.'

'Oh dear,' she said, sounding over-hearty. 'Do I detect an atmosphere?'

'Shall we say he hasn't matured and leave it at that?'

'There's a king-size tea inside,' she said. 'Maybe that'll help.'

Then with devastating directness Cuthbert pointed at Cuffy and stated the obvious. 'That man smells.' Peter ushered the boy towards the cottage, leaving his wife to repair the tinker's damaged feelings.

She remained stoically cheerful. 'Sorry, Cuffy. I must say you do look in a particular mess today,' She attempted to straighten his jacket and tie. 'We're going to have to smarten you up a bit if you want to go to Mandy's wedding.'

'How did you know that?' He was surprised.

'She told me.'

'I didn't think she'd heard.'

'She heard all right. But you don't make it easy.' Sally scanned the rosebed in search of a bloom. 'My horrible cousin might not be blessed with diplomacy but he does have a knack of pointing out the truth.' She looked round at him. 'Can't we do something about it?'

'Two things I can't abide – baths and schoolboys.'

'We'll talk about it later.' She found a rose. 'Meanwhile, you cut a dash as you walk home, eh?'

She put it in his buttonhole and he looked down at it. 'Waste of a good rose that,' he commented. 'It looks out of place away from its friends.' He was conscious of her perfume – and she of his, although she gave no sign. 'Are you lonely up on that hill all by yourself?'

'Me? Lonely? Never. Me and my old horse, we look down at the village and I think . . . I think I probably got as much as any man could want.'

Bernard had been put out to grass some four years

earlier and, apart from a touch of rheumatism, was a healthy enough companion for Cuffy. The tinker had adopted him and whatever the state of his finances he always ensured his old friend enjoyed a nightly treat of oats. He ladled them into a bucket that evening and confided in the horse. 'We're not lonely, are we?' He splashed in some water from the stream and placed the bucket in front of Bernard. 'Reckon I would be if you wasn't around.' He looked up at the sky, and across to the clouds around the summit of Ashbury Hill. 'We got to see you through another winter, my old Bernard. We just got to do that.'

The converted bus contained the bare necessities of life. A table, a place to sit, another to sleep, Calor gas cooker, and a paraffin lamp. He lit the baby oven and put in the meat pie. Sally's rose went into the tooth-mug. He removed his jacket and picked up a fishing rod. Then he paused, recalling comments made about himself by Jake, Peter, Mrs Simpkins, Sally, and most bluntly by the awful Cuthbert boy. He lowered his face towards his chest and sniffed carefully several times. Perhaps he could detect a *faint* odour. Nothing much, but possibly enough to spoil his chances of an invitation to the wedding. He thought of Mrs Higgins. She was a good lady, that one. A friend. He reckoned he took more notice of her than of anyone else he knew. With a glance out of the window at the fast-flowing stream, he put down the fishing rod.

There was a deep pool among some rocks where the water was dark and relatively still. Cuffy slowly removed his clothes, the resolve weakening with every layer, and walked tremulously from the bus. He stepped into the water and with courageous agony lowered himself until his shoulders were submerged beneath what felt like crushed ice.

Bernard looked across at his friend taking a bath. It was a sight his tired old eyes had never previously witnessed throughout a long life.

CHAPTER FIVE

THE REVEREND Arthur Norris, vicar of St George's Church of England in Shillingbury, was wielding a broom behind the altar with more enthusiasm than expertise.

He liked occasionally to buckle down to the mundane tasks of this world. It kept him in touch with reality, rendered him truly a servant of the Lord and, anyway, he found it rather fun. The good ladies of the village, who dutifully kept the fine old church clean, were far less happy about his energetic efforts to dispose of dirt and dust. Most of it shot up into the air where it hung chokingly for an hour or so before sinking slowly back to the ground after he'd gone. The rest failed to find its way to the dustbins because Norris had discovered a cavern beneath a loose flagstone near the organ, which dated back to some bygone age and proved a more convenient receptacle for his sweeping.

He loved the church. He could feel the history all about him, a living monument as well as a place of worship, evidenced by the brasses, gravestones and parish registers dating back to the sixteenth century. There was an atmosphere within the dignified stone structure which positively aided prayer. Of course one should be able to communicate with God in any surroundings but Norris was human enough to find it much easier when an organ was playing softly and sunlight streamed through stained glass windows. Over in the vicarage, he carefully preserved the churchwardens' accounts from the seventeenth to the nineteenth centuries. He would spend many a winter's evening trying to translate from the Latin the church's diocesan and archidiaconal records, experiencing a real thrill as a passage became clear and he discovered a new insight into the past.

Norris lifted the flagstone, propped it up with a tin collection box, and swept the rubbish into the cavern. Then, leaving the air heavy with suspended dust, he walked from the church towards the vicarage. He saw the figure of a clean and slightly groomed Cuffy passing on the other side of the low wall and hurried over to him. 'Ah, Cuffy – I was hoping to see you this morning.'

'Was it a job, Reverend, Vicar, sir?'

'You could call it a spiritual job,' smiled Norris. 'I thought you might have joined us at Morning Service. We were a little light on worshippers.' The tinker resigned himself to the inevitable lecture. 'You should try harder, Cuffy.'

'Yes, Reverend, Vicar, sir.'

'No man can take from a community without putting back his share. In your case that can only be with faith, you being a touch short on substance.'

'A touch short, yes.'

Norris regarded Cuffy as essentially a simple man and adopted a fanciful, simplistic way of putting over his message. 'When I am in the church, alone with God,' he said in a slightly sing-song voice, 'He sometimes asks me about you.'

'Does He now? And Him that busy,' commented Cuffy, who wasn't simple in the least.

'He asks me, "Where are those guests I have invited to my table but who have failed to turn up?"'

'I'm only in my little bus. He could always drop by if He wanted.'

Norris shot him a disapproving look, and suddenly broke off. 'There's something different about you this morning. Are you all right?'

Cuffy was puzzled by the switch of characters. 'Was that you asking, then? Or are you still being Him?'

The vicar found himself studying a clean and fresh man who had replaced overnight the grubby tramp. 'Have you – er – had a *bath*?' he asked, wonderingly.

'If cleanliness is next to Godliness I'm as good as up there sitting at his right hand,' Cuffy assured him.

They walked together to the vicarage where Norris asked Cuffy to wait a moment or two, a qualm of conscience causing him to hurry inside. He'd heard from Mandy about the mud-caked tinker with ambitions to attend her wedding, and his charitable instincts had been aroused. He emerged with a carrier bag. 'If these would be of any help I have no further use for them.'

'If you don't want them I'll take them off you, Reverend, Vicar, sir.'

'It's not that I don't want them' said Norris with tetchy annoyance. 'I do wish you wouldn't accept gifts with surly stipulations.' His eyes widened in alarm as Cuffy delved deep into the bag. 'Don't take them out here!' he added urgently. His warning was too late. Cuffy pulled out a large pair of brilliant red and yellow check trousers. 'They must have seen you coming in these,' grinned the tinker.

'A moment of weakness. Put them away.' The vicar gave an embarrassed wave to a passer-by.

'I'll wear them on high days and holidays and think of you, Reverend, Vicar, sir.'

'Then keep your thoughts to yourself. We are none of us constantly perfect in the eyes of the Lord.'

'You couldn't be anything but perfect in them trousers,' said Cuffy.

By lunchtime on Sunday, Cuthbert had had enough. But really enough. He was up to there with the village and everybody in it. He couldn't imagine how anyone could exist in such a dead-end hole. He'd wandered down to the boating lake, moodily messed about on the landing stage, unhitched the swinging boom, and was idly pulling it back and forth.

He looked up and saw Cuffy approaching from the direction of the vicarage. Cuthbert was not blessed with many ideas, and none of them inclined towards the constructive, but he had an idea then – one that prompted an unkind smile and a new energy.

'Hey!' he called. Cuffy looked across, his eyes narrowing with instant suspicion. 'I didn't mean to be rude yesterday,' continued the boy. Cuffy's eyes were alert – unforgiving yet. 'I've been given permission to use the rowing boat, only I can't undo the hitching knot. Could you lend a hand?' The tinker's eyes darted from side to side, wary of a trap, but he altered course and crossed to the landing stage. 'Then I'll get in and you can push me out a bit,' finished Cuthbert.

Cuffy passed the boy and stooped to examine the knot secured inches above the water. As soon as his back was turned the obnoxious kid swung the boom with all his might. He'd reckoned without the sharp survival instincts of a man to whom nothing had ever come easily. Without even looking, Cuffy dropped as flat as a pancake whilst nine feet of boom passed harmlessly over his head. The only casualties were the new check trousers which dropped into the water.

The tinker fished them out sadly and slowly turned his eyes to Cuthbert. The boy stood uncertainly, wondering whether to run for it. The tinker remained crouched, a hand resting on the other end of the same plank on which Cuthbert was standing. A sudden movement, a massive heave upwards, and the boy found himself sailing backwards through the air with only time for a slight scream before splashing heavily into the water. He surfaced gratifyingly covered in green slime and generously caked in mud. 'You wait, till my cousin hears about this, you perambulating old dungheap!' he spluttered. 'I'll get my own back, you see if I don't.'

Cuffy looked down at him. 'That boy smells!' he commented before walking away.

When Mother Coleridge had died, alone in front of the television set, for three days her sightless eyes stared at the passing pageant of news and entertainment before a neighbour called the police; and then it was only to complain about the volume. It was strange how even a close-knit community could live through a daily routine for so long without spotting the absence of a familiar character. On the other hand Saltie used to swear that if he dared to have a lie-in on a Saturday morning at least six people, seeing the bedroom curtains closed after breakfast time, would hammer on his front door to enquire if he was dead.

As for Cuffy, he just sweated and shivered through a bout of flu all by himself in his bus at the top of the hill.

On Wednesday evening Peter said, 'Have you seen Cuffy lately?'

'Now you mention it, no,' answered Sally.

'He wasn't at the station tonight, that's all. He hardly ever misses a lift home with me.' In fact, Peter had climbed into his car lost in private thoughts so worrisome that Cuffy could have been doing a handstand on the bonnet and he wouldn't have seen him. The London music scene seemed dead so far as he was concerned and he was beginning to harbour serious fears about work. His was a chancy profession at the best of times, and losing the

American tour at the start of the busy season had left him out on a limb – and London was an unfriendly place when times were tough. Sally had finished speaking and was looking at him curiously. 'Sorry,' he said. 'What did you say?'

'I said I might climb up to his old bus tomorrow – we owe him a favour for dunking Cuthbert.' Peter grinned and banished unspoken fears to the back of his mind for the time being.

She rose early the next day but instead of going riding she packed a few tins into a basket along with a small loaf, some butter, and a packet of tea. Then she set out to climb the hill. The bus had a closed-up look but, as she neared the door, Bernard the horse ambled over to say hullo. She gave him a passing pat. 'Where's your friend then, Bernard?' Then louder, 'Anybody home?'

A faint voice responded from inside. 'In here. The door's open.'

Cuffy lay on the iron bedstead covered by a motley collection of blankets, wearing his shirt and scarf. He must have been very ill but had recovered to the point of being pale and weak. Sally took in the situation at a glance and set about making him comfortable. The confined smell of illness was unpleasant but she gave no indication of it as she leaned him forward to rearrange the pillows.

His eyes were large and dark with concern as he looked up at her. 'I knew someone'd come,' he whispered.

'How long have you been like this?'

'Monday night. Heavy cold.'

'You've had more than a heavy cold, old friend. Do these windows open?'

'I've never tried them.' He leaned back, the company making him instantly feel better.

'Let's see if we can blow away some of your germs.' After some difficulty, she slid one open. 'When did you last eat?'

'Monday I think. I haven't felt hungry'.

'But you might fancy some nice hot tomato soup now?'

'Yes, if you don't want it.'

She found the Calor gas burner, some matches, and cleared a space to unpack the basket.

'Bernard hasn't been fed for days,' Cuffy told her.

'Bernard's got four acres of grass. He can wait. What

brought this on?'

'I think it was my bath.'

'You had a bath? When?'

'Saturday. After our chat. I had a good wash-down in the river.'

She looked at him, the tin of soup in her hand. 'You got into that river simply because of our talk?'

'It was horrible cold.'

She thought, knights of old claimed the fair maiden's hand for less than that. Aloud she said, 'Where's the tin opener?'

'In the drawer with the handle.'

She found it. 'The one with the piece of string?'

'That's the handle.'

'Ask a silly question!'

He lay silently as she opened the tin, found a saucepan of sorts, and lit the gas.

At last he said, 'I been laying here thinking. Just allowing thoughts to come and go. Except Tuesday night. I got frightened Tuesday night. I wanted someone to come Tuesday night.'

'You needed a doctor,' Sally said. 'I'll work something out for another time.'

'I knew someone'd come in the end. I just feared it *was* the end.'

There was no bread knife; she did her best with a small blunt affair with a blackened handle. 'Don't tire yourself talking.'

'I been talking all night. Have to talk to think; otherwise the thoughts whizz round in my head without any order to them.' His voice was growing stronger – her presence acting like a tonic. 'At first I thought it must seem I don't fit in around here. Shillingbury people aren't like me. They got farms, jobs, families, money in the bank, and motor cars. They're happy with what they have, so I should be unhappy because I got nothing.'

'But you're not,' she said, surveying an uneven slice of bread.

'I'm not. I'm part of their lives, you see. I *do* fit in.' He explained, as the confused jumble of thoughts which had besieged him over endless hours seemed to take shape. 'I go into the Oddfellows Arms and order a drink, wave my five-pound note, and Terry says she's clear out of change today. It makes her feel good to pretend. The widow Simpkins knows I'll ask her to marry me every time I pass. She acts narky, scolds me, but it makes her feel good.'

Sally smiled. 'Poor Mrs S.'

'Jake gives me all his mucky jobs and a chance to earn some spends,' the tinker went on. 'Mandy gives me a good feed from her kitchen, and your husband gives me rides in his car.' The philosophy resolved itself. 'Although I'm not anybody I sort of fit in with everybody else, see.'

She paused as she buttered the bread. 'And what do I do, Cuffy? How do I fit into your life?'

He lay back and considered. 'By not feeling sorry for me.' The answer came clear and sure. 'I don't care much for people feeling sorry for me because I don't feel sorry for myself. You talk to me like you want to hear what I got to say.'

She poured the soup into a tin mug and carried it with the plate of bread and butter to the bed. 'Yes, well I don't want to hear any more until you've drunk up this soup.'

He took it and at once raised it to his lips. Then, a rare feeling of gratitude stirred somewhere deep inside him. He looked up at the girl. 'Thanks for coming,' he said.

'I'm going to find a doctor and come back and see you later. Okay?'

'Okay.' There was one more thing to straighten out before he could permit himself a drink. 'Will you give some oats to Bernard? There's a sack under the bus – and I mix it with a splash of water from the stream.'

'Right.'

He nodded contentedly and took a comforting drink of soup. His eyes came round to her as she opened the door and he pointed. 'You also give me a rose,' he said.

She glanced at the solitary rose, bent sadly over the side of the tooth-mug, petals fallen. She was greatly touched. He managed a wrinkled smile. She gave him a slightly crooked grin . . . and was gone.

Jake said, 'Funny, one never thinks about Cuffy being ill. I suppose one day he just won't be there any more and that'll be that.'

He leant against the back door by the kitchen. Sally, wearing jodhpurs and jumper, had stopped on her way to saddle up Lady. 'It must have been frightening in that old bus by himself.'

'Aye. That's the part as'd get me down.' He followed her as she walked towards the stables. 'I'm dreading the day Mandy goes off – I don't know what I'm going to do in this place. Still, I'll be better off than Cuffy, I dare say.'

'You'll have the farmhands all day.'

'Aye, but it's the evenings.'

'Mandy says you watch the box till that dot goes.'

'Maybe, but you need someone to grumble at in the mornings.'

'She says all you do is grunt before your second cup of tea.'

'But you can't grunt to yourself, can you?' Jake countered. 'Where's the fun in that?'

He paused as he saw Harvey, in his postman's uniform, leaning his bike against the tractor. An unusually puzzled Harvey carrying a telegram for someone whose surname was new to him. 'Follett,' he said and spelt it for them. 'Is it someone staying with you, Mrs Higgins?' Even as Sally shook her head Jake was wearing the smug, self-satisfied expression of being one-up on the postman. It was Cuffy; except who on earth would send Cuffy a telegram?

'What's it say?' asked Jake.

'I'm not permitted to reveal the contents of Her Majesty's mail,' said Harvey.

'I hope it's not bad news,' said Sally. 'I never like telegrams.'

'Oh, he won't mind this one,' Harvey assured her, forgetting all about Her Majesty. 'He's won the pools!'

Willing hands helped the tinker downhill from the bus, his face paper-pale against the brilliant hues of the Reverend Arthur Norris's trousers. They took him to Rose Cottage where Peter studied the results printed in the previous Sunday's paper. There had been a fair number of draws but it still looked like a possible first dividend pay-out for about twenty-five thousand pounds.

Harvey and Jake stood either side of Cuffy, already protecting him against unknown hazards that came from winning fortunes. The tinker was anxious to make it clear that he always put his Xs in the same squares, and said so several times. The trouble with such haphazard methods lay in the fact that one was just as likely to pick up a couple of second dividends as win nothing at all. He could quite easily have won more than twenty-five thousand.

Cuffy tried to allow the conversation to wash over him. Instinctively he felt unsure. He was a great one for normality and the day was not proceeding as days normally did. In his experience this was not a good sign. The farmer and the postman were smiling at him, giving frequent winks, and pats on the shoulder . . . this just wasn't normal.

In the Oddfellows Arms Jake took it upon himself to offer guidance on the protocol of punters celebrating big wins. Cuffy was allowed to reach the bar first where he promptly ordered his usual pint before turning to see Jake and Harvey staring at him expectantly. 'Aren't you having anything today?' he asked out of interest.

'That's very nice of you,' responded Jake quickly. 'I think I'd enjoy a whisky and soda. What's your fancy, Harvey?'

'I'll have the same please'.

Jake nodded to Terry behind the bar and when her back was turned, he nudged Cuffy confidentially. 'I dare say our Terry here would welcome an opportunity to toast your good fortune,' he advised. Cuffy nodded vaguely and then saw that the Reverend Arthur Norris had joined the party just in time to greet the happy winner in the chair.

'I got your trousers on,' Cuffy whispered in a friendly way. The vicar managed a *sotto voce* embarrassed laugh before accepting Jake's offer of a glass of white wine.

The drinks were laid out on the bar. Four glasses were raised towards him, the smiling faces going out of focus as Cuffy was possessed of a dreadful premonition. He pulled out his five-pound note and, before it had been proffered, the piece of paper seemed to be whisked out of his grasp. There came the sound of a 'Ting' as the cash register was operated, then some oddments of change were returned to his hand.

It was the first of a whole series of incidents which left him bemused and worried. Everybody he knew began to behave differently towards him and things simply weren't the same any more. He enjoyed being taken by Sally to Banbury where the hairdresser wrapped hot towels around his face before shaving his beard, and shampooed his hair before cutting and trimming it into a style. In the outfitters he rather fancied the purple striped jacket which he thought would go well with his red and yellow check trousers, but she persuaded him to take a complete suit in grey with shirts, ties, and socks to complement it. The new brown shoes were painful, positively painful and he said so. What was the point of spending money on things that *hurt* – but Sally had laughed so he pretended he'd said something funny.

Despite feeling uncomfortable he went along with her whims until she took him into the estate agent. They showed him houses, bungalows, cottages . . . but he baulked and refused to consider anything he saw. After all, what would Bernard do in one of those stupid gardens?

When he felt strong enough he walked to the station. Peter seemed genuinely pleased to see the new-style tinker and opened the door for him. Before starting the engine he rummaged into his briefcase and pulled out several glossy-paged brochures. 'Brought these for you,' Peter said.

'What are they for?' asked Cuffy.

'Motor cars. You're going to be busy from now on – you'll need wheels of your own.'

Cuffy objected. 'I like *your* car.'

'Well, you're not buying this.'

'I don't want to buy it,' explained Cuffy, frustration welling up inside him. 'I just want to *ride* in it.'

They drove into the village but the old man didn't enjoy it as much as before and sat quite still, pensive and sad.

Later he walked round to Mrs Simpkins' house and was taken aback to see her putting on a fair display of struggling with the mower. He broke into a run. 'What are you doing cutting the grass?' he asked.

She took in his smart suit and styled hair. 'You're a bit above this now, aren't you?'

He spluttered slightly. 'But I *always* cuts your grass. I come round special because I missed last week, seeing as I wasn't well.'

She smiled at him, a warm intimate smile. 'That's very kind,' she said. 'Very kind indeed.'

'I bought you a present too.' He pulled a bag from his pocket. 'The only worthwhile thing I bought all day.'

She opened it, her delight turning to surprise when she

pulled out a small can of oil. He took it back from her without ceremony. 'We'll get this old heap working properly now.'

'How nice of you, Cuffy.'

As he worked he asked, 'No chance of naming the day, Mrs Simpkins?'

She liked a joke. 'Well, now you're a man of means – I'll have to think about it, won't I?' She turned from him and walked back to the house. His eyes followed her in frank alarm which he quickly disguised when she called over her shoulder. 'I didn't make you a meat and potato pie. I thought you might like something here. A sort of celebration now you're so smart.'

Things weren't going right at all. He *liked* meat and potato pie.

When he passed the vicarage on his way home the front door opened almost as if Arthur Norris had been watching for him. 'I'm glad I saw you. I wanted a word.'

'Am I to get a sermon, Reverend, Vicar, sir?'

'A sermon?' The vicar laughed disparagingly. 'My dear chap, sermons are for the pulpit not the public highway.'

'Where you been standing has never made no difference yet,' remarked Cuffy.

Norris felt it right that he should make a few points about the tinker's most fortunate windfall because, undoubtedly, there would be those who would find themselves unable to view his good fortune without a measure of envy. Some might even try to persuade him to part with some of it by drawing his attention to certain causes where money could be put to good use. He cited, as an example, the rain which entered the west tower; the longer it was left the worse the damage would become, until the cost of repairs would far outstrip the church's limited means. Cuffy nodded sympathetically because, in fact, the rain came into his bus just in the spot where he sat of an evening. He caught it in a bucket.

Norris said, 'The Lord is more disposed to look down on His house filled with worshippers rather than buckets. Anyway, the roof was only an example. There will be others wanting your ear for less worthy needs. It is a matter for your judgement. Simply remember that the church was there when you were in need of help.' He paused, awaiting some sign that his message might have fallen on fertile ground.

Cuffy nodded slowly. 'Thank you, Reverend, Vicar, sir. It was a sermon after all.'

Norris was never sure whether the tinker was the simple man he seemed or whether his brain was sharper than appeared to be the case. Sometimes he suspected Cuffy was laughing at him, which thought was rather worrying; until good sense told him that street survival should not be confused with the brainpower of a thinking man.

When Cuffy arrived at Jake's yard the farmer was mucking out a cowshed. 'Come to see how the workers live, have you?' he asked in a perfectly amicable manner.

'I wondered if you had any little job for me,' said Cuffy.

'Little jobs?' Jake smiled briefly. 'That's rich that is. Standing there in your brand new whistle and flute enquiring into little jobs.'

'I can soon change my clothes.'

'Look, you can put those bad old days behind you for good and all now.'

'I don't want to put them behind me,' Cuffy objected, wishing somebody would understand him.

'Well, I'm glad you don't want to change anything now that money's no object,' said Jake good-naturedly. 'But you needn't go hankering after digging ditches. You're too good for that sort of thing.'

'Seems I've become too good for all the things I enjoy.'

Jake looked at him for a moment. 'Come inside and have a cuppa. We were about to break anyway.' He saw his daughter going into the kitchen and called for her to put a kettle on. Then he and Cuffy walked slowly to the door, the farmer clasping his hands thoughtfully behind him. 'The thing is,' he said, 'new vistas have opened up for you. The power of money is a wonderful thing, Cuffy. It opens up doors that would otherwise have remained forever closed.' He attempted to appear worldlywise. 'It'll seem strange at first, of course it will. And in that respect if I can be of any assistance you have only to ask.'

'What sort of assistance, Mr Jake?'

'The spending of money is an art,' Jake explained patronisingly. 'It's not a pastime to be entered into lightly. Sometimes the expenditure of large sums cannot be undertaken by one man alone.'

They reached the kitchen door and Jake stood to one

side indicating the way with a slight inclination of his head. For an instant the tinker experienced a surge of suspicion, but he accepted the unspoken invitation and entered first. 'Have you spent large sums in your day?' he asked.

'I have had my moments,' Jake assured him grandly.

Mandy looked up from setting out the cups and saucers. 'Oh? What moment was that, Dad?' she enquired cheerfully. 'The time you squandered four sixpences in a row down the slot of a one-armed bandit?'

'We'll have none of that, my girl.'

Mandy grinned as she crossed to the breadbin and took out a loaf. 'Take no notice of him, Cuffy. If you need any advice get it from a qualified accountant, not from somebody who comes over giddy playing Black Jack with haricot beans.'

'Mandy!' exclaimed Jake, annoyed.

'Well, come off it, Dad,' she said, reaching up for the cake tin on a shelf. 'Suddenly coming into a fortune isn't easy. It really isn't. I've read about how it's ruined people's lives often enough. All Cuffy's short of is advice from well-meaning friends.' She crossed back to the kitchen table and nudged the tinker as she passed. 'You'll be able to go on your travels, though, won't you? No difficulties about that.' She put the loaf and the tin on the table. 'Cake or sandwich?'

Cuffy said, 'Cake.' Then, after a moment, 'Er – '

'Both?' asked Mandy.

'Yes please.' And that did it. Suddenly his mind clarified and confusion was swept aside. 'That's it!' he exclaimed.

'What's it?' asked Jake.

The tinker took a deep breath. 'Mandy always asks if I want cake or sandwich and I always says cake and then I hesitates and she says both and I says yes please. It's normal you see.' He rushed on while the thought was still clear in his head. 'Only these last two days nothing normal has been happening to me. I'd like to have a holiday right enough, fly in an airy plane, sail on a ship; just so long as nothing changed while I was away. I'd want to come home to my normal life, and friends . . . and little mucky jobs.' He looked up at Jake, almost shyly.

The farmer shook his head. 'Oh dear, oh dear,' he said.

It was dark by the time Cuffy climbed the hill towards his bus. He appeared incongruous in his new suit. As he neared the top he suddenly knew something was wrong, very wrong. He just knew. 'Bernard –' he called out anxiously. He climbed faster, panic filling his breast. 'Bernard –' he shouted louder.

It took him five minutes to find the horse. Bernard was lying motionless in a corner formed by a knoll of trees and some shrubs, as if the animal had deliberately sought out a sheltered spot. Cuffy ran through the grass, soft mud doing no good to new shoes. He scrambled down beside him, lifting the horse's head into his lap. He was still breathing, short panting gasps.

Cuffy cradled and stroked the head for three hours before Bernard died. Then he wept.

CHAPTER SIX

FOR PETER it was the nights which were worst.

When a songwriter has his first real hit, the professional and financial reaction is awe-inspiring, and even the most level-headed composer will experience the first heady tastes of a new lifestyle. On the other hand one flop brings in its wake casual waves and distant smiles from yesterday's friends; a succession of flops bring total obscurity. Tin-Pan-Alley is the loneliest place in the world for the out-of-fashion songwriter.

On the night that Bernard died two men in Shillingbury passed a sleepless night. Cuffy sat with dip pen and bottle of ink, frowning in concentration over his first desperate attempt at writing fiction. Peter lay in bed, listening to Sally breathing quietly beside him, and found himself unable to subdue the haunting fears of failure.

They came together the next morning. Cuffy, dressed in his old clothes, sat in front of Peter, watching him intently while he checked the football coupon with a newspaper. 'I wanted you to look at it for me,' he explained, 'Because it didn't seem right somehow.'

Peter shook his head. 'It isn't right, Cuffy. To start with you put a draw for Chelsea versus Leicester – it was three-nil.'

'I always put them in the same place every week, see,' said the tinker helpfully.

'And the next one's wrong,' said Peter. 'And the next . . .' He looked up from the paper. 'Cuffy, you got them *all* wrong. You didn't forecast *one* correct result.'

'I don't go by the teams or anything. I just put them –'

'– in the same place every week,' Peter finished for him. 'You told me. You also told me you never kept a copy.'

'Nor I don't. I wrote that last night. I always puts my crosses in the same place, so that's what I sent to Liverpool. Anyway, I did get a telegram,' he added carefully. 'There was nothing wrong with that.'

Peter's eyes narrowed, as far back in his mind a dreadful thought was born. 'A telegram – from Liverpool.'

'That's right.'

'Wait a minute.' Peter got up and crossed to the door. 'Sal,' he called.

'Yes?' from somewhere upstairs.

'A slight problem.'

'Coming.'

He returned to the tinker. 'Have you still got that telegram?'

'It's up in the bus.' He was relieved when Sally entered, her smile welcome and warming.

Peter said directly. 'The telegram from the pools. I think it could be a hoax.'

'Oh no!'

'And someone took the trouble to make sure it came from Liverpool.' He repeated, more pointedly than was necessary, 'From Liverpool, Sal.'

She closed her eyes briefly as the implication hit her. Cuthbert. She couldn't believe that even Cuthbert . . . 'Oh Cuffy, whatever can I say?' Then to Peter, 'Surely no post office would accept a hoax telegram from a kid. Especially in Liverpool.'

Cuffy's eyes flickered slightly at this and he looked down at his boots as Peter commented, 'The simple truth is that his so-called winning permutation was a load of old rubbish. What did the telegram say, Cuffy?'

'I can't read so I don't know. Harvey just said as I'd won.'

Sally was all for telephoning her uncle immediately but Peter wanted to think things through first; her Dead End cousin would only deny it anyway. As for all the money the tinker had spent, the gas fridge and the portable television could go back to the shop – they'd make noises but it would be possible to get over that. But the clothes, the hairdresser, the pub drinks bill . . .

'It was experience,' said Cuffy philosophically. 'Nothing has been normal these last two weeks. Nothing at all.'

'You can say that again,' Peter muttered grimly.

'Nothing has been normal these –' began Cuffy obligingly until Peter interrupted.

'Cuffy!'

There came a 'Rat-tat' at the door as Harvey delivered the morning mail. Peter hurried out and caught up with the postman before he reached the gate. A few confidential words brought him up to date with the hoax which meant it would be round the entire village by lunchtime. It would be easier for Cuffy if everybody knew in advance and he was spared the repetitive embarrassment of breaking the news himself. In return Harvey told Peter about the horse. Cuffy had said he wanted it buried in the corner of the field – a request that was almost bound to be turned down. Strange that the tinker hadn't mentioned Bernard; strange also that he'd said nothing about a second letter he'd received two days earlier. The letter bearing a Liverpool postmark.

Peter's mail comprised one circular. Nothing else; no commission, no cheque . . . not even a note from a friend.

As Cuffy left Sally picked him a buttonhole. 'We'll help all we can.'

'When you come up to the bus you asked me how you fit into my life.'

'And you said it was by not feeling sorry for you.'

He nodded. 'Well, don't spoil everything now.' It was said with uncharacteristic self-conviction.

Peter came over to them, pulling a note from his pocket. 'You'll need this,' he said as he gave it to the tinker. 'And don't spend it. I want it back when you've finished with it.'

'Ten pound!' gasped Cuffy. 'I'll *never* finish with it. A ten-pound note will last me forever.'

By ten o'clock Cuffy had started out on a methodical tour of Shillingbury. Both hands deep in the mackintosh pockets, his steady, unhurried lope took him first to the vicarage.

'Cuffy, my dear fellow,' exclaimed Norris. 'What a grave misfortune.'

'Yes, Reverend, Vicar, sir.' Harvey had unfailingly obliged by blowing on the hot embers of gossip.

'We must pray that the unfortunate child will come to realise how wickedly he has behaved.'

It had been a cruel trick but, surprisingly, the tinker interrupted Norris's smooth flow of comforting dialogue even before it was properly under way. 'I'm sorry about the hole in your roof,' he said. 'Maybe I could climb up and take a look?'

'The church restoration fund has a target of forty thousand pounds,' Norris pointed out piously. 'If the problem could be solved by sending a man up to take a look, we'd have set a somewhat lower figure.'

'There's only one thing for it then. We'll have to send up a prayer. The power of prayer is a wondrous thing.'

'Is it now?' said Norris. 'Why couldn't somebody have told me that before?' He recalled thinking only the week before that the evenings were drawing in and the nights becoming chilly. He had one or two spare oddments of warm clothing he could look out and Cuffy said he'd take them off him if he didn't want them. It was a hard day for the tinker and Norris refrained from uttering his customary rebuke about ingratitude. 'But,' he reminded him instead, 'if you could lend your voice to those of us who go in for this praying thing, we do it all together in the church on Sundays, you know.'

Sarcasm having been met with sarcasm, Cuffy ventured towards his next port of call. He enquired of Mrs Simpkins if she was still wanting to marry him. She rose to the bait and declared that anything she might have said a few days earlier was designed only to raise him towards higher planes of conversation. Cuffy seemed to be hearing exactly what he wanted to hear as, slowly, he brought his situation under control. It was established that meat and potato pie day was Friday and, when her face became suffused by compassion for the truly terrible day he was living through, Cuffy, on the other hand, seemed to think it was getting better as it went along.

In Jake's yard the farmer walked him towards a mountainous dung heap. 'Them pigs, when they're being taken to market . . . well, sometimes they seem to know what's in store for them. And when a pig gets frightened it don't do it in a gentlemanly way like you and me. So I got about three ton of little frights in a great big heap over here, all of which needs to be carted to Top Field and spread ready for next season.'

'Muck spreading,' sighed Cuffy.

'Well, yes. You got it in two words there.'

'At a pound an hour?'

'You drive a terrible hard bargain. There's three days work, I reckon.'

'I'll make a start in the morning.'

'You'll take your tea breaks outside,' warned Jake. 'I'm not having you in the kitchen in the state you'll be in.' Suddenly the farmer dived into a pocket and pulled out an

84

envelope. 'You'll save me the postage if you'll take this now.'

Cuffy knew what it was. His eyes became blurred by tears which prevented him seeing the invitation even if he could have read it. 'Miss Mandy's wedding –'

'You're as much a part of Shillingbury as anyone else around here. So you'll be welcome.'

The tinker nodded, too overcome for much else. Jake was walking towards a field and he followed him blindly. 'When you're carting the muck to Top Field use old Yorky here. He's over eighteen and should go out to grass. You got a bit of space around you so you might as well get to know him, now his working days are over.'

Cuffy was hardly able to speak. He tried several times but his throat was tightly constricted as Yorky ambled over to greet him. Eventually he managed a whisper which Jake had to incline his head to hear. 'If you don't want the horse I'll take him off your hands for you.'

When the five-thirty drew into the station Cuffy was standing by Peter's car. Minutes later he was sitting happily in the passenger seat as the MG sped through the countryside. As they pulled up outside the Oddfellows Arms Peter asked, 'What did you do with the cheque, Cuffy?'

He'd been expecting the question; somehow he'd been aware that Peter knew something. 'What cheque was that?' he tried.

'Oh, come on! If we're going to be friends, you and me, we've got to be straight with each other.'

'It were a hoax', said Cuffy stubbornly. 'You said so yourself.'

'And what about the letter you got from Liverpool?'

'What letter?'

'If that's the way you want to play it, okay. But you know, and I know, it's not true.'

Cuffy climbed out of the car slowly. It'd been a good day and he was loath to see it go wrong now. He leaned on the door and looked down at Peter. 'There are some things that become true because you want them to. This last week I've been as unhappy as at any time I can remember. All because of that talk about a cheque. Now it's gone away and not you nor anybody is going to bring it back. Because after a day like I've had today, I ask you this, Mr Higgins – who wants to win the football pools?'

With a small wave of his hand he turned and walked into the pub. He marched straight up to Terry behind the bar and ordered a pint of the usual.

He watched her as she filled the tankard and nervously his hand went to an inside pocket to take out the ten-pound note. When the barmaid placed the drink before him he put it down on the bar. A moment passed, their eyes met, she picked it up . . . 'Ten pounds – you have gone up in the world. I'm sure I can't change as much as that. Better chalk it up until next time.'

To his infinite relief she pushed it back into his top pocket. 'If that's what you want,' he said as he picked up the tankard and took a long drink.

The day was over. Cuffy sat in the bus by the light of his paraffin lamp. He was staring at a cheque – the only cheque he'd ever received in his life and certainly the largest sum of money he was ever likely to see. His mouth twisted with quizzical humour as he realised that no bank would now cash it; Vernon's representative had seen to that when he called. The cheque was cancelled and a new one drawn in favour of the church restoration fund – from an anonymous donor.

He sat wistfully. After all, it had come as a considerable shock to learn that money was not as valuable as he'd thought.

The simple fact was he was better off without it.

He held the end of the cheque over the top of his lamp. It quickly caught a flame and, turning it in his hand, he watched it burn.

CHAPTER SEVEN

THE WILDEST stretch of imagination could never describe Harvey as a gardener. His daily journeys past the front gardens of Shillingbury as he delivered the mail provided him with an ever-changing horticultural display and qualified him, in his own opinion, as a critic. His memory for the Latin nomenclature would last sometimes the distance of three houses, with the result that he could enquire of John Addison at number nineteen the name of the shrub massed with starry-white flowers, in order to comment acidly to Mrs Thompson at number twenty-two on the poor showing of her *Deutzia gracilis*.

The cottage gardens were a rewarding sight throughout the year. He took positive pleasure from the heathers and evergreens of winter, with shy snowdrops and gentle winter jasmine, reaching towards the bright daffodils, polyanthus and grape hyacinths of spring. Later the bolder tulips standing to attention beneath magnolias, camellias and rhododendrons bridged the seasons to the roses, iris, berberis, laburnum, and cascades of brilliant annuals. In their turn came the forerunners of autumn tints, chrysanthemums, dahlias, and colchicums. Finally, the sadly glorious colours of the autumn, and the brief rest before the first winter aconite peeped through to start the cycle again.

The only thing to come between the postman and his transient studies of other people's gardens was a telegram. His passion for delivering news became heightened by the delivery of a yellow envelope; telegrams brought with them a sense of urgency and he would hurry unseeing towards the home of the addressee, unerringly reciting the contents before the envelope was opened. 'It's from your father, Mrs Higgins,' he said to Sally at Rose Cottage. '"Arriving Wednesday. Staying indefinitely. Dad."'

'Harvey, you deliver confidential mail with all the secrecy of a town crier.'

'Why does he send a telegram? He only lives five miles away.'

'Because it pleases his sense of the dramatic.' Sally was about to close the front door when Harvey remembered the other public service he performed. 'You haven't seen Horrible Humphrey, have you?' It was a question asked regularly on his rounds because Mr Charles' over-sexed mongrel escaped into the road several times a week. 'He's going to get himself run over one of these days.'

'Let's hope they find him before he starts another population explosion,' said Sally.

Harvey sniffed. 'Any intelligent bitch would turn her back on him.'

'That's the last thing any intelligent bitch would do.' Sally stepped back into the cottage but paused again as she saw the figure of her father approaching.

Harvey touched his cap to him. 'Hullo, Major. I just delivered you.'

George Langton was an imposing man, military in bearing, but his every gesture, demeanour and voice was in the full tradition of Henry Irving, each utterance a proclamation demanding attention. He was carrying an ornate clock as he ignored the postman and marched up the path to Sally. 'You got my telegram?'

'It beat you by a short head.' She gave him a kiss. 'Nothing wrong, is there?'

'Nothing.' A perfectly timed pause, before, 'Except that my world has disintegrated.' He swept into the cottage. Sally gave Harvey a here-we-go-again look, before following her father indoors. By the time she reached the living-room Langton had already taken up a commanding position in front of the fireplace, still holding the clock. Peter was standing facing him and carrying a greenhouse plant in a clay pot. The two men looked as if at any moment they would toss them to each other in a bizarre juggling display. 'Thirty-five years of loyal, unswerving service,' her father was saying, 'and suddenly it's thank you, goodbye, and a bloody clock!' He dumped it on the piano.

Sally said, 'You mean you've been retired?'

'Sacked. No need to play with words.'

'You mustn't think of it as being sacked, sir,' Peter began.

'All right,' interrupted Langton. 'Stabbed in the back.'

'Dad, honestly –!' objected Sally. 'You know the company retirement rules and you've already wriggled round them for two years.'

'It happens to everyone sooner or later,' agreed Peter.

'Wouldn't happen in the army,' barked Langton. 'If they think a man's past it in the field, they stick him in the War Office, not the bloody wilderness.' His gaze fell on the plant in Peter's arms. 'You trying to hatch that?'

'Oh, er, no. It's a melon plant.'

'It's a what?'

'A melon plant. I want to grow melons.'

'Good heavens.'

Peter put it on the piano by the clock. 'Can I offer you a drink?'

'Don't offer it. Just give it me!' He turned to his daughter. 'You don't know how a thing like this shakes your confidence.'

'Well, it shouldn't, Dad,' said Sally, sitting on the settee. 'Now you're free to do all the things you've never had the time for.'

Langton relaxed slightly and sat opposite her. 'What things?' he enquired.

'You and Mummy could travel. Take a cruise. See the pyramids.'

'I chased Rommel around the pyramids.'

Peter came back with a Scotch. 'What about France?' he suggested.

'I was last man off at Dunkirk.' He took a sip then said helplessly. 'My job was everything I am. I don't know anything else.'

'Have you told Mummy?'

'No. I can't face two traumas in one day. I'll stay with you for a while.'

'Dad, you're being dramatic again. Finish your drink, pull yourself together, and Peter will run you home.' She had been nineteen before discovering that her father, for all his bluster, took to the hills at the sound of a firm voice making a practical suggestion. He plonked his glass down on a sidetable and rose to his feet. 'What do you think she'll say?'

'Knowing Mummy it'll be something like –' Sally clapped her hands to her face and cried, 'My God, George, what's to become of us?'

He nodded morosely, knowing his daughter had almost certainly got the inflection right as well as the words. He watched Peter collect the clock before following him out of the room. Sally heard him declaiming in the hall, 'Not only betrayed by my colleagues but spurned by my own daughter.'

In the car Langton listened to his son-in-law trying to convince him that it wasn't the end of the world. He'd got more energy and determination than most men and it was simply a question of harnessing it to something new. He'd always wanted to build a house but his trouble was he hated working alone. There had been a camaraderie in the army and he'd never done anything on his own. If he were to try and find something he and his wife could tackle together it would undoubtedly rule out the house – Martha's brickwork was awful.

They pulled up outside Greenacres, the name that some previous owner had bestowed upon Langton's house, and the 'Major' climbed out of the car and stood, head up and shoulders square, ready to face court martial. Peter cast an eye over the overgrown jungle that for that same owner of earlier years had once represented God's Little Acre, and was blessed with an idea. 'There is,' he ventured, 'a challenge, quite literally in your own front yard. With an even larger one round the back.'

'A challenge?'

'Take a look around.'

Langton made a three-hundred-and-sixty degree turn but could see nothing worthy of the word – the stupid boy was rambling again. 'Come on, man. Get to the point.'

'A hobby is something you have to discover for yourself, sir.' Peter grinned and drove off. Langton shrugged, turned, and saw his wife Martha staring from the living-room window with a gloom-laden face. It was going to be a difficult conversation.

The living-room was as untidy as the garden outside, the result of years of impulse buying. Once a week for the twenty-nine years of their married life, either Martha's or George's eye had been attracted by some *objet d'art,* picture, ornament, piece of furniture, or plain bric-à-brac. It had been purchased, brought home, and put down – rather than placed – in the first available space. Martha was a striking woman from whom Sally had inherited her bone structure, eyes, and bearing. She shared with her husband the great moments of drama as they played out every one of life's scenes for all it was worth.

Langton placed the clock on the mantelpiece, considered it for a few seconds, then turned towards his wife. 'I take it you've heard,' he began quietly in order to allow a maximum build up to his big speech.

'Sally telephoned. She said I was to remain calm. I am calm, George.'

He could feel the atmosphere pervading the room. The struggle against mental pressure, hysteria straining for release. Martha remained calm for a further five seconds before clapping her hands to her face. 'My God, George, what's to become of us?'

He tried not to wince at the anticipated words. 'There came a summons to the chairman's office.' He saw her half close her eyes, conjuring up the image. 'Company directors were gathered. Drinks, conjecture on the reason for our being called. Then the speech. It was – moving.'

'I can visualise the scene,' whispered Martha.

His voice increased in volume by a notch. 'When he announced it was I who was to retire, there could clearly be heard an intake of breath.'

'From relief,' she nodded understandingly.

'From concern,' he corrected. 'An expulsion of breath would signify relief. This was a positive sucking in.'

'It's as if I was there.'

'A voice was heard to cry, "Oh no!" '

' "Oh no"?'

' "Oh no." A still small voice rising above the general anguish.'

'Whose small voice?' she asked.

'*My* small voice,' he replied with plaintive annoyance. 'I have, after all, built the company from its embryonic birth to the position it enjoys today.' His voice became a shout. 'And when it's that idiot managing director's turn for retirement, I shall personally dance for joy in front of his very eyes!'

'Didn't he contribute to the general anguish?'

Langton snapped at her. 'There was no anguish, you daft ha'porth.'

'I will stay calm.'

'Only general trepidation as to whose neck was for the chop.'

'And it turned out to be yours.'

'Whereupon there was a sharp sucking in of relief.'

The ornate clock suddenly erupted into life from its new home on the mantelpiece. A whirr, a clunk, then the full Westminster chime as it struck three. Langton and Martha watched it, awestruck. When at last it fell silent they looked back at each other. Martha, still calm, asked, 'Are we going to live through that entire performance every hour for the rest of our lives?'

Later that evening Langton drew the curtains against the fading light. Then he opened them again and stared out across the quarter acre of rotting vegetation. He must have looked at the garden, a thousand times without noticing it – without even *seeing* it, his thoughts on other things. It was a challenge. By golly, it was something to stretch a man, something worthy of his energy and determination. He had a head on him, that boy, *he'd* spotted the possibility. Martha used to say, when they were younger, 'Set yourself a target, make it just a little harder, then *take a crack at it!*'

He hurried to the telephone and dictated a telegram. 'Higgins, Rose Cottage, Shillingbury, stop. Urgent I see you, stop. Do not go to bed, stop. Regards, George Langton.'

He walked briskly through the night air, his mind besieged by an onslaught of exciting ideas. He'd seen quite simple people working in their gardens. People without benefit of education or an army background. If they could do it he was damn sure he could. It was a challenge. Roll up the sleeves and get down to fundamentals. Dig for victory, walk arm in arm with nature, grow his own, and to hell with the Common Market. He spoke aloud in the silence of the night, 'You're nearer to God in a garden than any place else on earth.'

It was a question of vision. Planning on the grand scale. The great gardens of England – Wisley, Kew, Sissinghurst – they didn't come about by scattering a packet of seeds. They were campaigns of military magnitude. The Chelsea Flower Show . . . he slapped his side as he walked, he must join the Royal Horticultural Society.

In Peter and Sally's sitting room he gratefully accepted a whisky. 'I'm afraid we're out of soda, sir,' said Peter.

'Good,' commented Langton.

'Are we talking about your garden?' Sally asked, unbelievingly.

'The best idea he ever had,' said her father. 'I shall attack from the rear first, you know.'

'You mean you'll do the back garden first,' nodded Peter. 'Good idea.'

'Do I gather,' enquired Sally of her husband, 'that it was you who talked him into this?'

'It seemed a good idea at the time. I might just decide to help him.'

'You and Dad discussing gardening? It's like Lee Marvin talking to Mohammed Ali about dressmaking.'

Langton raised his glass. 'My garden shall be a canvas. And on that canvas I shall paint my vision of the future.'

It was a perfect line on which to make an exit so Langton cut short his stay rather than waste the effect. As he swept out of the room Peter called, 'And when do you start this – er – painting?'

'Tomorrow. Attack at dawn.' The front door slammed behind him.

The next morning Langton was waiting outside the Public Library when it opened. Minutes later he emerged reading a book on gardening and carrying three more. In the newspaper shop he added three gardening magazines, and in the book shop he purchased a *very big* picture book of fine English gardens. He finished up in The Corner Shop watching Mrs Cavendish pin a card to the display board:

Retired Gentleman requires part-time help in garden. Apply: Greenacres, Banley.

It was past midday before Peter spotted the card. He jumped into his MG and drove the five miles to his father-in-law's house. He was surprised to see a taxi waiting outside, its engine ticking over. Before he was halfway down the patch the front door burst open and Martha exploded out of the house. 'He's gone mad. This time he really has become demented.'

'What's he done?' asked Peter, as a more conventional greeting seemed uncalled for.

'Longevity runs in his family,' explained Martha. 'Nobody dies before they're eighty. Which gives him a comfortable eighteen years to do his garden. So will you explain to me why he seems hellbent on finishing it by lunchtime?'

'Are you going away?' Peter called, as she strode towards the taxi.

'I'm going to stay with my daughter for a while.'

'You mean my wife?'

'Oh yes,' she remembered. 'And with you.'

'Do we know . . . does she know you're coming?'

'I have just despatched a telegram.' He might have guessed. The Langtons' passion for telegrams was going to make the most terrible hole in their combined pension.

Peter attempted a philosophical shrug as he watched the driver rev up his engine until the taxi and its occupants were lost in a dense cloud of blue smoke which set off down the street like an asphyxial typhoon. His heart sank slightly as he surveyed the dense mass of overgrown shrubs and weeds, but he headed towards the side of the house, intent on blazing a trail through the wilderness in search of Langton.

He found him in a small clearing, seated at a kitchen table set among tall weeds. He was working with ruler, dividers, pencils, graph paper amid a heap of reference books and gardening magazines. Peter pushed his way through a hedge and edged his way towards the table.

Langton glanced up briefly. 'Can't stop. Following a train of thought.'

'Yes, of course.' He moved round to take a look. 'May I see?'

'Establishing tactics. Devising a battle-plan.'

'Ah,' said Peter, trying to sound intelligent.

'No point in hacking away without a sense of purpose.'

'No, no.'

Langton put down his pencil and leaned back in the chair. 'Imagine it, my boy. Allow a vision to superimpose itself upon the jungle you see before you. There, a terrace providing the perfect suntrap for Mediterranean plants.' He rose to his feet and strode among the giant weeds as he unfolded his dream. 'Beyond, a fence faces east of south to offer a home for climbers.' At this point he disappeared from view leaving only the sound of his voice accompanied by heavy crashing through the undergrowth. 'Before it, a herbaceous border whose plants will shade the roots of the gentle clematis, whilst allowing its flowered head to revel in joyous sunshine.'

Langton was not normally given to using such fanciful

descriptions, and, looking down at the table, Peter found the paragraph from which his fantasy was being quoted. As the older man reappeared Peter finished the line for him. 'Behind, the alpines tumble carelessly across the westward looking rockery.'

The book was taken from him and firmly closed. 'That's for reference only. The creative inspiration will be mine, of course.'

'Of course,' agreed Peter. 'I saw your advertisement on the Corner Shop board,' he added, changing the subject.

'A modest five pence per week. I decided it was the best course.'

'I had thought . . . seeing as we'd talked . . . you and me . . .'

Langton put down the book and looked doubtfully at his son-in-law. 'You? And me? Must confess, sort of thing in mind, general labour and all that.'

'I would enjoy creating something different. Something new.'

'Ah. There's the catch,' barked Langton. 'Only one commander-in-chief, d'you see? My garden, my vision.'

Peter pointed in all directions. 'There's enough scope here to keep two minds occupied.'

'The bigger the challenge the greater the achievement.'

'So you want to go it alone.'

'I think so.'

'With nothing more than a common labourer.'

'Afraid so. Afraid so.'

'Very well.' Peter turned to go. He was disappointed, there was no point in denying it. He had reached the hedge before a prick of conscience prompted Langton to call after him.

'I'd pay a pound an hour.'

Peter turned. 'I'd hardly be doing it for the money.'

'A pound an hour,' repeated Langton firmly. 'That way I'd call the tune.'

'Very well. A pound an hour for labour. The advice will come free.' Langton frowned. The card in The Corner Shop had said nothing about advice.

Peter drove him down to the Garden Centre where the difference between the two men became immediately apparent. Peter was a methodical person, a basic requirement for a composer. In his daily work he would try a phrase several times before committing it to manuscript; when orchestrating he liked to allow the sound of varying instrumental combinations to pass through his imagination before selecting the one which pleased him most. In the Garden Centre he examined an axe, felt the edge of its blade, took a couple of experimental swings to check balance, before pursing his lips thoughtfully, and turning his attention to a scythe. Then he chose a simple sharpening stone and considered that he'd probably found enough to keep him going for a day or two.

Langton, on the other hand, betrayed the weakness which had caused his living-room to become filled with bric-à-brac. He might have been in a supermarket the way he hurried from one display to the next collecting a varied assortment of accessories, impressed more by the shiny green and red colours than by their function. He staggered to the payment counter carrying a fork, spade, shovel, rake, shears, hoe, edgers, secateurs, sieve, dibber, trowel, trug and pressure spray. He crashed the lot down and stared at his companion with triumphant satisfaction.

By the time they returned to his garden Langton had bought one or two other eye-catching objects from the Centre, like a jackdaw in a gold-mine. The two men stood surrounded by their original purchases to which had been added a magnum bag of peat, a bird-bath, well-head, three china geese, a shiny gnome, and a lion rampant. The 'Major's' confidence had, however, taken a temporary tumble. 'One doesn't know exactly where to begin,' he said hesitantly.

Peter was ready with some advice. 'Well, what *I'd* do first, sir, would be to . . .'

Like a flash Langton over-rode him, making it clear there would be none of *that*. 'Be simple when I get started, you understand,' he interrupted. 'Oh yes, no problem at all. Be going like a train before you know it.' But again the fatal pause. 'It's getting *started*.'

Peter surveyed the scenery. 'The thing about painting a canvas is that there's nothing on it to begin with.'

'What on earth has that got to do with it?' asked Langton with an air of irritation.

'You can't draw a picture if the canvas is covered with scribble,' hinted Peter.

'I've got it!' Langton was off again, in full cry. 'Have a damn good clear out. Then we can see the measure of it. Weigh up the situation.' Peter smiled quietly to himself, pleased that his advice had been sought and taken, if not acknowledged. 'Excellent,' continued Langton. 'Now what's the drill? Tools.'

'You take the axe,' suggested Peter. 'I'll work with the scythe.'

'Clothes.'

'Clothes?'

'Gardening gear,' explained Langton. 'What does a chap wear?'

'Whatever you like.'

'Boots,' said Langton in his downright way. 'Boots, strong, gardening for the use of. And gloves; one pair per man. Must be correctly kitted out.'

Peter couldn't believe all this. 'I'm just going to take my jacket off and get on with it.'

Langton enquired scathingly, 'What? In your braces?'

'I don't wear braces, sir.'

'You are improperly dressed in my garden.' He glared at Peter who returned the look with a small defiance. This was not going to be an easy alliance.

Work commenced within the half-hour. Peter handled the scythe, swinging methodically and efficiently, edging forward a couple of inches with each cut in the prescribed manner and conserving his energy so that he would be able to continue through most of the day.

Nearby Langton, sporting plus-fours, bright pullover, and a deerstalker hat, wildly whirled the axe like a madman run amok. Round his head and 'crash' into an indiscriminate array of targets. 'Swish', 'slash', 'thump' – a clockwork toy overwound and out of control. His spring seemed to unwind and he slowed to a stop, breathing heavily, perspiring freely.

For a few moments he watched Peter swinging steadily. Then he picked up the sharpening stone and rubbed the blade as he would a carving knife. He took a deep breath and, with a sudden alarming new burst of energy, he was fully wound and whirling away like a devil possessed. He tired again, slowed and stopped. He glared towards Peter, then lifting his head, he surveyed the full extent of the task ahead of them before focusing back on the slight damage they had inflicted thus far. A masterly solution occurred to him.

He dropped the axe and left the garden.

Peter continued quietly for a full two hours. By that time he had cleared several square yards and had a bonfire going which he fed with the cut-down brush. He picked up the axe and neatly severed a fallen branch with a single stroke, allowing himself a superior smile as he tossed the two ends into the flames.

He became aware of the sound of a heavy engine approaching and paused in his work in order to listen. The jungle obstructed his view but whatever it was drew closer.

Suddenly, before his thunderstruck gaze, the ramshackle garage beside the house lifted bodily in the air to be flattened an instant later by the progress of a bulldozer. Langton, red flag in hand, waved the driver forward and onward as he clambered over the debris.

'Bring in the bloody tanks,' he shouted.

CHAPTER EIGHT

DAVID THE Vet's understanding of the inner workings within less charted regions of every pet in the neighbourhood was matched only by his knowledge of the mechanics beneath almost any bonnet. He had a passionate love for cars and everything to do with them. His prime ambition in life, apart from marrying Mandy, was to organise the first ever Shillingbury Rally. One complication was the predictable objections from Jake, the father of his fiancée, but the beast responsible for actually bringing the Rally to a standstill was Mr Charles' dreadful little mongrel, Horrible Humphrey.

Mandy had talked to Sally one afternoon to ask whether it would be convenient for David to see Young Upstart.

'Sure, if he can find him,' Sally responded. 'Most of the time he's on safari – in my parents' garden. He and Dad are planning a new Versailles.'

'Peter? Gardening?' queried Mandy incredulously.

Sally nodded. 'It's the full Laurel and Hardy bit. "That's another fine mess you've got us into, Peter",' she mimicked.

'It's about the Shillingbury Rally. David needs Peter's support – well, all your support come to that.'

'Because Jake's objecting?'

'Right.'

'Cars roaring through our village?' A second and equally good impression. 'We're not having it!'

'Almost his very words,' smiled Mandy. 'You know what he's like. He stifles progress and then complains about living in a backwater.'

'D'you want me to talk to him?'

'Oh Sally, would you? He respects you.'

'I can't think why.'

'Because you stand up to him. He likes a good argument.'

'Just so long as he doesn't lose it.'

Harvey was outside the Oddfellows Arms conducting what was becoming an almost perpetual search for Horrible Humphrey. Mr Charles was away on extended business and his randy and highly unloved dog had been put into kennels while the Big House was closed up. The wretched animal had immediately gone on hunger strike, either from loneliness or sexual frustration. The kennels knew Jake for what he was – an irascible farmer who spent the larger part of each day trying to cover up a heart of gold – and promptly telephoned him. Since then Horrible Humphrey pursued a policy of joining in either battle or intercourse with anything on four legs regardless of size and shape. Between bouts he would escape from custody and disappear completely before turning up at somebody's back door missing several handfuls of fur and, once, an ear. There was nobody in Shillingbury who would not be immensely relieved to see Mr Charles back in residence if only to be spared the worry of a mentally deficient dog.

At Greenacres Langton stood in the centre of his Little England and gazed mournfully at an area bulldozed down to flat desolation. Nothing rose higher than six inches. A large square of uncultivated nothing. Like a building site. Yesterday it was clothed, he thought, this morning it lay naked, stripped, ashamed. He had plundered its secrets, torn away the motley covering of tattered garments, and left it in undignified nudity. He felt an overwhelming sense of guilt, more like a rapist than an artist.

'We *were* a bit hasty,' said Peter when he arrived. 'I said so at the time. Some of those things we chopped down had been growing for longer than I've lived.'

'Hindsight!'

'A year will bring colour; maturity takes a decade.'

'Can't stand people who lecture.'

The methodical Peter would have scythed and chopped away for a couple of weeks with less sense of urgency. In that way the two men would have lived alongside the changing face and the resultant bare, featureless area would have come as less of a shock. The true gardener never appeared to hurry. Langton was not blessed with such patience. 'Don't see any future in harvesting the fruits of our labour after we're dead and gone.'

'My grandfather planted a tree on his eightieth birthday,' declared Peter.

'Ah, but did he live to see it bloom?'

'Not exactly. He had a heart attack and fell down the hole he'd dug. They had to dig him up to bury him.'

Langton didn't think it a particularly funny remark but decided to let it lie. Instead, he shook aside his despondency and burst forth with a direct quotation from the chapter on soil cultivation. 'No point in hanging about. Fall in for bastard trenching. Get the roots out, organic compost in, peat, moisture, nourishment.'

'I'll say this for you,' said Peter, 'You don't stay depressed for long.'

'Damn right I don't. Forward! Start over in the corner. Work side by side. Four hours on, two hours off. Sooner started, sooner finished.' He grabbed a spade and charged into the attack while Peter followed more slowly with the fork. Langton dug as he chopped, his spade a blur as it flashed in and out of the ground amid explosions of flying soil. Peter, by contrast, struck a steady tempo – in, lift, over. In, lift, over. Within moments the older man's flurry had run down and stopped. He surveyed the eighteen inches he had achieved then, leaning heavily on his spade, he glared at Peter. 'You don't work very fast,' he said accusingly.

'It's results that count,' responded Peter, continuing to dig.

'For a pound an hour one expects to see the odd bead of perspiration.'

'You expect to see a few clods of turned soil.' Peter indicated the pathetic patch in front of Langton. 'Not something that looks like a cat's been covering up its doings.' He continued to dig steadily. His father-in-law studied him and began to copy his movement. Sarcastic, but effective for all that. The two men worked side by side in silence before Langton stopped again after ten minutes. A second masterly solution had entered his mind. He stuck the spade into the ground and quietly left the garden.

An hour later Peter had made good progress. Some ten feet of the border in front of the brown fence had been turned over. He heard the sound of an approaching motor and paused to listen. Round the corner of the house Langton appeared behind a monstrous soil cultivator. The machine was operating him rather than the other way about and, with a terrible fascination, Peter watched him career back and forth in a series of high speed zig-zags. 'Advance!' shouted Langton, the adrenalin running high.

He shouldn't have waved his arm because that was the precise moment he lost control. Peter threw himself clear in the nick of time before the machine smashed its way through the fence into the lane beyond and a panic stricken Langton disappeared from the field of battle.

Jake's reaction to the proposal for a Shillingbury Rally was exactly as Sally had predicted. He didn't want to hear any trite remarks about an auto rally scarcely adding up to a social revolution because he, for one, had no intention of allowing village standards to teeter on the top of a slippery slope.

Sally became quite angry. 'There are people in Shillingbury – good people, just like you – who have actually asked us to alter the route so that rally cars will drive past their homes. There are farmers – good farmers, just like you – who have put their land at our disposal for the special stages.'

Jake could meet her anger with some of his own. 'There are folk – simple folk, just like me – who think that you and Young Upstart upset our smooth lives by pouring troubled water on the oil.'

Sally looked at him in silence for a second. Then, quite quietly, 'All right, Jake. I don't want to fight you. But if you insist on fighting me, *I'll* win.'

'I'm not fighting anybody. I'll not be made the villain of the piece. Why should I be made to fight to hang onto something I believe in?'

'Because you can't stop progress.'

He moved from his Matra Rancho to where she was loading items of riding tack into the MG. 'No, but I can *ask* you, can't I? I can ask you to make your souped-up cars go bucketing through someone else's village instead of mine.' He glanced at the saddle she was lifting into the back seat. 'Just as I can ask you to take your horse and riding tack out of my stables.' It had come totally unexpectedly. Even Jake was surprised by the threat he had uttered.

'Would you ask me to do that?' she asked.

'If needs be.'

She studied the farmer. His gaze was steady; he meant what he'd said. Further argument was forestalled, perhaps fortunately, by the arrival of an upset Mandy. 'Have you seen him?' she called. 'Horrible Humphrey – he's got out again.'

'Good for him.' Jake was upset and spoke thoughtlessly.

'Dad!'

'Dogs need to be free. To run and sniff other dogs.' He spoke loudly, giving vent to unreasonable anger.

'Well, don't shout at me,' said his daughter through tears of frustration. 'You're the one who said we'd look after the damn dog.'

Sally was the first to revert to reasoned behaviour. She crossed over to Mandy. 'Have you covered his usual haunts?'

'Everywhere,' moaned Mandy.

Sally found herself visualising a lonely, forlorn pet, putting a brave face to the world at the same time as harbouring a miserable loneliness for his missing master. Suddenly she knew where Horrible Humphrey was. Without logical thought but, instead, pure instinct. Whilst those around her cursed the ill-mannered animal.

They found him ten minutes later. Sitting on the very spot Sally had suggested they investigate. The front door-step of the Big House. A tiny scrap lost at the foot of massive architecture.

Jake – the other Jake – infinitely gentle, climbed out of the Matra Rancho and approached the dog, neither creeping nor hurrying, confident, understanding. 'Come on, boy.' His voice soft and coaxing. 'Are you so very lonely then? Hey, listen,' he was quite close now, 'what about you and me seeing if we can't hot up a nice bowl of milk, eh?' Horrible Humphrey watched him carefully but allowed the farmer to stoop and pick him up in his arms. 'Your master will be back in a week or so but, meanwhile, we must keep body and soul together, you know.' He carried him back to the vehicle and handed him in to Mandy.

Sally said, 'Jake, I don't begin to understand you.'

'Aye?'

'You can be so gentle when you want to.'

He climbed in and pulled the door shut. 'It's animals and me that has the understanding. Mainly because animals don't answer back.' They didn't look at each other as he started the engine. 'How did you know he was here?'

'Horrible Humphrey did exactly what I'd have done. If I felt lonely, lost, unwanted – I'd go home.' Only then did she glance at him. 'I'd go home to Shillingbury.'

He returned her look. Expressionless. Then he shifted into gear and they drove off.

The two men had worked hard, of that there was no question. But their labour lacked the element of skill which brings reward. Langton stood gazing across his vision of the future, contemplating sadly the flower beds whose inhabitants drooped limply, the pots and gnomes and troughs, the sundial, birdbath and china geese, looking like a tableau created by a tip-up lorry. In front of the greenhouse there was a plastic windmill overlooking a polystyrene 'brick type' wall surrounding an incredibly shiny blue pond over which they had constructed a rickety rustic bridge.

Langton and Peter were uneasy with one another. Each was painfully aware of personal inadequacy but unwilling to admit it, ready to blame but resentful of criticism. For weeks they had worked on wings of imagination but the moment had arrived when they looked out upon reality. 'Not good enough,' grunted Langton.

'No.'

'Bit of a dog's dinner if you ask me.'

There was a longish pause as their eyes took in the scene which bore no resemblance to anything described in the countless reference books. Peter shifted his stance slightly. 'No plan,' he said.

'I beg your pardon?'

'We had no plan,' he repeated stubbornly.

'Utter nonsense. The picture in my mind was crystal clear.'

'Instant gardening!'

The older man was on a short fuse. 'If you don't approve of my methods nobody's asking you to stay. Did I seek your assistance? Did I go down on bended knee and plead for advice? No sir, I did not! Put a card in the window for a jobbing gardener and you turned up.'

It was harsh comment. After all that Peter had done it

was harsh indeed, and unjustified. 'I've worked hard,' he objected, hurt.

'That I don't deny. Ability to work duly noted. Willing but slow would be my assessment.'

At which point Peter broke. 'If you weren't such a cloth-eared, stubborn thickhead,' he said, his voice rising, 'you'd listen to advice.' 'Sir', he added as an afterthought.

Both men had reached flashpoint simultaneously and the conversation continued in a series of sharp explosions. 'Insubordination, my God. If I'd had you in my outfit during the war –'

'You couldn't grow a box of mustard and cress.'

'Upset among the lower ranks. Troops panic due to being ill-equipped to appreciate the strategy of the officer mind.'

They were eyeball to eyeball. 'You mean,' shouted Peter, 'that somewhere inside the tireless brain which works aft of the drooping moustache, there is a *master plan*?'

'We might have lost a battle – we haven't lost the war.'

'You forget you're talking to the man who married your daughter,' yelled Peter, incoherent with rage. 'I happen to know that your army career lasted only until they discovered you had flat feet.'

Langton flung his hat on the ground. 'YOU'RE ON A CHARGE!'

Peter turned his back and walked angrily towards the greenhouse. He walked straight as a die, across the path, through a flower-bed, and directly over the pond. Langton shouted after him, 'Why are you not using the path?'

'Because the path is in the wrong place.' He continued to plough through a variety of obstacles as he headed unswervingly for the greenhouse.

'How can a path be in the wrong place?' spluttered Langton. 'You don't drive your car all over the fields and say it's because they put the motorway in the wrong place.'

Peter stopped. He turned . . . and walked dead straight back to his father-in-law. 'Any good gardener knows,' he said with pointed sarcasm, 'that one does not lay a path because it looks pretty in the picture book. Rather one waits several months until one can observe the tread marks which have appeared from constant use. And one puts the path *there*. That way it will be in the *right* place!' He turned on his heel and walked all the way back again, using the same route as before.

Langton, purple with anger, lost all control and proceeded to jump up and down on the spot. 'My God, it's a wonder you ever get anything done at all. Use the path, damn you, use the bloody path!'

Peter's anger was of the shortlived type. His arguments with Sally invariably blew up to a point when he would burst out with a line he rather liked, whereupon he would repeat it as if expecting a round of applause. In the greenhouse he said to himself, 'that way it would be in the *right* place' and smiled slightly in self-appreciation. His eyes focused on the melon plant before widening in wonderment. Nestling among the leaves was a melon. Small yet, but undoubtedly a melon.

He heard a footfall outside. An uncharitable streak took the upper hand, perhaps the argument was too fresh, and he hastily moved to stand between the melon and the door. Langton came in. Subdued. Unforgiving yet, but subdued. 'Council of War. Tonight.'

'Time?'

'Twenty hundred hours.'

'Place?'

'My house.'

'I'll be there.'

'I'll muster a bottle of Scotch.'

'Very good . . . sir!'

At eleven o'clock that night they were still there. Seated comfortably in his living-room, the lamplight attracting an occasional moth through uncurtained windows, the mock flame effect of the electric fire switched on but not the elements themselves. A nearly empty bottle of whisky and a soda syphon were on a low table between them and both men were nicely under the influence. They had talked things over, a full and frank exchange of views. An analysis of where things might have gone wrong, a polite regard for the other fellow's opinion, a deliberate and almost excessive courtesy towards each other. As the evening drew on, and the level in the bottle drew lower, courtesy developed into understanding, friendship, bosom pals. The pauses in the conversation grew longer, and there would be periods when they just smiled at each other.

Langton's face was round and genial, a smile excusing the slight slur surrounding difficult words. 'Didn't appreciate you were unaware of my master plan.'

'Completely in the dark about . . .' Peter's eyes tried sleepily to make both Langtons sit in the same place, '. . . anyplanatall!'

'Must have been confusing to you. Some of my actions.'

Peter nodded. He nodded several times. He spent several seconds nodding. 'I'll tell you what puzzled me,' he confided.

'Yes.' Langton leant forward impulsively and rested a hand on the young man's knee. 'Do tell me.'

'I will.' There was a long pause. Langton waited patiently. 'Just as soon as I can remember what it was.'

The two men leaned back in their chairs. Langton suggested helpfully, 'Was it something to do with the garden?'

'Yes.'

'Ah-ha.'

'Straight rows.'

Langton didn't quite follow. 'Straight rows?'

'You being an army man. I expected you to plant in straight rows,' Peter explained. 'Dress from the right,' he added with a giggle.

'Prefer the casual approach.'

'Higgledy-piggledy.'

'That's interesting,' said Langton with extreme politeness. 'You'd say higgledy-piggledy.'

'Definitely higgledy-piggledy. The plants appear higgledy-piggledy. Except the ones which appear dead,' added Peter, striving after the truth. He hoped he hadn't seemed too outspoken and took a thoughtful sip from his glass. 'I'm a straight row man myself,' he confessed. 'You know where you are with a straight row.'

'Ah. But nature does not grow in straight rows, d'you see?' Langton attempted to adopt a lecturing posture. 'When the wild bird broadcasts nature's seed in its own peculiar and slightly objectional way, it does not come in on a bombing run and drop on target.' His hand prescribed the motion of a bird in flight which Peter watched with scrupulous attention. 'Rather, it scatters it over a wide area. A little bit here, a little bit there . . .'

They both found this amusing and chuckled quietly and contentedly for several moments. A prick of guilt made itself felt deep inside Peter's memory. He was withholding information which should rightfully be shared. He wrestled with himself before, conscience winning, he leant forward. 'There is . . . in our entire garden . . . one single plant. Doing uncommonly well.'

'Which plant is that?'

'In the greenhouse there is a melon.'

'A melon?'

'In the greenhouse.'

Langton wanted to get it quite clear. 'In the greenhouse?'

'A melon.' Peter decided he must stop nodding; it was making him giddy.

Langton rose slowly and carefully to his feet. 'Then let us go and inspect it.'

Peter wished he had not blurted out his secret but it was too late. He followed his father-in-law through the kitchen where a torch was tested and found to be working. Like soldiers traversing a minefield the two gardeners helped each other past the ornaments which bedecked the lawn. In the greenhouse Peter solemnly shone the torch onto the melon. 'Isn't it beautiful?' he whispered.

Langton studied the round green object the size of a tennis ball with reverent care, and whispered back, 'That is undoubtedly a very fine, upstanding, healthy melon.'

'The first and only fruit of our labour.'

'We must mount guard over it.'

'Hardly necessary, d'you think!'

Langton looked over his shoulder as if expecting a guerrilla attack from behind. 'Protect it from pillage and rape. You never know the neighbours around these parts.'

'Leave it to me, sir. I'll pop in every morning and attend to its needs.'

Langton examined the fruit once more. 'That melon,' he declared, 'must not want for anything.'

As they returned to the house Langton walked ahead of the younger man. In the centre of the bridge which crossed the pond he paused and, turning back, asked the question which it seemed to him required answering. 'Tell me –' he began.

'There is no reward greater than the sight of growth,' said Peter.

'Quite so. But tell me – question I must ask . . .' he said apologetically. 'A matter of discipline, d'you see.'

'Sir?'

'Why did you not inform me immediately you discovered the melon?'

Peter searched his befuddled brain for an answer. None came, but circumstances rescued him because, with the sound of splintering wood, Langton once again disappeared from view. He splashed down heavily into the rock pool as the bridge broke asunder, and Peter looked down on a face contorted with agony.

'Are you all right, sir?'

'*I'm* all right,' gasped Langton, seeking strict accuracy even in pain. 'But I think I've broken my bloody leg.'

CHAPTER NINE

WITH THE arrival of midsummer the gardens of Shillingbury glorified in the free-growing period and reflected the pride and skill of their owners. There was some who favoured the herbaceous border, so beloved by earlier generations, where the choice of plants was restricted to those which could be cut down to ground level immediately after flowering, leaving only dead spikes sticking out of the bare earth for the longer part of each year. As gardens grew smaller there developed the 'mixed border' consisting of carefully selected flowering shrubs, evergreens, conifers, heathers, paeonies, phloxes and Michaelmas daisies, all choreographed to provide splashes of colour throughout the year. Other gardeners preferred freestanding beds offering short bursts of blazing colour from spring flowering plants, through the summer annuals such as petunias, antirrhinums and the like, to autumn displays of tagetes and dwarf pompon chrysanthemums.

No two gardens were alike. Mr Madigan had turned the whole of his back garden over to vegetables and grew a wide variety in sufficient quantities to feed a family of ten – which, with only Mrs Madigan's sparrow-like appetite to satisfy, largely went to waste. Mrs Wilson's front garden was entirely occupied by a magnolia tree of breathtaking beauty for just two weeks in spring unless a late frost browned the bloom, forcing the poor lady to wait another full year. Old John Villiers believed in a good mulch. His borders and beds were constantly covered with four inches of compost, sawdust, spent hops, peat, and mushroom manure which gave him rich green growth where geraniums carried leaves the size of soup plates but, unhappily, never a flower. Fred Dinely had planted a weeping willow on the day his son was born but by the time the boy left junior school there was no garden to play in and the bungalow was completely invisible from the road.

As the summer went by, and Langton languished in hospital cursing his plastered leg, Peter poured his severely limited artistry into Greenacres. Left to himself, he started all over again and tried to achieve single-handed what two had failed to do. He put all the plants in dead

110

straight rows, in dead straight beds, with dead straight edges. The pots and gnomes, and troughs, and rocks, stood in dead straight lines. He purchased turves and laid a dead straight lawn bisected by a dead straight path. He persuaded the leak from the pond to flow in a dead straight ditch dead down the middle of the lot.

When Sally arrived one Sunday afternoon he had squared off a rectangular bed like a crossword puzzle and was placing daffodil bulbs equidistant from each other prior to planting. Her mother had moved back to the house and Sally was about to run her to the hospital to visit her father.

'Any message for him?' she asked Peter.

'Just tell him to keep his chin and his leg up – and, that I'm winning the war.'

She nodded slightly before wandering away purportedly studying the garden. This was beginning to be something she couldn't handle; his obsession with the garden was a cover-up job, a means by which he could fool himself that he was working.

'Patti called.' He looked up with a sudden interest as she knew he would; Patti Maxton, lead singer with The Close Encounters, was a close friend.

'And?'

'She wants to talk about a new album. I promised you'd phone her.'

'Patti will never record an album this side of the tour,' he said briefly. It was impossible to get through to him whilst he was in this mood. 'Have you seen my melon?' he asked. She followed him into the greenhouse and together they surveyed the nearly full-grown melon. 'Not much wrong with that, is there?' He was half-proud, half-defensive.

'When are we going to eat it?'

'We'll organise a melon party.'

She stooped down and looked at it closely. 'Keep agrowing Buster. You've got a whole lot of mouths to feed.'

When they came out of the greenhouse they stood beside each other and looked across the garden. 'But it's no good, is it?' he said quietly. An admission, an opportunity for her to pitch in and help him. 'I can *see* it's no good,' he went on. 'But I can't seem to get it right.'

Sally moved tentatively. She was anxious not to destroy the moment. 'May I show you something?' She walked back to the daffodil bed and, picking up the rake, pulled together the bulbs from their meticulously careful straight lines. She gathered them all up into her arms and crossed to a newly planted tree at the edge of the lawn near the fence. She flung her arms wide and scattered the bulbs right, left, and centre.

'What the hell was that for?'

'You know when you walk in the woods, you see daffodils and bluebells growing among the trees? You'll never see them in straight rows. They're in clusters.' She smiled up at him. 'Plant them exactly where they've landed and they'll grow naturally – just like they do in the woods.'

Peter looked at the bulbs lying on the ground. Then, in his mind's eye, they became daffodils and for the first time he could actually visualise the scene. Slowly he was grinning – it seemed like for the first time in weeks. 'Why do you know everything?'

'You married a micro-chip.' She was immensely relieved and Peter, in an instant, returned to being something nearer his old self. There came a 'Yoo-hoo' from the house and Martha was walking towards them. She wanted to know what was going into the centre bed and, because the daffodils had only just been taken *out,* nobody had yet decided.

'Wallflowers,' said Martha firmly. 'They give a nice touch of green right through the winter and, if you set tulip bulbs between the plants, they'll all flower at the same time next May.' She picked up a trowel and the box of wallflowers and set to work with a quick wink at her daughter.

Sally wandered over to the pond, wondering if she could make it look a little less like a plastic bath by softening the edges with some natural stone. The three of them worked in silence for half-an-hour before Jake walked into the garden with Mandy. He gave the landscape an appraising look. 'Mandy said I should come and look at the garden before it's full of coach parties. I'm only joking,' he added hastily as Peter rose to his feet. Then, to Sally, 'Got a pond too, have we?'

'I'm trying to make it appear a little more natural.'

'Well, it should be at the foot of the rockery, shouldn't it?' said the farmer. 'That's where lakes form – at the bottom of mountains.' Peter looked a little apprehensive as Jake took hold of a large stone and, with Sally, began redesigning the pond and rockery. 'Have you noticed how all the rocks on the side of a hill face in the same direction?' Jake continued. 'Hundreds of years of prevailing weather causes that. And they all lean back a bit so the rain can reach the little alpine plants tucked in behind.'

Mandy was looking at the wibbly-wobbly rustic, considering whether it couldn't be turned into an archway leading to the lawn. She heaved at a post which came out of the ground remarkably easily.

Harvey arrived an hour later with a telegram for Martha. 'Please bring more grapes urgentest, signed George,' he recited.

'Cop hold of the other end of this rock, will you, Harvey?' asked Jake.

The postman joined the workforce and the six worked as a team until darkness fell. At one point Sally caught Jake's eye and they exchanged a quiet wink and smile. The feud was forgotten and, indeed, the whole operation was taking on the distinct appearance of an organised conspiracy.

By sunday lunchtime the garden was beginning to look a whole heap better.

'But he's not actually *doing* anything?' Langton was in a private room, sitting on the edge of his bed, but still in pyjamas and dressing gown. He looked sternly at his wife and daughter who sat in uncomfortable wooden chairs.

'No, oh no,' said Martha with a nervous look at Sally.

'Just keeping things tidy,' agreed her daughter, picking up the cue.

'Until you come home,' added Martha.

'And can tell him what to do,' finished Sally.

'. . . what to do,' repeated Martha.

The two women didn't sound very convincing. 'Meanwhile,' tried Sally, 'he's just doing a spot of weeding.'

'. . . spot of weeding,' came the echo.

'And generally keeping things tidy.'

'. . . tidy.'

There was a pause. 'How is the melon?' asked Langton.

'The melon? Oh, very well, thank you,' said Martha brightly.

'It sends its regards,' Sally added recklessly.

'Has it grown any bigger?'

They answered together. 'Yes,' said Sally; 'No,' said her mother. They looked at each other. 'No,' corrected Sally at the same time as, 'Yes,' said Martha. 'That is, Peter won't let us look at it very often.'

'You're sure he hasn't done anything in that garden?' Langton was becoming definitely suspicious.

Unfortunately, they both spoke simultaneously again. Martha said, 'No,' as Sally assured, 'Yes.'

'I mean,' explained Martha, 'no, he hasn't done anything.'

'And "yes" we're sure.' Sally's smile was not up to coping with her father's steely gaze. 'Nearly sure,' she mumbled.

Langton said, 'He's just keeping things -'

'Tidy,' Martha chipped in helpfully.

'But he hasn't *moved* anything? It was a positive question and was greeted with a longish silence, broken eventually by Sally with studied casualness.

'Only the path.'

'He's moved the path?'

Martha explained innocently, 'He said he was just putting it in the right place . . .'

'For you,' Sally completed the sentence, sensing it was going wrong.

'And the rockery.'

'And the rustic.'

'And the pond.'

'Just a bit. You can hardly tell the difference.'

Langton reached for the walking stick lying beside him on the bed and rose slowly to his feet. This was not a moment for hasty words. Army training reminded him that some crises required thinking about, so that the decision when it came was the *right* one. 'I'll kill him,' he said.

'Don't be so dramatic, George.'

Langton brandished the walking stick. 'What's he done? What's he been up to?'

'Dad, for heaven's sake. We've all of us made a few little suggestions.'

'. . . little suggestions.'

'Who,' spluttered Langton, 'is "*all* of us"?'

'Well, Mummy and me.'

'And Peter.'

'And Jake.'

'And Mandy.'

'And Harvey.'

'Are you trying to tell me an entire platoon has been working in my garden?' Langton wanted badly to stride back and forth across the room waving the walking stick over his head. Several pounds of solid plastercast rendered the gesture less than effective.

Sally spoke crossly. 'You should be jolly grateful people have been looking after things for you.'

'. . . jolly grateful.'

Then Langton sat heavily on the bed and looked at them with a great pathos. 'Can't you people understand,' he begged. 'I don't *want* people looking after things for me. I want to look after things *myself.*'

It was two weeks before he was able to stomp thunderously down his garden path, only to stop and stare aghast at the transformation which had befallen his vision of the future. He failed to recognise, and certainly refused to admit, that Greenacres had taken on a character. There was a first hint of graciousness, a young child who with maturity would become beautiful. All Langton could see was that it was *different;* grossly, fundamentally, inexcusably different.

Peter waited in the greenhouse, staring somewhat nervously from the partial concealment of the full-grown melon. He watched his father-in-law glowering at the changes in his garden, and the self-righteous convictions which had prevailed over several weeks began to fade slightly. Langton entered the greenhouse. 'You are DISMISSED!' he said.

While Peter had been indulging fulltime in his newfound hobby, David the vet had supposedly been organising the Shillingbury Rally. However, the life of a veterinary surgeon is as unpredictable as a doctor's – or a composer's for that matter. A mysterious virus attacked dogs all over the county and spread rapidly to epidemic proportions, the only palliative being to treat the illness as cat flu. David found himself working all hours of the day and night with the result that much of the detailed planning fell on Mandy who, in turn, roped in her friend Sally to help.

They contacted the local organiser of the British Rally Drivers' Association who proved enormously helpful and gave invaluable advice on ground rules, collaboration with the police, co-operation of councils and individuals, and generally provided great encouragement. He was not to know that, like most of the happenings in the village, the event would take on an entirely original twist and end up in a way which nobody could possibly have predicted.

It was hard work for the two girls, and made harder for Sally because it could not be said that her heart was in it. It seemed to her that when she and Peter had lived in London he was forever complaining about sharing her with all their showbiz friends. 'Now we're stuck out here,' she told Mandy, 'and when he's home – which God knows isn't very often – he seems hellbent on finding a hobby I can't share.'

'He's being very kind to Mr Langton.'

'No, he's not. He's doing it because he and I . . .' But Sally could not bring herself to tell Mandy about the row she'd had with Peter when he'd expressed an interest in their own garden, only to have been confronted by her own selfish objections. She realised now that he'd sought to smother his secret professional fears by an overt display of amateur labour, and she had been less than understanding. 'Take no notice of me,' she advised. 'I'm suffering from a touch of the "poor me" bit.'

'We all get it sometimes.'

'Let's you and me make history by winning the Shillingbury Rally!'

That Saturday night, as the ornate retirement clock on Langton's mantelpiece struck eleven, the 'Major' crept out and moved stealthily towards the greenhouse where he played his devastating, revengeful trump card.

116

He picked the melon.

He was up early the next morning but was loath to leave his bedroom. He stood by the window peering through a gap in the curtains. He knew his shout of dismissal would not be taken seriously and that Peter would return sooner or later; after all, he had already put him on a charge and threatened him with court martial – both to no effect. His son-in-law arrived at nine o'clock and, biting his finger-nails nervously, Langton craned his neck to keep the younger man in sight. When Peter walked out of his sight he ran into the back bedroom to follow his progress from there. He watched Peter surveying the garden with an expression on his face which Langton interpreted bitterly as 'smug satisfaction'. Then he saw him head towards the greenhouse.

He ran downstairs and sneaked out of the back door. He stood for a moment before, with sudden resolve, he squared his shoulders and marched into battle. He met his adversary in the centre of the lawn and was at once taken aback by the picture of white-faced anger that stood before him.

'You picked it!' A gasp of accusation.

'Now look here . . .' began Langton in a blustering way.

'You picked my melon.'

'I'm perfectly entitled –'

'You picked my melon.' Peter was having difficulty in finding words.

'It's not your melon,' said Langton, becoming heated. 'It's *my* melon. It's my house, my garden, my greenhouse, my melon.'

Peter's voice grew equally heated. 'I grew that melon. It's no use you saying otherwise. Yours died. Like everything else.'

Langton took two further strides and stood looking down into the other man's face. 'Let's have this out once and for all. Been boiling up for weeks and best get it over with. All this meddling! It's got to stop. I'm the commanding officer and you're the gardener. The jobbing gardener. Ever since you started you've been trying to *alter* things. "Tell you what you ought to do," you say. "You know what you *should* have done," you say. I'm in hospital for a month and you change the design. Dammit, you change *everything!* Those nasty little rows of wall-flowers! I'm in charge. It's my garden. My melon. Got to stop!'

The argument was going badly. Langton hadn't reckoned on the change of face – no more was this the lovable composer, but a man with a great anger. 'You're a featherheaded amateur,' Peter said, his voice shaking. 'You're all books and magazines. You're all talk.' A gesture with his arm embraced the complete area. 'You don't make gardens by buying rotary lawn mowers, flying things, cylinder jobs, flame-throwers, tractors, cultivators, electric hedge trimmers, sprays, powders, compounds. You do it with your *hands.* And a fork. And a spade.' He stopped, drew a deep breath, before continuing more quietly. 'And a bit of heart. You have to talk to the flowers. Encourage them. You? You charge at them with a bloody great machine and they don't know whether to duck or wave a white flag.'

'So that's the way it is,' declared Langton in a domineering voice. 'That's fine. That's very fine, that is,' he said less assertively. 'Now we know where we stand,' he added weakly before finishing up by repeating himself. 'You are dismissed.'

Peter didn't move. He simply held out his hand and stared right up at him. 'Then I'll just take my melon.'

Whereupon Langton exploded. 'You will not take your damn melon. Or anything else. On the day of my retirement I promised to invite my friends and colleagues to lunch. That's today. A lunch party. All my own produce. And we're starting with melon!'

'All your own produce?'

'Correct.'

'They're going to be awful damn hungry.' Peter stamped away with the last word. Langton kept the melon. Both men knew that neither had won the battle.

Thus it came about that the Langton luncheon and the Shillingbury Rally took place on the same day. It was also the day on which Horrible Humphrey escaped from care for what was to be the last time.

It was a long drive to the Rally start and the two girls left early to be there in good time. In fact, Mandy had brought

118

a picnic lunch and she and Sally munched sandwiches and drank Thermos coffee as they walked from car to car carrying out the necessary checks.

At Rose Cottage Martha arrived carrying her suitcase at the same time as Harvey delivered her telegram. They found the cottage locked and deserted.

In Langton's dining-room the table was laid for six. The 'Major' was wearing his best social smile as he served some rather small slices of melon to his guests. Jackson, the idiot managing director, had launched out on one of his interminable funny stories and, even as Langton tried politely to draw attention to the special nature of their first course without interrupting the joke, some directors began to eat. One sprinkled ginger and sugar generously over the tiny portion, another attacked his with fork and spoon, a third picked up his slice and demolished the fruit in three bites. All the while they laughed appreciatively at Jackson's anecdote, ignoring Langton's attempts to get in a word about the melon.

At last the story was finished. So was the first course. Langton's smile was stiff to say the least. Not one person had been aware of eating the melon.

At the Rally start the cars were in a long line, starting at one-minute intervals. Sally and Mandy were fifth to go – the farmer's daughter tearing open the secret envelope to ascertain the first map grid reference. Soon they were doing well, passing the appropriate checkpoints at high speed. Sally drove fast, carefully, assuredly – she was fond of Emma Gee and would prefer to lose the rally than press the car beyond its limits.

Horrible Humphrey wandered into Langton's garden just as the guests were leaving.

Peter arrived half-an-hour later. At first he thought there was nobody at home but then he saw the remote, hunched-up figure of Langton, sitting alone on the wooden seat at the far end of the garden. Something was wrong; he could see that from the set of his father-in-law's head. The unmistakable pose of a commander who has lost the war. Despite everything Peter experienced a twinge of sadness as he walked slowly and quietly towards the seated man. Eventually he reached Langton and sat down beside him. It was several moments before either man spoke.

At last, almost in a whisper, Langton said, 'You were right. I'm an amateur.'

'I lost my temper. Sorry.'

'Spent a fortune on equipment. Nothing to show for it. Nothing.'

'Always slow, the first season,' Peter said in a mollifying voice.

Langton shook his head. 'Washout. Failure. You run the show from now on.'

'Me?'

'You're the C.O. You give the orders.'

'I wouldn't dream of it. We must discuss things. The two of us. Together.'

Langton gave a grim smile. 'It turns into an argument more often.' They sat silently for several moments. Peter didn't move. Then Langton heaved a deep sigh. 'Had the lunch. Washout. Failure.'

'Oh.'

'God, how out of touch one becomes in just a few months. Didn't understand what they were talking about half the time. Superficial. Shallow.'

There followed another long pause before Peter asked, hesitantly. 'How was . . . how was the melon?'

'Jackson started one of his long stories just before we sat down. Huh!' Langton snorted. 'He can still ramble on just the same. Damned bore.' There came another sigh, echoing up from the lowest depths. 'By the time he'd finished, the melon was all eaten. Without a mention. Passed unnoticed. Not a word.'

Peter was lost for words. They were both lost for words. 'I suppose,' said Peter, 'I suppose there's not much you can say about a melon when it's just a starter.'

Very slowly Langton shifted his body slightly and produced a small plate covered by a saucepan lid. 'Saved you a slice,' he said. Peter was surprised. And moved. He took the plate and lifted the lid. It was no more than a sliver of melon, and a small sliver at that. 'Not a very large slice,' said Langton apologetically, 'because it wasn't a very large melon. And there were six of us sat down.' He watched Peter raise the sliver to his mouth, and then hesitate.

'You can't divide a melon into seven,' said Peter.

'Eh?'

'You said there were six sat down. You can't cut seven slices'

The older man gave a slight shrug. 'Oh well.'

'This is *your* slice.'

'*You* grew it.'

'No,' declared Peter firmly. '*We* grew it. You and me. Half each.' He broke the sliver into two minute pieces and handed one to Langton. They looked at each other, raised their portions in a silent toast, then nibbled and munched. 'Good flavour,' said Peter.

Langton said thoughtfully, 'It ought to be. It cost £7000!'

Unseen by either of them Horrible Humphrey left the garden as quietly as he'd entered it. He slipped under the back fence and took a few paces along the bank before moving to cross the road.

The two men heard the sudden sound of a car approaching at high speed followed by the fearful screech of brakes, and scream of skidding tyres. Then they watched with hypnotic fascination as a rally car crashed through the fence, tore through some baby shrubs, and finished up on the rockery. A moment later a second car took two newly planted trees before destroying the pond. It was followed immediately by a third which savaged the wallflower bed before muddily slewing to a standstill on the lawn. The fourth car seemed to sail clean over the top of the fence before totally demolishing the greenhouse.

They were too stunned to speak until Sally appeared through the shattered fence carrying Horrible Humphrey.

Peter stood up. 'Oh God, is he all right?'

'They just missed him. He's fine.' She looked at the drivers emerging from their cars, and then surveyed the battlefield that once was a garden. 'Dad, you really should do something about your garden. It's not as if you haven't got time now you've retired.'

CHAPTER TEN

THERE IS no community, large or small, which does not breed its own brand of small talk, the idle chit-chat of news-pedlars which remains harmless until it is manipulated into scandal. Historical events, where they are recorded by date and fact alone, are doubtless accurate enough; but when they are further illustrated by the writings within diaries, letters, or essays, the accuracy is almost certainly coloured by opinion and hearsay. The daily exchange of tittle-tattle, subject as it is to the emotions of the moment, includes incidents distorted by exaggeration and rapidly crosses the border into lands of unsubstantiated assumption.

In the main the Shillingbury Gossipmongers were well-known and identifiable. Harvey the Post could weave a fantasy around the postmark of any letter he delivered, Ma Cronin spread abroad the sayings of spirits from another world who spoke to her out of the living-room chimney, and Mildred Davenport, despite being house-bound and confined to a wheelchair, was closely involved in every titbit of social scandal within a twelve-mile radius. Mrs Jenkins lived next door to the buxom widow in Marsh Lane, which lady habitually invited tradesmen into her house for reasons unverified, but the variety of delivery vans parked at intervals in the lane for half-an-hour or more was evidence enough and did nothing for the reputation of the milkman who seemed able to manage no more than five minutes.

The Reverend Arthur Norris deplored the irresponsible loose talk he heard around the village, and stamped on the unkinder innuendos the moment they reached his ears. However, the cultures of scandal grew all around him as the necessary ingredients came together in the correct proportions, and during that long hot summer the vicar was amazed to discover that Jake was as guilty as the next man when it came to character assassination by gossip. The four instances which combined to blacken the names of Peter and Sally were his association with Patti Maxton, the letter on which he scribbled down a telephone number, the vicar's decision to allow a recording to be made in the church, and the arrival of one Richard Firman, builder and decorator. They fused together and exploded on the night of the Shillingbury Cloudburst.

True to her word, and despite his doubts, Patti Maxton had come up with an invitation for Peter to score a new solo album for her. Patti, the lead singer with The Close Encounters, was every man's dream of how a coloured girl should look. A wide smile, glorious eyes, ebony black hair. She was hardworking, professional, and successful. Patti and Peter owed each other a great deal; she for the chart-busting hit numbers he'd written for her, and he for the way she performed them. He knew her singing style almost better than she, which was scarcely surprising in that he had created a sizeable part of it. He wrote for her remarkable breath control which enabled her to contain a phrase and even crescendo out of the end of it when other singers would be gasping for oxygen; above all, he scored around her incredible sense of rhythm which remained rock steady whilst her voice throbbed and built until it burst around a seemingly abandoned tempo.

He worked fourteen hours a day to complete the arrangements in time for Band Call. By commercial standards he took an uneconomically long time over each orchestration. He wrote more quickly when he was contributing to a television show which would most likely be seen once only and, anyway, the sound quality from home receivers was not of a particularly high order. An LP, on the other hand, was designed to be played again and again, often on high fidelity equipment, and demanded more sophisticated and carefully thought-out composition. What he lacked in speed was more than compensated for by the concentration that went into each score. He made frequent journeys to Patti's houseboat where he tried to satisfy her appetite for rehearsal, and it seemed to Sally that she saw less and less of her husband.

She was glad to see him writing again but she was sufficiently clear headed to sense that things were not right between them. They were going through a difficult patch and, although it was hard to identify specific areas of strain, the second honeymoon which began when they moved into Rose Cottage was positively over. Whatever caused the 'atmosphere' between them, where each behaved with self-conscious consideration towards the other, the reality was that it was a bad time for Sally to meet Richard Firman.

He arrived in the village one Sunday morning, driving a small van, the side of which proclaimed: 'R. FIRMAN – Plumber, Electrician, Carpenter. Speedy & Efficient Service'. Firman himself was tall, strong, self-confident to the point of flashy arrogance which trait was softened by immense charm, great good humour, and an extremely persuasive manner. He drove slowly on that rare day in an English summer which had actually created a water shortage, and passing the church he listened idly to the sound of singing coming from within. Down to the pond on the Green, where the water level was well down as indicated by an expanse of dried, cracked mud around its banks. In the postage-stamp garden of one of the council cottages an elderly lady carried a bowl of washing-up water to moisten the parched annuals and, in a field, a young farmgirl emptied a couple of buckets into a cattle drinking trough. The car wash at the local garage was inoperative, a sign read 'Water Restriction – NO CAR WASHING'. He passed a farmyard and saw the farmer folding a large tarpaulin. An impulse prompted Firman to stop. He called 'Good morning' as he got out of the van and walked into the yard. Jake looked up but said nothing, he saw little point in greeting somebody he'd never met. 'I was wondering,' continued Firman, unabashed, 'if you'd like a tarmacadam job on your yard? I'll be working nearby next week and could quote you a good price.'

'Where are you working next week?' Jake saw Firman hesitate. 'There's nobody I know wants a tarmacadam job doing.'

'Well, this chap was hoping to keep it quiet,' said Firman with a frank, disarming grin. 'Anyway, he's only *interested*, but I'm hoping he'll come through with an order.'

'If he exists – which I doubt.'

'So do I,' admitted Firman with a shrug. 'But with your wide circle of friends, perhaps you'd be kind enough to remember me if anyone needs any building or decorating.' He pulled a visiting card from his pocket and passed it to Jake. 'My numbers on the back.'

'Richard Firman, eh?'

'That's right. Er, may I have the pleasure . . ?'

124

'Smith. Jake Smith. You can call me Mr Smith.'

'I'm pleased to meet you. Could I quote you for your yard?'

'No.'

'Fair enough.'

'We get lots of your sort,' said the farmer bluntly. 'Take the money and run.' He tried to hand the card back but Firman smiled at him without taking it.

'That was really frightfully offensive, you know. Any job I do will be done, and done well. I've never seen the English countryside, so I'm working my way around it. See it while there's still time.'

'You expecting it to disappear or something?'

Firman threw him an enigmatic smile. 'Let me give you a hand with that tarpaulin. What are you trying to do with it?'

'Fold it. What's it look like?'

Firman took one end and folded it across to the middle. 'The countryside will be here. But I might not.'

'What's that supposed to mean?'

'Awkward things, tarpaulins,' said the builder, ignoring Jake's question. 'Where's it go when it's folded?'

'In the barn. Why mightn't you be here?'

'Never mind. I shouldn't have said it.'

'But you did.'

The two men pulled the bulky ends together and stooped to lift it. 'Doctors can be as wrong as anybody,' muttered Firman as they carried it between them to the barn.

They dumped it in a corner and, straightening up, Jake asked, 'How long have they given?'

'Maybe a year,' Firman said simply. 'But I'm not looking for sympathy, I'm looking for a job.'

'I'll do what I can.'

'I'd be most grateful, Mr Smith.'

'You can make it "Jake".'

'I'm Dick.' He walked back towards his van, but then paused, and turned. 'I'd rather you kept the other bit confidential.'

'Who would I tell?'

In St George's Church young Mark Hamble was singing

'Bless This House', accompanied on the organ by Peter. The boy's voice was pure and sweet, the height of the stone-built edifice adding sufficient echo to bring a depth of quality to the sound. Peter listened intently, revelling in the acoustics; the Reverend Arthur Norris listened also, but his mind was on other things. He was puzzling over what he could do to attract more of the parish population to Sunday service. Later, he stood by the main doors bidding personal farewells to those of his flock who had made an effort to attend. He heard Sam, the tuba player from the Shillingbury brass band, comment to Harvey that the boy had sung well and, when Peter hurried out, he complimented him on an interesting choice of music. 'I hope you didn't mind,' said Peter apologetically.

'Mind? Good gracious no. After my reference to the church restoration fund, an emotional plea to 'Bless This House' worked wonders for the collection.' Peter grinned. Norris was able to count the congregation even in the brief movement of raising his eyes towards Heaven.

'Any more thoughts about my suggestion?' he asked.

'I can see no harm in using the church to make a record. Although I'm still not clear why you need a church.'

'Not *a* church, Vicar, *your* church.' Peter explained how artificial reverberation was used in a recording studio to give all manner of echo effects, but that ambient sound could often provide a dimension impossible to create electronically. He thought he was probably blinding the vicar with science.

After a polite pause, Norris enquired mildly, 'And you propose to bring your pop group to Shillingbury?'

'The Close Encounters, yes. With a small rhythm section.'

'And the finished record would be on sale in the shops?' The question was put with naive innocence.

'Hopefully. If the company likes it.'

Norris clasped his hands together and held them under his chin, a habit he adopted when thinking deeply. 'Peter, forgive my asking, but if you made a record here in the church, do I assume there would be a modest contribution to the restoration fund?'

'Of course. We'd make a donation.'

'A donation, ah, yes.' Norris smiled artlessly. 'I'd like to see the church get a piece of the action. Er – is that the right word?' he added shyly.

'Well,' said Peter doubtfully, 'it's not quite the same thing as a donation.'

'I'm afraid I'm not up to your line of lingo.' The vicar frowned slightly and pursed his lips thoughtfully. 'Shall we say a facility fee of two hundred pounds, and maybe a small percentage of the royalties?' he suggested.

Peter looked at him blankly. 'You're not serious . . ?'

'You understand I'm a child in these matters.'

'I'd hate to negotiate with you when you've grown up.'

After Peter had gone Norris allowed himself a surge of anticipation. Some of these pop groups earned fortunes, he thought, and the church's share might even see a commencement of work on the crumbling belfry before autumn. Resisting the temptation to rub his hands he hurried to join those of his flock who congregated around a table outside the Oddfellows Arms of a Sunday morning.

'In the parish church?' exclaimed Jake, as soon as he heard the news. 'I've never heard such nonsense in all my life. We're not having it. No more to be said.'

'I'd say that's rather up to the vicar here,' objected Sam.

'No, dammit, it's not. With respect, Reverend, there's the good name of the village to think of.'

Norris took a sip of his wine before looking at the farmer levelly. 'When were you last in church, Jake?'

'What's that got to do with it?'

'I was wondering why this jealous protection of your beloved village couldn't be extended to embrace the Word of God.'

'He doesn't need me,' grumbled Jake. 'He's old enough to look after himself.'

'So why shouldn't he listen to some nice music coming out of the church?'

'He doesn't get to hear much else coming out of there,' agreed Sam.

'Especially when we play,' acknowledged Harvey with frank honesty.

The farmer glared at his two fallen disciples before turning back to Norris. 'Because it's sacrilege,' he declared.

'It's not sacrilege,' said Norris hotly. 'Never going to

church at all, *that's* sacrilege.'

'And aside of all else,' Jake went on, adept at changing tack in an argument he was losing, 'Shillingbury's *got* a band. We don't need blackleg labour coming in and taking jobs that should rightfully be ours.'

A thought was beginning to form somewhere in the inner depths of Sam's mind. 'I'd like to be on a record, Jake.'

'Me too,' agreed Harvey.

'What are you two talking about?' Jake was angry now.

'If The Close Encounters make a record we could accompany them,' said Sam bravely.

Jake gave the calculatedly heavy sigh of a man sorely tried by surrounding stupidity. 'Sam, they're a pop group. They sing in tempo. Fast. Loud.'

'I know,' said the tuba player defensively.

'You get three bars behind when we play *The Dead March in Saul.*' Sam was squashed but not defeated. He resolved to raise the matter with Young Upstart personally.

The vicar broke in, gently. 'Jake, don't you think you're blowing this up . . .'

But the farmer interrupted as he rose to his feet. 'No I do not. I'm going to have it out with Young Upstart right now.'

The moment Peter arrived home he realised the time spent attending service had made him late for his rehearsal with Patti. He put the final touches to a score, telephoned his copyist in London to stand by for an all-night race against time, and bundled thick wads of manuscript paper into his already bulging briefcase. He wondered if he was going to make the one-thirty-five and, praying that Sally was in a better frame of mind, he walked into the garden.

He noticed the sun-scorched grass and the deep fissures which had opened up in the parched, baked soil. There was a wide crack running from the lawn into a herbaceous border at the back of the cottage. Sally, in swimsuit and shorts, was watering the shaded part of the border using a hosepipe. 'Are you going to drive me to the station?' The underlying feeling of guilt at leaving her yet again, this time for three days, caused his question to sound abrupt.

'I suppose so,' she replied tonelessly. The argument

between them had seemed to go on for ever.

'Don't overdo the willingness. Would you rather I took the car?'

'I don't mind.'

He spoke with an unnecessary air of patience. 'Sal, we've been through it a hundred times. My work is in London. I have to be there.'

'Practically the whole week, it seems; day and night.' She handed him the hose which he took without thinking.

'I haven't time to argue any more, I'll miss the train.' He looked down at the hose in his hand. 'Should we be doing this?'

'Why not?'

'I thought we were supposed to be having a drought.'

'It only needs seven consecutive days without rain for someone to make muttering noises about a drought.' Her temper had not improved and she was in a thoroughly bad mood.

'Except it's been seven weeks and everybody's shouting it from the rooftops. You must have heard.'

'I'll go and put some clothes on,' she said grumpily.

He was stuck with the briefcase in one hand, the hose in the other, and anyway, he was scarcely wearing the right clothes for watering the back border. 'Look, if it's any help I could leave the car at the station for you to pick up later.'

'I *said* I'll go and put some clothes on.' She walked away towards the back door leaving him hung. He continued watering until he heard the distant sound of the front door chime. Sally called down from the window above his head. 'You can answer the door if you like.'

'Thanks.' It was said sarcastically. He looked around for somewhere to put the hose. He saw the large fissure stretching from the wall into the lawn, so he directed the jet of water into it, then shoved the nozzle deep into the crevasse where it gurgled away contentedly into some unknown underground cavern. He hurried round the side of the cottage, glancing anxiously at his watch, and smothered a grimace when he saw Jake waiting outside the front door. 'Oh, hullo, Jake.'

'Not disturbing you, I hope.'

'As a matter of fact, I'm just dashing for the one-thirty-five.'

'Then I mustn't keep you,' but having said that Jake still unhurriedly followed Peter to the parked MG. 'I was wanting a word about this music-in-the-church business.'

'Jake, I haven't time for a word about anything.' Peter marvelled that word could have reached Jake so quickly.

'There'll be a deal of opposition,' the farmer warned.

'Who from?'

'Me.'

Peter tossed his briefcase into the back seat. 'Look, it's only a half-formed idea. I'll be back on Wednesday – we'll talk about it then.'

'Maybe too late Wednesday. Perhaps I'll have a word with your wife.'

'Ah.' Peter walked round the car. 'She doesn't know about it yet. I was going to surprise her.' He was unsure how Sally would react if he brought his work into the village, she had been totally unpredictable over several weeks. He delved into the pocket of his jacket and pulled out a sheet of paper. 'If there's anything really urgent, here's my hotel number and the number of the recording studio. Right?' He scribbled the numbers down, handed the sheet to the farmer, and climbed into the car as Sally came out of the cottage. She had changed into a cotton dress.

'Hullo, Jake. When are we going to get some rain?'

'Oh, this'll break any time now. All that high-flying cirrus tells me that.'

She slipped into the driving seat whereupon the telephone could be heard ringing inside the cottage. 'Let it ring,' said Peter.

'But it might be business. You wouldn't want to miss Leonard Bernstein or George Solti, would you? Better yet, it might be someone wanting *me*.'

Peter scrambled out of the car and ran angrily to the house, muttering as he went, 'And then, if it's all the same to everyone, I'd quite like to go to London!'

She smiled brightly at Jake. 'Sorry about that.'

'I hope I haven't called at a bad time . . .'

'Not at all. He gets this obsession about his entire career hanging on his catching the one-thirty-five.'

'I dare say these things are important.'

'Yes, but important to whom? That's what we ask ourselves.'

Peter hurtled out of the cottage. 'It's Mandy. For you. Sal, I really must *go*!'

She smiled at him sweetly. 'Why don't you leave the car at the station? I can always pick it up later.' She climbed out, Peter threw up his arms in despair but called after her with a new, firm tone to his voice.

'Sal —!' She stopped. He moved up behind her, ignoring Jake who hovered awkwardly. 'We're not going to say goodbye like this, are we?'

'Not saying goodbye like anything. Don't miss your train.'

'We never carried an argument overnight.'

'No argument. Go and do your big job in London while the little woman keeps the house clean for you.'

He bit his lip. 'Are you going to wish me good luck with the session?'

'Good luck with the session.' It was said flatly, without expression or feeling. He stood deflated, watching her walk quickly to the front door. 'Come in, Jake. I won't be a moment.'

Jake glanced at Peter climbing miserably into the car then, feeling distinctly uncomfortable, followed Sally inside.

She listened to Mandy's voice on the telephone without registering what the girl was saying. Through the window she could see Peter in the MG. Suddenly interrupting: 'Mandy, can I call you back? Couple of minutes? Would you mind?' She rang off and ran past Jake out of the room.

'Hey!' she called from the front door. Peter turned, smiling with relief at her change of tone. 'Good luck with the session.'

'Thanks.'

'Phone me?'

'The moment I check into the hotel.' A nod and half smile to each other. It was enough.

Back in the living-room Jake was studying the wall with a look of puzzlement on his face. 'How long has this been here?' he asked.

'Mm?' Then Sally saw the crack. Deep, wide, stretching crookedly from floor to ceiling. 'Good God,' she cried, appalled. 'How on earth . . ? I mean, I couldn't have missed it . . . it just wasn't there a minute ago . . .' Again

131

she ran out of the house but Peter was accelerating away, already out of earshot. She returned to Jake. 'It's not going to fall in on us or something?'

'No, no,' he assured her. 'But if you like I'll try and get someone round in the morning.'

'Thanks.' Just as the first scratch on a new car renders it a write-off in the owner's eyes, so the crack in the wall seemed to turn her cosy home into a tumbledown shack. She'd worked so hard on the cottage and her imagination ran in overdrive. She pulled herself together and turned back to the farmer. 'You called in to see Peter. Is there anything I can do?'

'Not really,' he replied slowly. 'I'll see him another time.' He looked at his boots for a moment then raised his eyes to the girl. 'There are cracks more serious than those in walls, you know,' he began.

'There are?'

'Like in marriages.' He regretted his presumptiousness when he found his look being returned without expression. 'Or is that none of my business.'

She spoke without offence. 'I think it's none of your business, Jake.'

'I'll get someone round to look at the wall for you.'

Peter sped into the station car park, screeched to a racing stop, and dashed from car to platform taking the bridge steps two at a time. It was normal for him but this time he had left it too late. The London train was pulling out. He paused for a moment's breath, returned to the car, tossed his briefcase into the back, started the engine, and headed towards London. He made good time, considering, and reached Patti Maxton's houseboat on the Thames two-and-a-half hours later. He enjoyed driving and all traces of bad humour had been dissipated by the sunshine and rush of cool air. 'Patti,' he called. 'It's me. An hour late.'

She stuck her head out of a hatch. 'Hullo, hour-late-me. Where you been?'

'Missed the train. Had to drive.'

'C'mon down!' Money and success had bought Patti the means to enjoy her own lifestyle. The first thing her income had purchased was space, independence and solitude. The houseboat was comfortable, luxurious, but more importantly, quiet and peaceful. She would sit on deck on a summer's evening and listen to the silence – it was something that offered more contentment than anything else. Below deck a large saloon housed her piano, a bar, telephone, thick carpets, deep chairs, with the cabin walls decorated by show-biz posters, a couple of gold discs, and numerous photographs, mainly featuring Patti in company with one celebrity or another.

By the time Peter came down the companion-way she was pouring gin into a tall glass, clunking in ice cubes, and topping up with tonic water. She held it out to him. 'Shipboard service gets slower every day,' he grinned.

'So do some of the passengers.' He kissed her. Just a kiss, it was nothing special. Then he took a long drink. He put the glass down in time to see her standing by his briefcase. 'Full of goodies?' she asked.

'Packed to the brim with sheer genius,' he said, crossing to the piano.

The sun was casting long shadows across the lane when Firman's van pulled up outside Rose Cottage. Walking up the path to the front door he cast an appreciative eye over the cottage, and an even more appreciative look at the stunningly beautiful girl who opened it in response to his knock. It was not an insolent stare, simply pleasant surprise and genuine admiration that brought a smile to his lips. 'Hullo. I'm Dick Firman. Jake asked me to call.' Sally viewed him with equal surprise and not without curiosity – builders didn't often come in this shape and size and loaded with such charm. 'I should really have telephoned first . . .'

'That's all right. Come in.'

'He suggested tomorrow morning,' Firman explained as she closed the door behind him, 'but I'm the impulsive type.' She indicated the crack in the wall and he moved closer to study it. 'I say, that's quite a crack, isn't it? I mean, it's not one of your hairline splits – this is a full-blown, uncompromising crack.'

'I'm glad you like it,' she said briskly. 'But what does it mean?'

'It means you have a subsidence somewhere.' His eyes roamed across the four walls and ceiling before coming back to her. 'May I take a look outside?'

'Of course.' Sally led the way through the kitchen and into the garden. He looked carefully at the outside walls before stepping backwards to see the roof.

'What worries me,' he said, 'is where any other cracks might show up.'

'Other cracks, he says!'

Firman explained that the clay soil in Shillingbury was subject to subsidence during long dry spells and not only was it serious but, he admitted frankly, it was also terribly expensive. Sally liked his straightforward approach and the way he treated it as a discussion rather than a builder quoting for a job. 'The trouble with subsidence is that the foundations sink until the weakest part of the structure gives way under the strain.' He rubbed a hand over his face. 'And a load-bearing wall isn't something I'd expect to be weak.'

'What would you expect?' She caught his look as it centred again on the roof. 'Uh-uh, you're just a bundle of laughs, aren't you.'

'I come from a long line of cheerful ancestors. Do you have a ladder?'

She indicated. 'Behind the garage.'

'I'll shin up and take a look-see.' He walked easily towards the garage. She heard herself calling after him. 'May I offer you a drink when you come down?' He turned, continuing to walk backwards. 'The thought of a cold lager will have me up and down that ladder so fast you won't know where I've been.' She smiled. He was easy to smile with.

An hour later she sat beside him in his van as they pulled up in the station car park. She surmised at once that Peter had taken the MG to London so Firman offered to drive her home again. 'Sorry to be such a bore,' she said.

'What began as a medium dull day is becoming more exciting every minute.'

'Driving me home is as exciting as it's going to get.'

Despite the friendly warning he stopped outside the Oddfellows Arms and offered to buy her a drink. When she shook her head he tried, 'Look, if you were going to eat all by yourself tonight . . .'

'Mr Firman, before we play the "Here-we-both-are-at-a-loose-end" scene, I'd like to be dropped either here or outside the cottage.' It was all guileless enough, the man was trying to date her and she enjoyed the experience.

Only Harvey saw them drive away from the pub; he came round the corner as they gathered speed and, being Harvey, naturally assumed Young Upstart's wife had found herself a new drinking companion. The separate ingredients were in the mixing bowl of gossip and the stirring began.

The telephone was ringing as Sally inserted her key in the front door. But it stopped before she reached it. She stared disappointedly at the silent receiver, hoping it would ring again. It didn't.

Peter hung up. He wondered whether to dial again but realised she must be walking back from the station and, without benefit of reasoned or logical thought, decided he would drive home again. He half listened to Patti as she sat at the piano and sang a phrase repeatedly, reading from the manuscript. 'You want to take it in one breath if you can . . .' Then she was standing immediately behind him.

'As an old chum, is everything all right?'

'Not especially.'

She turned him round gently and looked up at him, her head slightly on one side. 'You don't want to leave that one alone too often. She's not the solitary type.'

'So she tells me.'

Her arms slid round his neck. 'You don't take easily to country-style, do you?'

'I'm working on it.' She kissed him. They'd known each other a very long time. 'Did I ever tell you my wife doesn't understand me?'

'Regularly. The trouble is she does. So do I.' She kissed him again. After he'd gone she sat looking at the door for a full five minutes. Then she wandered back to the piano and tried the phrase in one breath. She hoped it would sound better the next morning.

By ten o'clock that night it was raining in Shillingbury. It had started with a few drops; big warm ones spluttering down and landing several inches from each other. Within minutes it gathered momentum. The sound increased, a rustle into a patter, a patter into a downpour. It grew cooler until, dramatically, a flash of lightning and simultaneous clap of thunder turned the tap full on. The rain fell in solid sheets, punctuated by flashes and crashes, the drops bouncing a full six inches from flat surfaces, the water gushing from pipes, flooding down streets, flattening parched plants which had waited so long only to find themselves unable to cope with the force of its arrival.

The cloudburst continued unabated for ten minutes before the pressure eased back to a steady heavy downfall. Sally had gone to bed early and fallen asleep the moment her head touched the pillow. She didn't hear the thunder and was unaware of the lightning. Nor did she notice the first half-dozen drops of water which fell singly onto the pillow inches from her head. Her eyes opened as two drops fell in quick succession and she was wide awake instantly, leaning over to switch on the bedside lamp. The ceiling paper was split and the rain was coming through with increasing speed; even as she watched a second hole appeared nearby.

She scrambled out of bed and rushed into the bathroom, instinctive survival moving faster than conscious thought. Grabbing an armful of towels and a plastic bowl, she tried to place them strategically, but gaps were opening up in the ceiling every few seconds until there seemed as much rain inside the bedroom as outside. She was not a girl to panic but sobs welled up inside her as she realised her efforts were a pathetic protection against the damage being done to the furniture, carpet, cushions and bedclothes. Her home was being flooded and, desperation giving strength, she lifted, pulled or pushed everything movable onto the landing. She ran downstairs and gathered together a selection of receptacles, buckets, jugs, more bowls, more towels. She worked sensibly and fast, but to little avail. She was weeping with rage and frustration.

When there was nothing more she could do she pulled on a pair of jeans, went downstairs, found the visiting card she'd left on the desk, and dialled his number.

'Mr Firman?' He knew it was her at once. 'I'm sorry to wake you up, it's Sally Higgins. Look, there's water pouring through the bedroom ceiling. I wouldn't disturb you at this hour but it really is cascading down over everything.'

Firman drove to Jake's farm, walked quickly through the deserted yard, and manhandled the tarpaulin into his van. He didn't ask permission, he wasn't keen to encourage help.

Sally met him as he struggled with it up the path. Without hesitation she grabbed one side of the bundle. 'Where to?' she shouted.

'Round the back. Sling it over the roof. Only way.' They laid the tarpaulin flat on the back lawn and he showed her how to keep folding it back on itself so that when they pulled one end of it would come clear easily. They worked side by side in the drenching rain. 'Is the ladder still in the same place?' he asked.

'Where you left it.'

'We'll need two. I've brought one.'

Five minutes later the two ladders were leaning up against the back wall of the house. Firman shouted, 'You'll have to help. Think you can?'

'Just tell me what to do.'

'We've got to manhandle the tarpaulin up as far as the eaves.'

She looked at the height. 'Not only are you a load of laughs you come up with comedy business as well.'

He lifted about a third of the length across her shoulders and her knees buckled with surprise at the dead weight. 'Okay?'

'I think so.'

He put a fold into the remaining two-thirds and, with a grunt, hoicked it onto his own shoulders. They approached the parallel ladders and began to climb. Sally felt as if her shoulders were being borne down into her stomach, her legs began to shake after half-a-dozen rungs, but Firman climbed easily close by her and she determined to get to the top somehow. He realised that if her end of the tarpaulin were to slide off her back it would inevitably pull him and his ladder to the ground but somehow he knew she was going to make it to the top. At last their heads were level with the eaves. He shouted, 'Right. Over your head and into the gutter.'

She had no idea how she was going to find the strength. Apart from anything else it meant her taking her hands off the ladder, but the rain and wind, together with the knowledge of what was happening to her beautiful bedroom nullified an inborn fear of heights. 'I need a drum roll for this,' she muttered and heaved at the bundled tarpaulin with all her might. He succeeded and she managed somehow. They both sagged over the tops of their ladders to regain breath before he called out to her.

'There's a rope tied to the corner eye-hole.' She found it. 'We've got to get it up to that ridge.'

'And all performed without the aid of a safety net.' She was frightened then; stepping off the ladder onto the slippery tiles was more than she'd reckoned on. She saw Firman ease himself up and commence a catlike crawl towards the chimney stack holding the tail of his rope. She shut her eyes tightly, as if to squeeze out the water, then stuck the end of the rope in her mouth and used both hands to pull herself up. There was nothing to cling onto and the roof slates were slippery; she found that if she remained as upright as possible she felt in less danger of sliding backwards. She made it to the ridge and, looking over her shoulder, saw he was already sitting astride the very top. She flung a leg over and found herself facing him at opposite ends of the roof. The wind tore at hair and clothing whilst the rain penetrated so that garments were nothing more than an encumbrance.

'Now all we have to do is tug like mad.'

They began to pull. Slowly the end of the tarpaulin unfolded from the main bundle and began to climb the tiles. After a while Sally flagged.

'I can't –' she gasped, '– anymore.' There was not an ounce of pull left inside her.

'Just hang on. When I've got this end up, I'll come and help.' He seemed to heave so effortlessly and she watched him haul away until he could reach the edge of the tarpaulin itself. He tucked it over the top and then tied the rope off to the chimney. He straddled his way along the ridge towards her until he could reach round and grab the rope in strong hands. They pulled together and the tarpaulin obediently climbed towards them until she was able to tie it off. They were both breathing heavily. 'This is the point where it usually stops raining.'

'It'll have stopped raining in the bedroom, anyway,' she observed, looking down on their handiwork.

'Let's go and have a look.'

'Back to the ladder?'

'Yes. Don't jump.'

'Funny man!'

At first it seemed easier going down than it had been climbing. Perhaps Sally was too relieved to be heading back to the comparative security of the ladders because suddenly her feet slid from underneath her and she felt herself begin to skid downwards out of control. Panic engulfed her as she splayed her hands in a vain effort to stop herself. Suddenly his arm was round her – strong, unyielding, safe.

'Me Tarzan.'

'Me Sally Higgins,' she answered weakly.

Firman practically lifted her onto the ladder and she felt her way down to the ground. When he joined her she was leaning flat against the rungs with her arms dangling by her sides. 'You'd better come inside,' she said, pushing herself upright.

In the cottage they looked at each other. Both were drenched to the skin. The shirt which an hour ago had been worn in bed now clung clammily against her body, her hair was flat and dripping, jeans sodden. She said, 'What was that you were saying about it turning into an exciting evening?'

'You're an incredible girl,' he replied with open and frank admiration. 'I've never seen anything like it.'

'Considering I flunked mountaineering and housebuilding at finishing school! You'd better have a hot shower. Upstairs. There's some spare jeans and a T-shirt in the cupboard.'

'What about you?'

'I'll be fine. I'll fix us a hot drink. Tea or coffee?'

'I couldn't have some hot chocolate?' he asked.

'Now that was something finishing school excelled at.'

He went through the living-room and upstairs. She turned into the kitchen, wearily filled a kettle, and plugged it in. She took a towel from the drawer and wiped her face and hair, suddenly shivering. Then, remembering, she referred to a number scribbled on the 'Don't Forget' pad and dialled it. She rested the receiver on the worktop while she took cups and saucers from the china-cupboard, until she heard the voice from the hotel answer. 'Hullo,' Sally spoke into the mouthpiece. 'Would you put me through to Mr Peter Higgins's room please?' There was a pause, while the voice checked a guest list. Then it told her that Mr Higgins had failed to check in. Yes, they were quite sure.

Sally replaced the receiver. She stood by the kettle until it boiled, just shivering – but by then it was not only because she was cold and wet. She was miserable to the depths of her being.

Fifty miles away Peter drove fast along the country roads, peering past overworked wipers. He went into a bend too quickly, ran out of road, and an uncontrolled skid put him into the ditch. All was silent and still – only the offside front wheel spun uselessly.

CHAPTER ELEVEN

JAKE, WITH Sam and Harvey, had left the Oddfellows Arms when it closed and arrived at the vicarage minutes before the cloudburst. The visit to the Reverend Arthur Norris had become something of a Sunday evening ritual, the vicar thinking that opening a possible back door to the farmer's attendance at church was better than opening no door at all, and Jake, because he enjoyed the relaxed atmosphere at the end of the Reverend's longest day of the week.

Norris sat deep in an armchair, head resting back, gazing at the ceiling, and allowing the continuing flow of Jake's words to wash over him. He was aware of the storm outside and knew it would be well past midnight before his guests left.

'I didn't mince my words neither,' Jake was saying. 'There'll be opposition, I said, a deal of opposition.'

Sam's voice had become a trifle blurred. 'What did he say to that?'

'He knew what I was hinting at,' the farmer replied knowingly. 'So he gives me his London numbers. And here's the thing . . .' He pulled out the sheet of paper, the drink having diluted his resolve to say nothing. 'See what he wrote it on.'

'Looks like a letter,' observed Harvey who was trained to spot such things.

'It *is* a letter. And not being backward in coming foward, I *read* it.' He held it at arm's length to bring the words into focus. ' "Darling Peter" ' he read. ' "See you at the boat four-thirty Sunday. Love Patti." '

There was a stunned pause. 'Phew,' said Sam. 'Young Upstart!'

'What did I tell you?' asked Jake, triumphant at having imparted such news.

Norris commented quietly, 'Poor Mrs Higgins.'

'Now listen,' said Jake, beginning to regret it. 'We've got to handle this very carefully.'

'We mustn't tell a soul,' agreed Sam.

'You're right,' the farmer nodded. 'When I tell Mandy I'm going to tell her not to say a word.'

141

'I'll swear Edith to secrecy,' promised Sam.

'You can always trust the missus,' the postman declared stoutly. 'She's the soul of discretion.'

'And when I preach it from the pulpit next Sunday,' Norris said sarcastically. 'I'll be sure to tell the congregation to keep it to themselves.' He rose to his feet. 'Really! You're a bunch of hypocrites. For all you know this Patti could be his sister. Or his aunt.' But when he looked down the three men stared up at him pityingly.

An hour later Jake had dropped Sam off outside his council house and was on his way to Harvey's place when the two of them drove past Rose Cottage. Their eyes centred in amazement on Firman's van parked outside and Harvey recalled seeing Mrs Higgins leaving the Oddfellows Arms with a stranger in that same van. It was very late and Jake wasn't thinking straight any longer: he knew he would have a hangover in the morning and vaguely wondered how he was going to crawl out of bed again in less than five hours. There were things going on in his beloved village which needed taking in hand; the trouble was his mind was too befuddled to assemble the facts clearly.

Harvey said, 'Young Upstart taking off for London as bold as you like and now . . .'

'Him and Mrs Higgins were having terrible words when he left – he was wanting her to wish him good luck with the session.'

'Is that what they call it nowadays?' sniffed the postman. There was a silence as he thought back into the mists of time, and memories stirred nostalgically. 'You and me didn't used to do so bad, did we?'

'Not after we was married, we didn't.'

'True enough.' Then Harvey let out a small sigh. 'They was never so willing once they knew you was married.'

Jake shook his head. 'I'm at odds with young folks, nowadays. They're that much more casual than we were.'

'And less careful.'

'They seem to imagine we never did it in our day. They have a quick how's-your-father up the back of the barn and think they just invented the wheel.'

'That letter,' said Harvey thoughtfully as the Matra Rancho slowed to a stop outside his semi-detached. 'You're not going to go waving it around, are you?'

'Only Mandy,' promised Jake. 'She's their generation. She'll know what to do.'

Harvey nodded and climbed out. Then he stuck his head in through the window, ignoring the rain. 'And while you're at it,' he suggested, 'ask her what she thinks of a pop group singing in the church.'

'I'll do no such thing,' Jake said with typical and glorious inconsistency. 'It's got nothing to do with her!'

They sat in the living-room, he in a chair and wearing the borrowed clothes, she, on a pouffe in a towelling gown, hair dry, no make-up, cradling a cup in her hands, vulnerable, defenceless. 'Is it a big job – the roof?' she asked.

Firman stirred and put his cup down on the low table. 'I don't know until I have a look in daylight.' Again the frank answer, no empty promises. She felt a deep and sudden insecurity from the fact that water had penetrated her castle roof. There could be nothing worse than seeing the personal materialistic results of her partnership with Peter lying awash and ruined by the flood. Her only link with reality seemed to lie with this man making it safe and strong for her again.

'How long have you been a builder?' she enquired.

'From a practical point of view, not long. Before then I drew the plans and somebody else built them.'

'And before that?'

'Well, I was in hospital for quite a time.'

She remembered. 'Oh God, and you on the roof getting soaked!'

'Don't worry,' he laughed, 'a drop of rain won't kill me.'

She watched him reach for his cup and take another sip of the chocolate. 'Mr Firman . . .'

'Please call me Dick.'

'May I ask you something personal?'

He was ahead of her at once. With a studiously blank face he finished the chocolate and put down his cup again. Then he gave a small, resigned sigh. 'Has Jake been talking?' Sally nodded. 'Damn him, I knew I shouldn't have mentioned it.'

'It is true?'

'Yes,'

'I don't know . . .' she said hesitantly, '. . . the conventional answer to that.'

'You're scarcely a conventional person.' He grinned at her, frank and admiring. 'In fact I've never met anyone quite like you before.'

She said, 'I suppose I haven't met anyone quite like you, either.'

He looked at her. Young, vulnerable, incredibly beautiful. She caught his look – was there the slightest raise of eyebrows? He really wasn't sure. He made a small, tentative movement – and found her smiling at him. 'Wrong!' she said.

He leant back in his chair hastily. 'I was afraid I might be.' The moment was broken and Firman stood up. 'Anyway,' he said, slightly embarrassed, 'Thanks for the chocolate. And the clothes.'

'You're welcome. Any time there's a cloudburst.'

'Goodnight – Mrs Higgins.'

'Goodnight, Dick.' She rose to her feet and walked with him out of the room.

He paused by the front door and looked up at the ceilings and walls. 'I'll be round as soon as I can in the morning.' Then, as if trying to regain stature after his miscalculation of moments before, he added, 'There's not much I don't know about this type of construction.'

He went. Sally was glad he'd said that. It explained how he knew where the water was coming in without her telling him.

The next morning the sun shone again, bringing a new texture of heat. The humidity which had built up over several days had been dispelled by the lightning and thunder, the rain had washed dust from the leaves and rooftops, trees spread vivid green branches over refreshed grass and reinvigorated growth. The lanes began to dry, and freshly washed cottages presented a new face to the cloudless sky.

In the farmyard Mandy leant against the Matra Rancho reading the note while her father watched closely for her reaction. He was surprised when it came. ' "Darling Peter, see you on the boat at four-thirty" means they're having it off, does it?'

'There's no need to be so . . .'

144

'I just wanted to understand what you think is going on.'

'I don't know, do I?' he objected. 'It's just that I like Young Upstart's wife.'

'So do I.'

'Well,' said Jake carefully, 'you're a friend of hers, you ought to show her the letter.'

'That would be the friendly thing to do, would it?' his daughter enquired directly.

He shifted uncomfortably. That blunt way of asking straight questions was inherited from her mother. 'What else?'

'*Not* show her the letter.'

'You mean keep quiet about it? Act casual like?'

Mandy pushed herself from the side of the vehicle and handed the letter back to him. 'I mean forget the whole thing, Dad. You keeping quiet and acting casual like is the equivalent of driving round Shillingbury in a loudspeaker van.'

'That's no way to talk to your father.'

She threw him a cheerful grin. 'I'll see what I can find out,' she promised.

When she arrived at Rose Cottage she found Sally struggling to dry out. The clothes hoist was filled with sheets, towels, and pillowcases; rugs, cushions and blankets were spread over every available surface facing the sun. From the open bedroom window Firman could be heard singing cheerfully, but tunelessly, a spirited rendition of 'When I See You in your Bright Blue Jeans'. Mandy helped her as she heard all about the disastrous adventure. 'The silliest thing of all,' Sally finished, 'was that while I was sitting astride the roof in the middle of the night during a tropical rainstorm, I suddenly remembered I hadn't returned your telephone call.'

'Forget it – it was only about the meals-on-wheels,' Mandy said. 'How long is Tom Jones going to fill your bedroom with music?'

'A couple of days or so.'

'When does Peter get back,' Mandy asked casually.

'Tomorrow. Why?'

'I just wondered.' Sally surveyed the chaotic garden and thought that, what with the items spread for drying and the tarpaulin over the roof, the place looked like a giant

145

jumble sale. 'Who told you it was subsidence?' Mandy enquired.

'Your father suspected it. Then this chap confirmed it. Dick Firman. Do you know him?'

'Never heard of him.'

'He said he'd have to raise the foundations. It's heart-breaking.'

'Did he say how much it would cost?'

'No. We've still got that little joy to come.' Sally had slept badly and was feeling the full emotional effects, hot behind the eyes and ready to burst into tears at the slightest provocation. She decided that doing the meals-on-wheels run would probably take her mind off things and, despite the other girl's assurance that she could manage it alone, felt there was nothing further she could do at the cottage until the builder had finished. As they walked towards the car Firman raised his voice in a renewed burst of song. Sally muttered, 'Raise the foundations, he says. You'd think this was bloody Venice.'

Mandy was unusually quiet as they drove from one old person's house to another delivering lunches and taking the modest payments. It was not a job she liked. Some of their customers were sweet, neat, and spotless; others had given up or grown too frail to cope, and lived in dirty squalor. All were lonely, fearful of rising costs, and desperately in need of company. They tried to prolong conversation while other meals in the car awaiting delivery grew cold. A few tried to smother the embarrassment of poverty by treating her as a servant and complaining about the quality of the food. One old man, nicknamed Desperate Dan, retained an echo of far-fetched ambition by inviting her to delve into his trouser pocket and fish around for the money.

All the old people were up to date with the latest gossip; Harvey had been as thorough as usual in spreading the word. She only hoped none of it was being thrown back at Sally.

At number twenty-six Mrs Dromgoole made no attempt to help as Sally endeavoured to create a space on the table to set down the lunch. 'Who are you?' she asked queru-lously. 'I haven't seen you before.'

'You saw me last week. I'm Sally.'

'Speak up, dear. You won't get anywhere in life if you mumble.'

'My name is Sally,' she bellowed, very distinctly.

'Oh, you're Sally. The one who's married to the punk rocker man.'

'Peter's not a punk rocker man.'

'You're very pretty to be married to a punk rocker man.' Sally explained at the top of her voice that Peter wrote music, and liked all kinds, but arranged pop music best of all. 'We don't want anyone arranging a pop festival here,' said Mrs Dromgoole testily. 'There's enough goings-on as it is.'

'What goings-on, Mrs Dromgoole?'

'If you don't know, dear, I'm sure nobody does,' the old lady said as she took some money from the mantelpiece. 'Sometimes I can't sleep for the noise of singing and shouting in the pub.'

'The only thing you can hear is the deafening din of village gossip.'

'What was that, dear?'

'Nothing, Mrs Dromgoole,' Sally said, taking the money. 'I was mumbling again.'

In the car she asked, 'What's up, Mandy?'

'Up?'

'You're too quiet. This isn't our merry, rabbiting Mandy. And I seem to be recognising the traditional Shillingbury behaviour pattern when someone falls from favour. So what am I supposed to have done?'

'Nothing,' said Mandy firmly. 'It's my dad, as usual. This time he seems hellbent on becoming the fount of all rumours.'

'About me?' Sally was hurt and shocked.

'You. Peter. Or both.' She pulled up at a crossroads to allow Sam's breakdown truck to go by. 'Look, forget it, will you. If anyone here was stupid enough to take notice of a fraction of the gossip that . . .'

But Sally wasn't listening. She was staring, horror-struck, at the car being towed in by the breakdown truck. It was Peter's MG.

In the garage she was almost shouting at Sam. 'Is he all right?'

'He sounded all right on the phone,' said Sam scratching his head. 'Aside of being cross, that is.'

Sally sagged with relief. 'What happened?'

'Seems like he ran out of road. About thirty mile away. I was on my way round to tell you.'

'May I use your phone?'

Mandy interrupted gently. 'Where was Mr Higgins going, Sam? Did he say?'

'He was phoning from a hotel, I think. So he must have taken the train back to London.'

Mandy turned to Sally, who was white and shaking. 'Why don't I run you back to the cottage and you can phone from there?'

'Can't wait,' said Sally briefly, hurrying towards the forecourt office.

'All right,' said Mandy understandingly. 'You must be worried.'

'Not worried,' called Sally briskly. 'Angry.'

Peter's head throbbed with a constant, relentless pounding, and his hand ached intolerably, but he was the first to admit he'd got off lightly. They were already an hour behind schedule and about to try a take when Sally phoned. Patti gave him a nod, she'd carry the musicians' overtime for *this* call. He hurried into the control booth and picked up the receiver.

Sally assured herself he was not badly hurt. Then the words came out, tumbling over each other, out of order, so much to tell, so much unhappiness, so much anxiety. 'Darling, you're being slightly incoherent. What sort of crack?'

'For heaven's sake, Peter. A crack's a crack.'

'But they do come in assorted sizes.'

'This one's enormous. Mr Firman says it could be caused by subsidence. He's a builder. Tall, strong, handsome, amusing, and very kind. We spent the night on the roof together.'

'I wish you could describe the crack as well as you can describe Mr Firman.'

She told him about the damaged ceiling, the soaked interior furnishings, and the necessity to raise the foundations. It would cost a fortune, she was all alone, he had an orchestra waiting . . . 'Come home earlier,' she begged.

'It's a two-day session with the tape reductions.'

'Come home tonight.'

148

'I tried last night.'

'Try again tonight.'

'Sal . . .'

Then sharply, angry, curtly, 'All right. Go back to your music!' There was a pause. She could hear the sound of the orchestra tuning in the background. Then his quiet voice –

'Sal, my head is bandaged, my hand is plastered, there's an army of little men slinging sledge-hammers around in my brain. I just thought I'd mention it.' There followed a second long pause. So long that he asked, 'Are you still there?' He heard her draw a deep breath.

'When I saw your car being towed in . . . I thought . . .' She tried to form a sentence, but the words died in her throat. Then, a choked, tearful, cry – 'Don't you ever send your car home again without you in it.' She rang off and sat quite still until Mandy came in, put an arm round her, and led her back to the car.

Peter returned to the conductor's podium but they went through four takes before he got the tempos right.

Sally had pulled herself together by the time they reached the cottage, and Mandy just dropped her before continuing on her way back to the farm. She wanted to put her father straight about matters concerning loose talk, and she was most anxious to let fly a string of sharp words in the general direction of Harvey the postman. Sally found Firman waiting for her in the kitchen. He sat drinking a cup of coffee, relaxed and completely at ease. She felt an unreasonable resentment. 'What are you doing here?'

'Waiting for you.'

'You've finished upstairs?'

'All done.' He saw her eyes go towards the coffee cup. 'I took the liberty of making myself a cup of coffee. May I get you one?'

'No, thank you.' She was looking at him, level, cool, unsmiling.

'I thought you wouldn't mind,' he said with easy charm.

'Did you?' In her own time she broke the look. 'I'll go upstairs and have a look.'

The bedroom was tidy again. Better than that, much better. The ceiling was repaired and papered, the rugs laid, the furniture returned and apparently dusted. In particular, by the bed, there was a vase of red roses. 'A small token for a lovely lady.' He stood behind her.

She turned slowly. 'You're extremely thorough.'

'I try to be.'

Sally walked past him and went downstairs, trying to regain control of herself and the situation. He seemed to be constantly one step ahead of her, making over-familiarity suddenly inoffensive. Perhaps presumptiousness became a necessary lifestyle when time was short. In the living-room she said, 'I like you – I suppose you know that. But you puzzle me. I think you know that too.'

'In what way?'

She shrugged her shoulders and gave him a small smile. 'Doing what you're doing. Driving from place to place. Don't you have a family?'

Immediately she knew she'd touched a raw spot. His face clouded and he walked to the window where he stood looking out at the garden. 'After the declaration of war, the first thing my parents really saw eye to eye about was the question of my evacuation. Not so much in the interests of my safety; more in order that they might concentrate their undivided attention towards turning the war effort to their own advantage. My father spent a sizeable proportion of his time avoiding conscription and my mother spent nearly all her time avoiding him. She liked soldiers a lot. More precisely, she liked a lot of soldiers. Sometimes two at a time. She tried very hard to keep her affairs secret from him because, being her husband, he felt entitled to a percentage of the take. He was in the acquisition and exploitation business. Which means he stole anything he could lay his hands on and flogged it on the black market.

'They lived well, my mother and father. They were busy living well when an incendiary bomb fell on their house at 92, East End Street, and set them alight. A high explosive landed on the same spot seconds later and scattered their ashes. They'd always expressed a preference for cremation.'

It had been spoken without self-pity, a matter-of-fact relating of a tragic childhood. Sally had never experienced the situation of a man unburdening his soul, a stranger, but someone who, for all that, needed a friendly ear.

Firman turned from the window and faced her.

'You didn't really have to tell me all that.'

'I didn't want to be a mystery – to you of all people.'

She handled it well, allowing a few seconds to pass before saying quite quietly, but in a down-to-earth way: 'What about the problem of my foundations?'

'Yes, well, raising foundations comes a bit pricey.'

'How pricey?'

'About three thousand pounds. But, for you, I work at cost.' He allowed himself a small grim smile. 'People are more important to me than money.'

She felt the situation slipping away again. 'I'm not important to you, Mr Firman.'

'You don't know how important.'

She rose to her feet and moved to open the front door. 'I'll talk to my husband about the foundations.'

That evening Sam, driving the local taxi, met Peter at the station. As they covered the six miles into the village, he expounded his master-plan about The Shillingbury Brass Band accompanying The Close Encounters. It seemed to Sam that Young Upstart didn't take too badly to the idea; maybe it put him into deep shock, or maybe he simply wasn't listening. Anyway, he didn't say no. Then again, he didn't say yes either.

Peter let himself in through the front door and dumped his briefcase on a chair in the living-room. 'Sal –' he called. He glanced around the room briefly, vaguely looking for the crack she'd been on about, before climbing the stairs to the bedroom. He looked out of the window to see if she was in the garden. Behind him he heard the bathroom door open quietly. She stood there, radiantly beautiful. 'Everything shiny and new,' he commented softly. 'Including you.'

'How was the session?'

'Terrific. How was this end?'

'We're dry again.' She moved to him and into his arms. They hugged each other tightly. 'Thank you for coming home.'

The sun was setting, throwing long shadows across the cemetery, as Arthur Norris closed and locked the main door of the parish church. He walked towards the vicarage but slowed his step as he saw the distant figure of Jake making his way to the Oddfellows Arms. 'Jake,' he called. 'Would you spare me a minute.'

'Evening, Reverend.' The farmer climbed onto the low verge and moved towards the vicar. The two men met half-way.

'Would you explain to the good Lord and myself what kind of scandal you've been spreading over the past forty-eight hours?'

'Scandal, Reverend?'

'Don't come the innocent with me, Jake.' The vicar's modulated voice made the rebuke the more telling. 'You turned up a titbit of juicy gossip and you've been delivering it around the houses along with the milk.'

'I'm sure I meant no harm.' For once Jake seemed uncertain and aware of being in the wrong.

'From the crucifixion to the atom bomb the disasters of this world have been caused by people who meant no harm.'

'I'll maybe call on them in the morning.'

'If you do you can pass a message from me. They and their singing group will be welcome in the House of the Lord at any time.'

Jake was puzzled. Genuinely so. It was right enough that he was scarcely a religious man but he'd always felt the church upheld certain standards and respected them. 'I don't understand you, Reverend. What do you hope to get out of it?'

'I'll tell you what I hope to get out of it, Jake. The sheer satisfaction of seeing pews filled with people, the church overflowing with goodwill. And if, as an added bonus, we manage to achieve some kind of communication between our generation and theirs then I'll ring every bell in our crumbling belfry.'

Sally drew the curtains across the window and switched on a lamp. 'So when it became obvious he planned to ease something approaching three grand out of you and make a pass at me, I opened the front door and showed him out.'

He poured the drinks. 'It must have been rotten for you.'

'No, it wasn't, actually.' She sat beside him. 'He's lonely, frightened, desperately trying to squeeze too much into too little – he's charming, amusing . . . and sad.' He held out her glass. She took it and sipped thoughtfully. 'That is, I *think* he is.' He waited. 'I have the strangest feeling that for two days I've been living among a constant succession of half-truths.' He was listening intently. 'I get the impression everyone is concealing something. I don't know what. In some cases, I don't want to know what.'

He was looking at her then. 'You're including me in that, aren't you?'

'I don't want to know what time you left Patti to drive home.'

'I told you. I phoned but you –'

She interrupted quickly, urgently. 'I don't want to know.' She stared into her glass. 'I know what time it was when I phoned the hotel . . .'

He was at a loss, but he left it alone. It was better left. He finished his drink and stood up. 'Another?' She shook her head. As he poured a Scotch for himself, he said, 'Anyway, mysterious background or not, your Mr Firman's done a fantastic job on the wall.'

She continued looking into her glass. 'He did the bedroom, not the wall.'

He looked around the room. 'Maybe I'm going mad. But which wall has the crack in it?'

'Peter if you can't see . . .' Sally tailed off as she stared blankly at the wall. There was no sign – not the tiniest suspicion – of any crack. She got up quickly and peered closer. He looked on with studied interest. Then she pointed a finger at the wall and spoke slowly, 'There was a crack in that wall. It stretched from floor to ceiling.'

'I believe you. I believe you.'

They went to bed early. Their bed was bathed in the light from a full moon. They lay wide awake, with their backs to each other. Each was conscious of the other; aware of too many arguments in recent weeks, the strain of insecurity, the trembling doubts made worse through being unspoken. Wanting so much for things to be right between them, yet unsure of how to mend the rift. They lay silent for a full forty minutes before he spoke, almost in a whisper. 'How long can we keep this up?'

'Keep what up?'

'Living in Shillingbury and working in London?'

'Let's try. I want it to work.'

He rolled onto his back, arms behind the head. 'On Sunday the session seemed the most important thing in my life. Today I realise importance is relative. I should have been here with you.'

She looked at him. His face was half-lit by the moon and she watched it for several seconds. 'I love your music,' she whispered. 'I used to think that anyone who could create such beautiful sounds must be wonderful to know.'

He shook his head slightly. 'It's a world of fantasy and make-believe. I need someone to keep me in touch with the earth people.'

'The earth people are right here in bed with you.'

They turned and kissed tenderly. Then she murmured, 'If at any time – when we're apart – you're unfaithful to me . . . I don't want ever, ever to know.'

He raised himself up on one elbow. 'Is that what all this is about?

'When you and I first met I was the career girl who could handle anything and everyone. Remember? Yesterday, when they brought in your car, I discovered that I'm only complete when we're together. I love you.'

They kissed again, this time more passionately. Then they lay comfortably together, calmer and infinitely more contented. Still neither slept. Sally allowed thoughts to filter slowly through her mind. Any marriage must have its minor crises, particularly in the early years. Each day she learned a little more about the man she loved and slowly became used to the realisation that it was she who was the stronger of the two. This would have disconcerted her two years earlier but now . . . perhaps she rather liked it. She could hear it raining outside. She would never be able to listen to the sound of the rain without reliving that awful night. Wait a moment, though, it couldn't be raining – she was looking at a full moon shining out of a clear sky. A tiny thought flickered somewhere at the back of her memory. 'What did you do with the hose?' she asked.

'What did you say?'

'Sunday. I gave you the hose. What did you do with it?'

'Oh.' He pondered a moment. 'I stuck the end down a dirty great dried-up crack in the ground.'

'Did you turn the tap off?'

'No.'

'Neither did I.'

'We must have been no end of help with the drought.'

She thought to herself: the cracks in the ground near the cottage had disappeared. They would have, because Firman had said it was all clay around these parts; and clay expands when wet and contracts when dry . . .

Suddenly she was hitting Peter. 'What on earth –' he began.

'Why the hell didn't you tell me?'

'I didn't think –'

'For two days you've been pouring hundreds of thousands of gallons under the cottage.'

'And all the time I've been making beautiful music with Patti, I've been raising the foundations at the same time.'

'If you had any idea –'

'Perhaps I am a genius after all –'

'What I've been through –'

'Better yet, I even get to bed with the lady of the house.'

He took her in his arms, kissed her strongly, passionately. Then rolled on top of her.

'Don't you think,' she murmured between kisses, 'you ought to go and turn the hose off?'

'Now? You're joking!'

'Darling, we can't possibly leave it running all night.'

Jake was unskilled in the art of apology, mainly because he had little practice. He stood before Peter and Sally tongue-tied and acutely embarrassed. They tried to look encouraging as he cleared his throat for the fifth time. 'I didn't mean any harm,' he said at last. It was not how he'd intended to begin and he found he could not continue.

'Was that it?' tried Sally.

He turned to Peter and said, with terrible significance, 'When you wrote down your London number . . .'

'Yes?'

'On that *piece of paper* . . .'

'What piece of paper?'

The farmer had never yearned more for a larger vocabulary. 'You know, that certain piece of paper you wrote the telephone numbers on . . .'

'Of the hotel and the recording studio.'

'The recording studio, yes,' Jake seizing the cue like a

lifeline. 'Right. So when you gave me the number of *the recording studio* . . .' His eyes swivelled desperately to Sally and back to Peter. '. . . and I might have said . . . not understanding like . . .'

Sally asked helpfully, 'Would you like me to leave?'

'No,' said Jake turning back to her. 'Because that night, during the storm . . . late . . . the builder and all that . . .'.

'And all that?' she asked.

His face reddened. 'I don't know about *all* that,' he corrected hastily. 'I just thought . . . with his van outside . . . *some* of that . . .'

Peter asked, 'Would you like *me* to leave?'

'No!' said Sally. Jake's message was slowly getting through.

'So if I said anything amiss . . .'

'Jake,' she asked in bewildered amazement, 'are you suggesting that Richard Firman and *me* . . .'

The penny dropped with Peter at the same time. 'That piece of paper . . .' He explained to Sally, 'It was Patti's letter confirming Sunday.' Then to Jake, 'Did you really think . . .?'

'I apologise if I caused any inconvenience,' the farmer struggled to regain some dignity from the debacle. 'I was only trying to protect our village from the ravages of a permissive society.'

'Okay, Jake,' said Peter. 'Perhaps you'd like to inform the village that we're un-ravaged.'

'Show business isn't all Harold Robbins, you know,' Sally told him.

'I'll put it straight. You see if I don't.' Jake hurried out of the room, glad to get away. Outside the cottage he remembered his promise to the vicar. 'The Reverend said to tell you your Close Encounters can sing in the parish church if you want.'

Peter sighed. 'Yes, well, that *was* a secret!' He winked at Sally – he'd explain later. 'I'm sorry you don't approve, Jake.'

'You can't teach an old dog new tricks. I'd always thought it was because the old dog is better able to judge whether the new trick's worth learning.'

'Would it be a better trick if The Close Encounters were accompanied by The Shillingbury Brass Band?' Peter asked. Jake was not sure if he'd heard aright – neither, for that matter, was Peter.

'The boys and me would be prepared to help you out.'

They shook hands on it. After Jake had gone Sally said, 'You're quite a person, Peter Higgins.'

'I think I'm a nutter.' They kissed on the front path. The crisis suddenly a closed book, secure in each other, contented, relieved, happy. It was a long kiss.

Harvey, cycling past with the second delivery, rode smack into a wall.

Sam always took credit for the fact that the brass band accompanied The Close Encounters in the church, and probably he was right to do so. The fact was that, faced by the unfamiliar sight of an apologetic farmer struggling red-faced to admit to spreading malicious gossip, Peter had not known quite what to say; later he admitted it just seemed a good idea at the time!

The first rehearsal was a great disappointment to the band. As Peter distributed the parts of his special arrangement the old men were working themselves up either to rock and roll or play it real cool, so it came as something of a let-down when they discovered they had a hundred and sixty-eight bars rest to start with, before they found themselves playing an unbelievably slow version of 'Bless This House'.

In the Oddfellows Arms Jake said, 'I don't understand it. I won't say I don't like it, but I don't understand it.'

'I don't even like it,' complained Harvey who'd been expecting to beat out a new rhythm on his big drum.

'It's not so bad for you, just thumping away,' pointed out Sam. 'But holding long bottom notes on a tuba is like blowing into the Q.E.II's siren.'

'The Close Encounters'll never be able to sing that slow,' observed Jake. 'Their trousers is too tight.'

Harvey added, 'I thought we was going to get something with a beat to it. I was going to dress up.'

'Dress up?' questioned Jake sharply.

'You know, put the gear on.'

'Put the gear – ? In *church*?'

'We can't take part in a rock concert wearing uniform. I was going to put on a pair of jeans.'

'A pair of Jean's whats? asked Sam, who wanted to know.

'If we're going to do this thing,' argued Harvey, 'I reckon we got to do it properly.'

Jake summed up the exchange. 'Well, I don't understand it. Then, I dunno, that's the story of my life.'

Next door, in the saloon bar, another mystery was solved with the arrival of Patti in the village. She was awestruck by its sheer beauty and peace, like taking a walk through history. Then, catching sight of someone through the hatch opening on to the public bar, she asked, 'Hey, does he live in the village too?'

Peter and Sally followed her look. Peter was surprised. 'No, he must be visiting. I haven't seen him for years.'

'What's he doing nowadays?' wondered Patti. Then they became aware of the total bewilderment suffusing Sally's face.

'Uh-huh!' Sally exclaimed painfully. 'Stand by for an announcement from the girl with egg on her face. That is Richard Firman – builder and decorator.'

'That, my love,' Patti assured her, 'is Peter Martin – out-of-work actor. He made his name in that play by Somerset Maugham – you know? – in the sanatorium, where the fellow only has a year to live.' Her voice prattled on as background to a rushing sound in Sally's head – of shame at her stupidity mixed with sheer disappointment. She knew he was a charming ne'er-do-well, but she'd thought he'd told her the truth. She *wanted* it to be the truth. Patti was saying, 'Last time I saw him was in a hotel in Majorca. So far as I could see he was still playing the part – but for real – ' Then Sally was aware of Peter's look. He could see right into her eyes, into her thoughts, into her mind; and his look was one of deep sympathetic understanding.

She searched out Dick's digs and walked round to see him. He'd taken a room in a house, one of a terrace, shabby, cheap. His van was parked outside and he was loading it up, preparatory to departure. He stopped momentarily when he saw her, but then carried on without saying anything.

'I guessed you might be leaving,' Sally said. 'I thought it might be nice if someone said goodbye.' He ignored her. She waited while he walked back into the house and returned carrying a cardboard carton filled with books, papers, oddments. It went onto the back seat. 'There's really no need to crawl away into the night,' she said. 'I'm not angry. Quite strangely, I'm not angry.' He took off his jacket, turned, and slung it inside. 'Only disappointed.' He stopped then, turned back and looked at her. 'Why did you give up acting? They tell me you were good.'

'I am good. Who says I gave up?'

'This – is *acting*?'

'What else? Create a character, work up the plot. Fulfil the engagement, move on to the next date.'

'You removed the roof tiles. Deliberately.'

A small shrug. 'One has to set the scene.'

'You'd have taken our money.'

He was pleasant. Unashamed. Apparently without guilt. 'As my fee. You enjoyed the performance, didn't you? Isn't that what you pay for at the box office? By the way, the takings were a bit down this week.'

She looked at him, and slowly pulled a sheaf of notes from the pocket of her summer coat. Enough to cover materials, and a bit over. She held it out in silence. He took it, quickly, into the pocket.

'Was it –' she asked, '*all* acting?'

'No.'

'Your childhood?'

'Was true. Every word. You're the only one I ever told.'

She searched his eyes, wanting so much to believe him. 'I bet it'll stay in the act from now on.'

'You think I should keep it in?' he asked.

'Oh yes.' She was thrown by a sudden and annoying tear. 'It's the best bit.'

She turned from him and walked away down the street. She didn't see his beaten, baffled expression as he closed the van door and drove out of the village.

There was not an empty seat to be found in the church. Young enthusiasts seemed to have come out of the woodwork; in fact many had travelled miles to hear the group on a wide variety of outrageous forms of transport. They'd recognised the unusual venue and dressed with reasonable suitability. Norris spoke a few words of gratitude from the pulpit before introducing The Close Encounters. There was applause as Patti entered with them.

Norris looked down with great satisfaction on his congregation as teenagers and villagers, young and old, sat alongside each other.

As Peter mounted the podium there came a minor disturbance at the back of the church as The Shillingbury Brass Band made *their* entrance. It was widely known that the worthy old men were nothing if not wholeheartedly enthusiastic. Sam was a 'mod', Reggie a 'rocker', Harvey a 'teddy boy', Jake had gone 'country and western' and it was anybody's guess what Basil had gone, but his winkle-picker boots made him several inches taller.

Unaccompanied, Patti sang the first few bars of Peter's unusual arrangement of 'Bless This House'. Then The Close Encounters, backed by the rhythm section, pitched in with a fast disco tempo, building up quickly to the swinging beat which was their hallmark. The audience began to clap the off-beat. Young and old joined together. Finally the climax. Patti and the kids changed key and hit an even faster *alla breve* tempo of the counter theme. Peter cued in The Shillingbury Blowers. They took up the melody they'd rehearsed. The church was filled with sound, glorious and noble, moving and exciting. Modern and old-fashioned merged in magnificent harmony.

Jake caught Peter's eye and smiled. He'd taken his first step along the road of understanding between generations, and it was Young Upstart who had shown him the way.

CHAPTER TWELVE

THE ROMANS first invaded England in the late August of 55 B.C. when ten thousand men sailed under a full moon from Boulogne and rowed straight into a north-easterly gale. Feeling none too well, and weighed down by heavy armour, they fought their way up a shelving beach in the face of ferociously accurate javelin hurling from well-trained tribesmen, until Caesar was obliged to concede that his legionaries had no stomach for the undertaking and embarrassingly withdrew. The full-scale invasion of Britain came ninety years later and the place names dating back to these early times are divided broadly between pagan and Christian origin. Eight hundred years after that the men with winged helmets sailed their longships from Denmark and, by the tenth century, the East Midlands had been divided among the Danish armies whilst, further south, the Anglo-Saxons settled in the counties around London.

The countryside around Shillingbury became a sort of 'no man's land' where no leader was sufficiently confident to build a castle on the one hand or a cathedral on the other, with the result that the area remained nervously defensive and largely agricultural. The word 'shilling' was thus derived, not from the coin as might be imagined, but from a pagan tribal name, whilst 'bury' is a prehistoric word with a defensive connotation. Overlooked by a high hill and surrounded by fine woodlands Shillingbury enjoyed an excellent look-out vantage point as well as natural defences. At the same time the rich clay soil offered sustenance to successive crops.

The peaceful regime came to an end when the Danes overran Mercia, and the lives of simple folk were subjugated beneath the trials of strength until Ethelred rebuilt the ruined walls of Worcester and the region came under the beneficent influence of the Church. At this time an incident occurred which was to form the basis of the Shillingbury Legend. A child-king of Mercia was murdered and the rumour spread that as the boy had disappeared under mysterious circumstances, the penalty for mentioning his name would be death. The story went that a ploughman working in the fields had been confronted by a man who came forth out of the sky and guided him to a grave where he found the bloodstained body of the young king. The murderers were arrested, brought to justice, and the belief was born that from thenceforward whenever the village faced any crisis the Man from the Sky would return bringing with him understanding, peace of mind, and prosperity.

He came again that summer on a sweltering hot day in July.

It was a Shillingbury morning much the same as any other. Harvey read what he could of the first delivery before popping the letters through the front doors of the appropriate houses. Terry swept a languid broom among the tables and chairs outside the Oddfellows Arms, Mrs Williams in the General and Fancy Drapers turned a cardigan faded by the sun in the optimistic expectation of equalising the colour by also fading the other side. Madigan the Fish wielded an artistic paintbrush over the lettering 'Fish and Chips', and the early Midland Red bus picked up passengers from the long-distance stop near the Green and accelerated away.

In Peter and Sally's bedroom the village sounds percolated through the drawn curtains. Sally's eyes opened, immediately awake. She looked at her husband who took longer. Eyes open, shut again, a couple of blinks . . . even then it was an unwilling consciousness. 'Good morning,' she said.

He flopped an arm round her, kissed whatever was nearest. 'Happy birthday, darling!'

She smiled. It was, after all, his first thought on awakening. After a few seconds he rolled onto his back, stretched out an arm to the bedside unit, opened the top drawer, and took out an envelope. The arm described a circular movement in her direction. She took the envelope whereupon he subsided into two minutes more of slumber. She laughed at the card, then read the message within, her expression softening as she did so. She kissed him. He grunted.

Then to more practical matters. Without disturbing him she took a further peek into the envelope, upturned it, a small shake. Her head turned partially to take in the headboard behind; a gentle lean outward to scan the floor by the bed. Nothing. Perhaps it was on *his* side. She raised herself on one arm and leant over him. His eyes opened. She dropped him a casual smile and slowly withdrew to her own side. With a monumental effort he hauled himself from the bed even before all systems were functioning normally, left the room, and flopped heavily down the stairs. Sally sat up, a headshake to loosen hair, eyes bright, expectant, pretty. He returned with a handful of letters, a postcard, the newspaper. 'I wonder if anyone's popped in a postal order.'

'I'm nearly old enough for it to be a cheque.'

He sat on the edge of the bed and scanned the headlines. She opened the cards. 'Aunty Vi. Mum and Dad, "Sorry we missed your birthday",' a look heavenwards of amused tolerance. The next card brought an affectionate, 'Ah!'

He looked up sharply. 'Who's that from!'

'Tony.'

'Is he supposed to send you birthday cards now you're married to me?'

'Of course he is. He's terribly good looking and has a lovely sense of humour.'

'It's funny how men with good teeth are always first to see the joke.'

'I'm glad you're still jealous.' She put the cards down and stared fixedly at his back. 'Are you working today?'

'Later.' She began to worry. 'I thought we might go for a spin later. I'll buy you a birthday lunch.'

'That'll be nice,' she commented, none too enthusiastically. 'Where to? London?'

'Wouldn't you prefer somewhere local? The Horse and Hounds.'

What sort of present was *that*? 'Why the Horse and Hounds?'

'The food's good there,' he said. 'You can eat out of doors on a day like this.' He left a pause, a long one. Enough for him to read a complete news item. 'Besides, there's a hitching post.' He got off the bed and drew aside the curtains. Sally suddenly felt a surge of excitement as she scrambled out to follow him. She ran to his side and looked down, childlike, out of the window.

A pony and trap by the front gate. Pretty grey pony, gentle face. The trap freshly painted, new harness, shining brasses. On the seat a large painted board – 'Happy Birthday, Darling'. She hugged him, almost crying with joy. 'I *love* it!'

At midday she drove him along country lanes, sunshine dappling through the trees, the pony's trot the only sound to be heard. She was picturesque in summer dress, hat, white gloves, parasol beside her. He graced the occasion by sporting a country jacket and tie. They passed the Big House and took the link road towards Banley. She was ecstatically happy.

Lunch tables were set on the wide lawn outside the Horse and Hounds. Several diners looked up admiringly as they drove in and she parked neatly between a Daimler and Mr Charles' elderly Rolls-Royce. 'I say, that was a rather splendid entrance.' Mr Charles sat at the adjoining table. Jacket with leather cuffs and elbows, deerstalker hat, silver handled cane. Horrible Humphrey sat beside him.

'Hullo, Mr Charles,' Sally greeted him.

'New?'

'Birthday present from Peter.'

'Oh, many happy returns. You've undoubtedly raised the tone of the car park.' Peter and Sally sat down, exchanging a quick look of mutual hope that Mr Charles would not be staying. They ordered aperitifs, the waiter gave them menus, and Horrible Humphrey quietly moved to a new position beneath their table. 'Tell me,' continued Mr Charles genially, 'do either of you speak French?'

'*Un peu,*' replied Peter without looking round.

'Like a native or like a tourist?'

'Like an idiot.'

Mr Charles was waving a letter. 'This came through the post this morning – all the way from France.'

'What a triumph for the Post Office,' murmured Peter. Sally shot him a warning glance.

'It's in French,' continued Mr Charles. 'One or two bits I don't understand.' Sally took it from him, noticing the stamp had been torn off and the envelope mutilated. 'Harvey,' explained Mr Charles. 'He wanted the stamp for his daughter's little boy. I do wish we had a postman who didn't so resent parting with letters.'

'Which part are you having difficulty with?' asked Sally.

'Roughly speaking the bit between *Cher Monsieur* and

164

the indecipherable signature at the bottom.'

The letter came from the mayor of a village in the Dordogne called St Jean-Luc. Peter and Sally were of little help with its translation but figured out that 'St Jean-Luc jumellée avec Shillingbury' was almost certainly a suggestion about twin towns. Their conversation was disturbed by a sudden alarmed stiffening of Peter. 'Mr Charles, your dog is . . .'

'Oh, is he?' said Mr Charles, looking under the table. 'Humphrey, stop doing that! Tell me, what do twin towns actually do?'

'The councils get together, don't they?' Sally suggested. 'They sign a treaty to create understanding, build friendships, exchange visiting groups.'

'There are one or two people I'd like to exchange. I'd swap my housekeeper at the drop of a hat for someone who'd refrain from serving mashed potatoes as if they were on the centre court at Wimbledon.' They did not get much further with their French and Mr Charles rose to leave five minutes later, announcing his intention of seeing whether The Corner Shop had a map of St Jean-Luc. It was highly doubtful – they'd only just got a map of nearby Banbury, and *that* was covered with little pictures of 'Ride-a-Cock-Horse'. As he headed towards his Rolls-Royce, Horrible Humphrey tagging along behind him, Peter commented ruefully, 'That wretched dog appears to have eaten one of my shoelaces.'

'Is that what he was doing?'

'No. That's what he was doing afterwards.'

It was Mrs Simpkins who translated the mayor's letter. She obliged with little difficulty. 'Dear Chairman –'

'I thought it said "President",' interrupted Mr Charles.

'"Monsieur le President" is French for "Chairman."'

'Pity. Carry on.'

'"Following the recent provincial elections I was honoured to become appointed Mayor of St Jean-Luc, an enchanting village in the Dordogne region of France."' Her spectacles tended to slide towards the end of her nose causing her to tilt her head far backwards in order to see through them. '"It is many years since I lived in England and I would like to take this opportunity of inviting your council to consider the possibility of Shillingbury becoming a twin town with St Jean-Luc."'

'Yes, we gathered that bit.' Mr Charles wondered if she would reach the end of the letter before her head fell off.

'"If this idea appeals to you perhaps I could fly over to discuss the drawing up of a treaty between our two towns. I have the honour, dear sir, to remain your most etcetera etcetera . . ." and I can't read the signature.'

Mr Charles leant across the table and took the letter from her. 'Mrs Simpkins,' he said admiringly, 'you never cease to amaze me.'

'My French is a little rusty now,' she said modestly. 'I learned it during the war.'

He peered at the signature. It was a bold scrawl. '"Jules . . ."' he tried.

Mrs Simpkins' stomach seemed to leap, leaving her breathless, as quite suddenly she *remembered*. 'May I see that again?' She studied the letter, trying to prevent it from floating in and out of focus. 'Julien,' she read. 'Julien Lacoste.'

'You knew him?'

'Oh yes,' she breathed. 'I knew him. It was Julien who taught me to speak French.' She removed her spectacles and replaced them in her handbag. 'I was in love with him,' she said simply.

He arrived a week later.

The village had become accustomed to the sight of Sally, seated in the trap, trotting Jingle through the countryside. She had fallen immediately in love with the alert and willing pony and found lasting satisfaction in using so leisurely a form of transport to explore the historical wealth of the neighbourhood.

She was moving fairly slowly along a tree-covered lane, cool in the shade, lit by a thousand rays from sunshine dappling through leaves, when her attention was caught by the sound of an approaching aircraft. It was low, somewhere near. They came out of the trees into the open, experiencing the sudden shock of torrid heat, and Sally looked up searching for the plane.

It appeared at treetop level. A single-engined private plane roared overhead, startling the pony, before climbing steeply. Then the pilot proceeded to present an aerobatic display somewhere over the village; victory rolls, stall turns, a falling spin, loop the loop. It climbed again and Sally thought the performance was finished when the plane seemed to level off, the engine note changed, and a figure fell out of it. She gave a start of alarm which became relief when the falling object blossomed into a parachute. The air was still and it was clear to her that the landing zone would be near at hand, so she and Jingle trotted briskly towards it.

The parachutist landed expertly about thirty yards from the lane and Sally arrived at about the same time. She jumped down from the trap, hitched the reins over a fence, climbed it, and found herself at the edge of a cornfield. She was scarcely dressed for this kind of thing but she ran towards the man who, by this time, was gathering his chute and unclipping the harness. 'Are you all right?' she called out.

'Thank you. I am very well.' He smiled at the girl wearing a cloak and struggling towards him through corn which was ready for harvesting and did little to help her progress.

'I thought you were in trouble.' She was nearer, and slowed to a walk when she saw the man was uninjured.

'Had I known I was to be rescued by Alice in Wonderland I would gladly be in trouble.' She reached him and he gave her a small bow. 'My name is Julien Lacoste.'

Julien was about fifty-eight but looked considerably younger. Fit, bronzed, handsome, charming – and French. He had a ready laugh, warm humour, he was rich, mischievous, successful. Some men have it all. As he bundled his chute and unzipped his flying clothes, he told her he had once arrived in Shillingbury in precisely the same way; it was when he was eighteen, one of the Free French in the Battle of Britain, when he had parachuted down filled with bullet holes. He was undeniably a character, he described himself as an ageing playboy, but with sufficient money and panache to follow his whims.

'Welcome back,' said Sally as he helped her over the fence. 'May I drive you to the village?'

'Perhaps to the aerodrome? My little girl is in the plane, they will have landed by now.'

'It's rather a long way with only one horse power. But my husband will run out and pick her up in the car.'

'You are very kind.' She clicked Jingle into motion and turned round in the direction of the village. He looked at the view. 'I had forgotten what a lovely country this is.

Has Shillingbury changed much since the Battle of Britain?'

'Shillingbury hasn't changed much since the Battle of Hastings.'

'Good.'

Peter was none too pleased when his work was interrupted by a request to collect Monsieur Lacoste's little girl from the airfield. He could not help noticing that his wife seemed to be reacting in the normal feminine way when a good-looking Frenchman paid extravagant continental compliments. He drove to the airfield and pulled up near a number of neatly parked planes. Somebody pointed out the new arrival and he walked over as the pilot was standing on the wing, off-loading suitcases and assorted baggage. 'Excuse me,' he called, 'I'm looking for a little girl. Chantale Lacoste.'

The pilot turned. 'Well, you have found her.' Peter reacted in the normal masculine way when suddenly confronted by an exceptionally pretty girl. She was very young, probably not more than twenty-five years of age, her head set proudly on the long graceful stem of her neck, blonde hair piled carelessly on top of her head, a flawless complexion, laughing blue eyes, and soft full mouth. Her flying suit failed to disguise the slimness of her body and the coltish elegance of long fine limbs.

Peter introduced himself. 'You? A little girl?'

'To Papa I am still a little girl.' He helped her down and picked up a couple of cases. 'So he landed all right? Without breaking anything?'

'He flattened a square yard of our corn harvest and then entered the village riding in a pony and trap. All he needed was a Charles Aznavour song to make it the opening scene of a musical.' As they walked towards the car he asked, 'Where is your pilot?'

'I am the pilot.'

'Scene Two is going pretty much to form as well.' He talked freely, flattered by her apparent interest in his work as a composer and delighted that she knew one of his songs. She made his job sound romantic and he felt comfortably successful, forgetting that he'd written little of note over several months. 'When I first met my father-in-law he said, "Ah, you're the chappie who plays the piano, composes music, and conducts the orchestra.

But, tell me, what do you do for a *living*?"' He laughed at his own joke and Chantale joined in politely.

'We have that story in France too.' Then, catching his rueful look, 'Forgive me, I did not mean to put you down. I was trying to impress you that I was not a little girl.' In fact, Chantale was an actress. Her father had given her a good education and, at first, seemed disappointed when she announced her intention of going on the stage. However, his attitude had changed when she won herself a place in the Conservatoire dramatique and emerged very creditably two years later. She did not mention her mother. Peter bundled the cases in the back of the car as she climbed in. 'Where are we going?'

'To find your father. And explain to my wife how I thought you were a little girl.'

'That will be Scene Three,' said Chantale.

They were in the Oddfellows Arms. 'You and Peter,' commented Julien, 'you look a happy pair.'

'Couple,' corrected Sally. 'We say couple. Yes, we are a happy couple.'

'What does it mean, this word couple?'

'Pair.' She introduced him to Terry behind the bar. '*Comment ça va,* dear – what can I get you? Champagne?'

'Thank you, no,' smiled the Frenchman. 'Too much champagne makes me a gay person.'

'I'm going to love your English,' said Sally. 'Let me buy you a pint of beer.'

Julien was looking at Terry. 'I remember your father. He was here in the war.'

'Yes, dear, that's right. Dad stood right here behind the bar until the day he died. Pulling on this handle was the last thing he did,' said Terry, filling a tankard. 'He put the drink down and dropped dead without taking the money.'

'We must pay you quickly.' Sally smiled at Julien. 'Would you like to tell us if the beer is as good as it was?'

He took a long, full drink, then raised his head in thoughtful consideration, as if he was tasting wine. 'To drink a glass of English beer is like coming home from the desert,' he pronounced. 'Already I am treating myself like I am at home.'

How is it the French always make English sound better than we do, wondered Sally. Aloud she said, 'Our Terry is quite a character.'

Julien looked at the buxom girl moving away to the other end of the bar. 'She has a nice couple,' he murmured.

Considering the Mayor of St Jean-Luc and his daughter had dropped in out of the sky entirely unannounced, Shillingbury gathered itself together with remarkable alacrity to accord him the reception his status demanded. Mr Charles put them up at the Big House and, by the weekend, had laid on an excellent dinner with distinguished guests from the neighbourhood. He told Peter and Sally that Mrs Simpkins had revealed her *affaire du coeur* after she had translated Julien's letter. She had been a probationary nurse at the cottage hospital when he was shot down. She'd nursed him, fallen in love with him, and had waited for him ever since.

While the guests were enjoying pre-dinner drinks in the drawing-room Sally looked round the strangely old-fashioned scene. The ladies wore long dresses, the men black ties and dinner jackets. Mr Charles carried with him a style of living which she could appreciate without wishing to emulate. It was an impressive room: solid heavy furniture, brocade curtains across high windows, Persian carpet, good pictures on the walls, magnificent wood panelling, and a massive fireplace. Her eye fell on Mrs Simpkins who stood unaccompanied near the bookcase; she stood motionless, never once shifting her gaze from Julien who moved easily from group to group, chatting, relaxed, contented.

Sally moved over to him unobtrusively. 'Julien, keep looking at me and don't turn around until I've gone. On the other side of the room, standing alone, is a lady wearing a green dress. You've looked directly at her twice without recognition and you mustn't do it again.'

'Who?'

'Margaret.'

He drew breath, half closed his eyes, and allowed a hundred distant memories to sound echoes in his mind. 'Marguerite,' he breathed. 'My God, she was eighteen when I last saw her.'

'Now make a joke so that I can laugh and wander over to Mr Charles.'

There wasn't a joke in him at that moment. Instead he said, 'Thank you, Sally. Already you are a good friend.'

'That's funny!' She laughed, and left him.

He timed his move perfectly. As if finding himself on his own he allowed his look to scan the room. Even then he nearly missed her again, it was the green dress that saved him. Perhaps, also, the way she held her head, her quiet poise, both hands holding the sherry glass. He allowed recognition to light up his eyes and hurried over, taking both her hands in his. 'Marguerite!'

'I thought you had forgotten.' She looked up at him, uncertain, nervous.

'Comment aurais-je pu t'oublier?'

'Les anées sont pries sur tu, Julien.'

'Toi aussi, tu es magnifique. La jeune fille que j'ai connu est devenue une femme distinguée.'

'Toujours aussi flatteur. Tu ferais prendre des vessies des lanternes.'

The moment passed. At dinner they were placed at opposite ends of the table but three or four times his eyes caught hers and seemed to smile gently. The conversation centred on the idea of twin-towning with St Jean-Luc. There would be bickering on the parish council as to who should, or should not, participate in the exchange scheme, whether it could be regarded as a proper charge on the rates, would wives be invited – Mr Charles had heard it all before.

The discussion went on and enthusiasm ran high. Underlying it all was a feeling which Mr Charles found himself unable to identify. There was something about Julien Lacoste, he couldn't put his finger on it, but the Frenchman seemed to draw one out of oneself. There came a moment when Mr Charles heard himself asking, 'Why did you wait thirty-two years before paying us a visit, Monsieur?'

'How can I answer?' A typically French shrug. 'The weeks are filled with work, the years come and go.'

'My wife and I used to travel,' confided Mr Charles. 'Just holidays, you know. Picking up useless information about unremarkable places. I can't see much point in it now.'

As he spoke it seemed to him that he and Julien were the only two people in the room. The eyes were on him, listening, concentrating, understanding. 'How long have you been alone?' he asked.

'Just over a year,' Mr Charles told him.

'Then the loss is till fresh.'

'One carries on, you know.' It was the first time Mr Charles had alluded to the death of his wife in four years.

There were to be those who would say that Sally's 'man from the sky' was something considerably more than he appeared.

Jake's opinion on the twin-towns scheme, in common with many other matters on which he held a view, could be contained within a single sentence. 'Twin Towns? I've never heard such nonsense in all my life. We're not having it – no more to be said.' He was well aware that many of the towns in the area, large and small, had formed a liaison with a similar town in France but, so far as he was concerned, the council needed their heads examining. He had short shrift for the French. 'There they go, practically running the Common Market, and just waiting for an opportunity to unload a butter mountain and wine lake all over Shillingbury.' His answer to any argument that it was as harmless as a few people trying to build up a cultural understanding was as predictable as the explosive force with which it was delivered. 'It's *agri*cultural understanding we want. And the only people who's got that is *us*. They're not even intelligent enough to realise we're right and they're wrong!' He had never been one for seeing the other fellow's point of view and, being a big man physically, his word was frequently the last.

His single-minded beliefs in that which was right and that which was wrong extended to the inclusion of his daughter's life. Mandy handled him better than anyone else since her mother had died. She was the apple of his eye and he made no bones about it; he tolerated her repartee with a humour reserved for her alone and genuinely admired the way she ran the farm as his equal partner. However, their present argument struck at the root of their entire relationship. David planned to take her away with him to Australia as soon as they were married. His insistence that Australia held out opportunities which did not exist at home ruffled Jake's patriotism; 'the grass was always greener' until you'd climbed the fence and the distance between them represented a mighty high fence. 'The lad's all right in his way,' he'd said to Mandy, 'but I won't pretend I didn't hope for somebody who'd understand our way of life. I want to give you the farm, keep it in the family . . . I don't want to see you hurt, girl.'

'You're hurting me now, Dad,' was all she'd said. Later, she was genuinely worried about upsetting her father. They'd been a close-knit family and the whole business of emigration seemed to be a tug-of-war with her loyalties in the middle. As usual she poured out her concern to Sally. They were close friends but, for once, the older girl seemed preoccupied with a problem of her own, and responded by relating the most recent argument with Peter.

He'd been commissioned to write an advertising jingle. It was small reward for the effort he'd made over the past months to row himself back into the limelight and, anyway, there was no guarantee it would be used if the client didn't like it on first hearing. He'd written dozens of jingles in the past and, although they could be enormously remunerative, Peter had tended to compose them between other major jobs. But *this* one he was treating as if it was a symphony. Sally had been enthusing over provisional plans for the twin-town ceremonies but he'd paid scant attention. 'We're going to organise a bistro on the Green,' she'd told him. 'You know, check table cloths, candles in wine bottles, French onion soup, pâtés, crêpes, wine, accordion music.'

'Great,' he'd commented without looking up from his work.

'We're covering the trees with fairy lights. It'll look very pretty.'

'Terrific.'

'Aren't you interested?' she'd asked.

'Of course I'm interested, darling. Only I've got this . . .'

'Julien's talking about the treaty being signed up at the Big House during a banquet. Darling, why don't you compose a special anthem which could be sung by the schoolchildren?'

He'd looked up then. 'You're joking!' She hadn't been joking. 'How can I find the time? This is important.'

'It's a sixty-second jingle,' she'd burst out.

'It's thousands of pounds. If I get it.' Suddenly he'd become insecure about writing a jingle, for God's sake. 'What on earth do you imagine pays for the . . .' He'd stopped dead, then added lamely,' . . . housekeeping and things like that?' She knew he'd been about to say 'the pony and trap' and was angrily upset.

Mandy considered Sally was being harshly unsympathetic over the bad patch Peter was experiencing, but then she didn't really understand show-business people. Sally felt that Mandy was too weak where her father was concerned and should take a firmer stand over the Australia business, but then she didn't understand the farming fraternity.

On the other side of the village, in the Big House, Mr Charles was talking to Julien. 'I spent forty years in the Law Courts, watching the disciples of crime process their weary way to the cells, dreaming a dream of the day I would be free to concentrate on the future.'

'In what sphere?'

'The conservation of energy. The natural resources of this world are burning away faster than governments will admit. We must look to tame the powers of the sun, the wind, the mighty oceans, the untapped potentials.' The Frenchman looked at him with his penetrating blue eyes. Quite inexplicably there floated into Mr Charles' memory a quiet comment of his wife from years ago: *He has such a way with words you actually think he knows what he's talking about.* A slight smile played around the corners of his mouth as he continued. 'I constructed in my garden a windmill. The revolving vanes atop a slender tower were linked to a dynamo for the generation of electricity.'

'And?'

'Whenever the wind blew the whole damn thing fell over.' The two men laughed. It was the first time Mr Charles had related a joke against himself. It was just a little extraordinary in its own way.

In her small bungalow Mrs Simpkins was going through her wardrobe. It had been a long time since she had looked at her dresses, really looked at them with a critical gaze. Then she turned her attention to herself. A long, cool, self-appraisal in the mirror. Little could be done to repair the ravages of years but maybe the face and figure were not so far gone that a diet, visits to hairdresser and dress shop, could not temporarily arrest. She would like to look her best for Julien – after all, she'd always known he would return one day.

CHAPTER THIRTEEN

THOMAS HARDY wrote that 'every village has its idiosyncrasy'. By the same token every village wears its country's characteristics with the same unconscious habit that people display their nationality by dress and bearing. The fundamental appearance of St Jean-Luc made it indisputably French whilst Shillingbury had a thousand-year history of being indestructibly English. Thus it was an unwise decision on the part of the parish council to attempt to create a little France in the heart of England. Mr Charles had applauded the concept of 'rattling the side-drum of Shillingbury whilst the British Tourist Board blindly banged the big drum of Stratford-on-Avon', but their idea of decorating the Green to resemble a bistro and presenting prizes for the most French-looking shops was not soundly based.

The village began to take on a strange new look. Workmen prepared the Green by hanging festoons of bunting, intermingling tricolours with Union Jacks, and they erected gaily bedecked stalls on the grass near the pond. The shops responded to the spirit of town-twinning, led by Mrs Williams who hid the old lettering of General and Fancy Drapers with a new sign *Boutique Haut Couture* under which smaller signs promised *Can-Can Petticoats*, *French Directoirs & Knickers*, *Parisienne Hats*, and *Umbrellas of Cherbourg*. Madigan the Fish was less successful with *Poissons et Pommes*, the Plain and Fancy Bakers offered *Croissants et Ghettos*, the lending library promised *An Exhibition of French Masters*, under which some joker had added 'Bring on the French Mistresses', and Old Mrs Harcourt displayed a handwritten notice in her cottage window, *French Lessons Given* and spent the days looking out with innocent optimism.

The countryside basked in continental sunshine and outside the Oddfellows Arms tables with check cloths and bright umbrellas had been set, whilst Terry had donned a striped apron and beret to serve drinks. Reggie, wearing what could be described only as 'French costume', moved among the customers playing accordion music. Shillingbury looked like an unsuitably dressed and over-made-up elderly lady setting off to a fancy-dress party.

'Is this wise, we ask ourselves?' queried Sally.

'Don't you like it?' responded Mr Charles in surprise.

'Why would the inhabitants of our twintown want to come all the way here to see a bad reproduction of their own country?'

'Dammit, it's a tribute to them!'

She shook her head sadly. 'It's so typical of Shillingbury. Our heart's in the right place even when we pick up the wrong end of the stick.'

'You're a bit of a wet blanket, I must say.'

Sally's view was shared vociferously by Jake who openly opposed any fraternisation with the French; that is, he did until he met Julien. Jake was sitting with Harvey at one of the pub's tables, glaring disgustedly at the burlesque characterisation of Reggie, when Terry brought over their pints. 'Terry,' he said thoughtfully, 'me and Sam, and Harvey and Reggie, come in here regular once a day and you pull a pint for each of us. That's twenty-eight pints a week, which is one thousand five hundred a year. At forty-five pence a pint that'd be . . . let me see now, what'd it be, Harvey?'

'Oh well, it'd be at least . . . at forty-five pence . . . easily . . .' answered Harry who was none too quick at mental arithmetic.

'Six hundred and seventy-five pounds a year,' filled in Terry.

'As much as that?' exclaimed the farmer with feigned surprise. 'Well I never. 'Cos that's exactly what you'll be losing to The Sow and Pigs if you don't get Reggie and his comic French costume out of here.'

He turned as the shadow of a man fell across him and a quiet French voice said, 'Hullo, Jake.'

Jake rose slowly to his feet as he peered at the stranger. 'I'm afraid you have the advantage . . .'

'Julien.'

A search into the memory. A cog clicking into place, bringing first disbelief, followed by slow recognition, before finally reaching that point of magnificent inconsistency which so typified Jake's life. His face became wreathed in smiles. 'Julien! Well, I'll be –' The proffered hand was pumped up and down. 'I'd have known you anywhere!'

'You haven't changed.' The meaning was ambiguous.

'Well, I *must* say . . . fancy that!' Jake shook his head in wonderment. Then, 'You remember Harvey, don't you?'

'You are Harvey?' asked Julien.

'That's right,' Harvey said.

'Are you sure?' With a smile.

Jake asked, 'So what are you doing in England?'

'A whim. An idea.'

'You're not to do with this town-twinning nonsense, I hope?'

'That, precisely, is my whim.'

'Then we'd better have a talk about it, you and me,' said Jake severely. He pulled across a chair and sat the Frenchman down firmly. 'But tell me, what's new?'

Julien smiled again. 'When I look at you, and hear you speak, I realise that absolutely nothing is new at all.'

Less than a hundred yards away Chantale, making a simple summer dress look like a thousand-franc model, walked up to Rose Cottage. Sally saw her out of the window and waved. 'Good morning.'

'Good morning,' called Chantale. 'I am sightseeing. I want to see where you live.'

'Come inside and take a look.' Chantale hurried her step and five minutes later the two girls were drinking coffee in the kitchen.

'This is enchanting. How old is the cottage?'

'Parts of it are over four hundred years. A local blacksmith built it for his bride in 1498. The original baking oven he made is still there, at the back of the fireplace.'

'You have made your home look so chic.'

'Thank you. I've never thought of an English period cottage as chic.'

'If it is simple, tasteful, and very expensive, that is chic.'

'Oh well. It's what Peter calls me anyway – simple, very expensive . . .'

Chantale envied Sally her home. She herself had not yet owned anything of lasting value, living either with her father or in theatrical digs and provincial hotels. A part of her yearned to settle down somewhere, find a husband, start a family. She admired the assured way Sally ran her house yet became instantly professional when Peter came in and played them both his jingle.

He sat at the piano and spoke as he played. 'We open on a shot of acres of young corn swaying gently in the wind – which is violins . . . with the melody underneath on horns. Then the flutes and clarinets pick out cascades of greens and yellows rippling across the meadows.' His hands conjured pastoral chords from the keyboard. 'Landscape shots through trees; great fat well-nourished cattle, and stupid sheep posing like they're auditioning for a Constable painting.' He brought in a disco-rhythm beat with his left hand. 'Then The Close Encounters take up the theme . . .'

When he finished playing Sally said, 'It has a good feel to it.'

'Yes?' Peter spoke eagerly, hungry for praise.

'I think it's going to work – you know, with the orchestra, all the reverb, and multi-track effects.' She paused, then asked perceptively, 'Do you think a country-side setting and The Close Encounters go together?'

'Why not?'

'It doesn't seem the right sound. Like backing *Saturday Night Fever* with Beethoven.'

His face snapped shut; he was not ready for criticism. 'Darling, you can tell me about anything except what is, or isn't the right sound.'

Chantale broke a short tight silence. 'It's a pretty melody.'

'We're recording it tomorrow.'

'Where?'

'Studios. In London.'

The French girl turned to Sally, young, eager. 'Sally, could we go and listen? I've never been to London.'

'I can't.' Then, reasonably, 'Neither can you, really. Mr Charles is taking us to Booker Aerodrome.' She smiled as the younger girl pulled a face at the prospect of visiting the famous aircraft museum. 'Obviously not your scene.'

'I prefer music to aeroplanes.'

'Well, I *must* go. Out of courtesy to your father.' Chantale was about to interrupt with a disparaging comment that he would have eyes only for the aeroplanes, when Sally continued, 'But if you prefer to go to London, I'm sure Peter will be delighted to take you.'

The girl looked at Peter, and then back at Sally. 'You would not mind?' she asked in surprise.

'No', Sally assured her, somewhat briefly. 'Why should I?'

Julien could not have been taken anywhere he would rather have been than the Museum of Old Aircraft at Booker. As they walked slowly past the magnificently maintained exhibits, he told Sally that, despite owning his own private plane, he travelled remarkably little. He lived in a village where the horizons were so close that even Paris was an adventure. Rather, the sky was his playground; he flew for the joy of living and lived for the joy of flying.

Later they sat quietly after a picnic lunch. Sally broke a longish silence. 'Julien.'

'Yes?'

'Why did you come back to Shillingbury?'

'When I was elected Mayor of St Jean-Luc I felt it was a perfect opportunity.' He'd answered readily, too readily, and stopped when he saw the girl shaking her head.

'No. The twin town was an excuse, not a reason. If you wanted to recapture wartime memories you could have done that years ago.'

'I was happy here.' He thought about it a few moments longer, then added, 'I did not realise how happy until quite recently.'

'And you're thinking about the future rather than the past.' She flashed him a frank and disarming grin. 'I'm terribly bad at minding my own business,' she excused.

Julien lay back in the cool grass, a tree shading the midday sun. He looked up at the blue sky and high-flying summer clouds and placed his hands behind his head. 'During the war, after I had come out of hospital I lived on the farm belonging to Adam Smith.' He went on quietly, 'A fine man, a rare person. His son Jake was four years younger than me. Adam taught us both together. Everything we know about the land came from that man. After the war I went home to France, and grew the grape with single-minded dedication.'

'Your wife –' said Sally, thinking of Chantale, 'she must have been beautiful.'

'She was the most beautiful creature who ever trod the earth.'

'Where is she now?'

'Alive. But no longer with me.' He closed his eyes, maybe against the light, perhaps to shut out a memory. 'I worked all the days to make and sell my wine, you see. I was ambitious and I did well. Soon I was able to buy a plane, and when I was not in the vineyard I was high above it . . . working and playing my way through life with self-centred blindness. I did not see my wife was drinking the wine as fast as I was making it. By the time I did, it was too late. One day I decided I must "find" my daughter before she was lost to me as well. Chantale opened my eyes to the true meaning of companionship. We do everything together. Work, play, talk, laugh. When I watch her act on television, on the stage, once a small part in a film . . . I am proud so much I could burst. Today she thinks only of her career; but soon, she will marry . . .' He broke off.

'What will you do then?' Sally asked.

He stirred and raised himself up on one elbow. 'I am a playboy. I will play harder.'

'But alone.' Then, because she had spoken aloud the words he'd kept secret from even himself, 'I'm sorry.'

'I am not good at being alone,' he admitted. 'I am too selfish, I think.'

'I don't think you're selfish at all.'

'You are a clever girl, Sally.' He rose to his feet, the easy movement of a fit man. 'I have said to you things I have not dared to admit to myself.' He began collecting together the picnic things; the conversation was over. The man from the sky was himself vulnerable, Sally thought.

In a London recording studio The Close Encounters put down a track of Peter's commercial as a demo for the client. Peter conducted the accompanying orchestra and, behind him, Chantale listened with rapt attention. She thought Peter was probably the most wonderful person she had met. They lunched together at the White Elephant and afterwards walked in warm sunshine through Hyde Park towards his publisher's office near Marble Arch.

'How long have you and Sally known each other?'

'Four and a half years. She worked in the recording

studio where we were this morning. That's where we met.'

'It is good for you she understands about music.'

'It certainly helps when it comes to putting up with my temperaments. She's a very good judge normally, but when it comes to knowing "the right sound" she leaves it to me.'

'Because you know best?'

'I sincerely hope so.'

They walked a little way before Chantale voiced her thought. 'I think you know best. I like your music, Peter.' Her words provided the spur he needed.

'In that case, let's go and see if the client agrees with you.' It was always the moment he dreaded. Maybe Chantale would be a good omen. 'It'll put us out of our misery,' he added realistically, as he altered course and steered her towards the Park Lane pedestrian underpass.

Phillips was in his office when they arrived. A room of modern design and furnishings, expensive, near lush, but untidied by hi-fi equipment, tables submerged beneath discs, cassettes, and sheet music copies. He listened carefully to the tape but Peter knew before it was half-through. He just knew. An ice-cold block coagulated in his stomach and he made no movement when the tape finished and Phillips removed it from the machine.

'No?' he asked without looking up.

'Sorry. It's not what I'm after.'

'Oh.' Peter took the tape from him. 'What – er – *are* you after?'

'I dunno. But it's not *that*. I mean, this is the English countryside image we're projecting, okay?' His hand fanned slowly through the air as he painted the mental scene. 'Rural, reliable, great traditions of hand-reared quality. You *live* there, for God's sake.'

'I don't live anywhere like you just described,' muttered Peter bitterly.

'To start with I think you're obsessed by the sound of your pop group which, in this case, isn't right for the product.'

Chantale interrupted defensively. 'Do you not like the melody, Mr Phillips?'

'The melody's fine. Great tune.' He moved back to his overburdened desk and sat in the tall ornate swivel chair behind it. 'But I've got a million pound account here and we've got to come up with something better than a good tune.' A foot came up on the desk and the chair demonstrated it had reclining qualities in addition to swivelling. 'We need a *sound*. A sound that conjures up an image of . . . purity.'

Peter stood up miserably. 'Well – that's that! Come on, Chantale.'

Phillips called after him as he went through the door. 'If you come up with any ideas, call me. Okay?'

'Sure,' said Peter.

It was a solid thud to the body. He could sense the bitter taste of failure then, made worse by his being discredited in the face of his young admirer. Success was capricious and transient, flatteringly attentive one moment, rudely rejecting the next. It had been several months since he'd earned any real money but that was nothing compared with the pulverising damage Phillip's turn-down had inflicted on his self-confidence.

The forthcoming French Festival meant different things to different people. Julien Lacoste had caused each of many persons to take out a private worry and have a good look at it. Mr Charles began to wonder whether he was committing the unforgivable sin of wishing his days away, Mrs Simpkins realised she had frittered away a near-lifetime waiting on a memory, Peter was hiding in a dark corner of depression, and Sally saw with sudden clarity that the time was come for a clear-cut act of faith.

Mr Charles had said, 'I don't believe you have a worry in the world.'

Sally had replied vigorously, 'You're joking. I have a husband who, when last seen, was seriously discussing becoming a trappist monk, while an extremely pretty French actress has gone ga-ga over him. And I'll tell you something, Mr Charles – I'm *jealous!*'

'I'm sure you can handle it.'

'You can bet on that.' The idea had formed in the small hours as she listened to her husband lying restless and insecure beside her. 'It's all to do with the right sound,' she'd said to Mr Charles.

'The right sound. I thought it was to do with the sexiest dress.'

'You won't believe what I'm going to wear.'

Up on Top Meadow Julien Lacoste cast an expert eye over Jake's land. Acre after acre of immaculately tended fields spread away from them as far as the eye could see. The field they were in was ready for harvesting, the barley of rich quality, tall, ripe, and clear of the cheapening wild oat.

'Excellent,' said Julien. 'You are a good farmer.'

Jake nodded. 'This is the field my dad gave me when I was a young 'un. Only it grows larger as I grow older.'

'You work it yourself?'

'Always.' Jake paused in their comfortable walk and surveyed his handiwork. 'Dad told me, "Work it well and you'll be rewarded on earth and blessed in heaven." He's been right on the first point. Now I'm getting closer to Judgement Day I don't want to let up in case he's right on the second as well.'

Julien looked at him shrewdly. 'What will you do when this field, and all the others, grow *too* large?'

'I'll worry about that when the day comes,' Jake said curtly.

The Frenchman pulled a knowing face as he noted his friend's over-quick answer. 'I think you worry about it now,' he said, continuing to walk.

'I'll put in a manager, I dare say.'

'Or a son-in-law. That was the idea, was it not?'

Jake caught him up. 'Why do you say that?'

'Because you are selfish.'

'Now wait a minute –'

'Calm yourself.' This time it was Julien who stopped walking and turned to face the other man. 'I am selfish. All men are selfish. You know, we become set in our way of life, when some young man wants to take away our daughter. Suddenly, we realise what she means, what she is, what she does. He is a threat to continuity.'

'Mandy's fallen in love with this young chap,' Jake told him. 'A vet, he is – David. He's all right as they come but, I don't know, we're a close-knit family and he just doesn't fit in. Now he wants to take her to Australia as soon as they're married.'

'Chantale has yet to find such a man but already I am nervous.'

'I'll tell you the truth,' declared Jake, stepping nearer to

Julien. 'It's not nervousness. Nor yet selfishness. It's jealousy. That's worse, isn't it?' -

'It is something I well understand,' Julien said softly.

'I hadn't. Not until now.' They began to walk again, each nurturing their own thoughts. Jake was not a thinking man by nature but the problem of Mandy was something demanding of thought. Suddenly he said, 'I've just remembered – that's what it was about you. You always made me stop and think things through.'

The bright blue eyes glanced across at him, an understanding grin accompanying the look. 'We had good days. During the war. You and me.'

Jake knew what he meant. He knew precisely what he meant. 'No wonder we worry about our daughters. If the young men today are half as bad as we were . . .'

'Or as successful.'

The treaty was signed three days later on the occasion of the Shillingbury Fete. The village green was completely transformed. Trees and stalls were decorated with fairy lights, candles sputtered on the tables, pools of light picked out features and areas, French-style music drifted over the scene from loudspeakers, the weather provided as balmy an evening as any to be found near the Mediterranean.

Jake was there with Mandy, Mrs Simpkins wore her most dazzling new dress at the Crêpes Suzettes stall, occasionally tossing (and missing) a pancake. Nearby Harvey urged people to try his French Onion Soup which, having peeled sixty pounds of onions, he himself was unable to appreciate. Reggie with his accordion clashed discordantly with the recorded music. Chantale made a most stunning entrance, white dress, blonde hair, bewitching smile. She passed a young man, dressed as a 'French Baker' and he offered her some gateau which she laughingly refused, leaving him momentarily crestfallen.

Mr Charles' distinguished old Rolls-Royce eased its way quietly onto the Green and he stepped out with Julien. 'Your English village is wearing French clothes,' exclaimed Julien.

'We dressed it up a bit. In your honour.'

'I am flattered.' He was also surprised.

'By the way,' said Mr Charles. 'I took your advice. Momentous decision.'

'A cruise?' guessed the Frenchman correctly.

Mr Charles nodded. 'The Greek Islands. Never seen them and, anyway, it'll be better than hiding away in the Big House.'

'I'm glad.'

'I'm most grateful to you. You made me stand back and take a look at myself.'

'You'll be gone for several weeks.'

'Yes, I'll drop you a postcard.'

Sally peeped out from the flap of a tent. She could see Reggie staring fixedly in her direction. Peter came up behind her. 'Are you sure we're doing the right thing,' he asked. She nodded. Then she gave the sign.

The recorded music was faded back and Reggie played a loud introductory chord on his accordion. The crowd looked up as Peter and Sally appeared from the tent and walked to the centre of the Green. People laughed and clapped appreciatively and quickly gathered around in a large circle.

Peter and Sally were dressed and made up as Clown and Auguste. Peter was the original white-faced clown, in traditional sequined costume and tall pointed hat. He bowed extravagantly and, raising a trumpet to his lips, began to play. Before the first few notes were completed he was interrupted by Sally dressed in the baggy black suit, boots, and red nose. She stamped around him drowning his solo with ill-tuned blasts on a clarinet. It was a faithful reproduction of the famous Cairolli Brothers act, generously shown them by the son of the famous clown. It was a performance they did well, having played many charity shows, parties, and cabarets. They put in all the tricks to the thorough enjoyment of the crowd and the evening air was filled with the warm sound of laughter and applause.

Jake stood in the shadows watching the performance. He became aware that Mandy had moved up beside him and carefully adopted a studiously expressionless face.

'Dad.'

'Aye?'

'The Fete's going well.'

'Aye.'

'It's as good as anything you'd find in France.'

'I don't reckon much on travelling anyway. There's plenty of books as'll tell you all you want to know.'

She looked up at him with a flash of her cheeky smile. 'You get a nosebleed the moment you go further south than Berkhamsted.'

'I don't need none of your lip, girl.' But their customary badinage was exchanged quietly, without conviction, as if their hearts weren't in it.

'Dad –'

'I know.' It was spoken gently. Sadly.

'I have to go, Dad. David needs me . . .'

'Aye. He's your husband.'

'And you?'

He breathed in, squared his shoulders, and looked determinedly towards Peter and Sally. 'Did I ever say I needed you?' His voice was gruff, belligerent, arrogant. 'Did I ever say I needed anybody? I can look after myself. Your place is alongside your man. After all, it's not as if it'll be forever, is it?' It had not come out quite as he'd intended but it was a good effort for all that. She stood silent. So silent that he nearly spoiled the whole effect by repeating, 'Is it?'

Mandy rested a hand on his arm. 'No, Dad,' she promised quietly.

He nodded. 'Very well then. I don't know what you're fussing about. Cut along and let me enjoy this.'

He stared fixedly at Clown and Auguste. Mandy felt proud of him, sad for him, and deeply happy that such an understanding could exist between father and daughter. Only after she had gone did he turn his head and look after her. He allowed himself the luxury of a tear.

Extraordinarily, while the comedy act was in progress, a not dissimilar scene was being played out on the other side of the Green. Julien saw Mrs Simpkins enjoying the charade and joined her. 'I have much laughter in me tonight.'

'My French is better than your English,' she commented.

'I remember you learned more quickly than I did.'

'And forgot more slowly.' She had not meant to say that. Or anything like it. The words had escaped, unprompted, unthought.

'I'm sorry,' he said.

She turned and looked at him. 'It was a full year before I really believed I wouldn't hear from you.'

'What can I say?'

There was nothing he could say. She wondered why they were even discussing it and marvelled that she'd admitted her disappointment so readily.

'I meant everything I said,' he tried to assure her. 'At the time, I meant it.'

'The memory is faded, gone, forgotten.'

'Not forgotten.'

'Yes, Julien, utterly forgotten. And your captivating, broken-English, sweet talk can't bring it back. Because if it did, after all these years . . . it wouldn't be fair.'

He could see she meant it. He permitted himself to voice his own thought. 'I wonder where our lives would have led if I had stayed in England after the war.'

'We'll never know.'

Chantale stood nearby, the centre of a small admiring group. Julien's eyes went to her and, as if by telepathy, she turned right round and looked at her father. She sent an unspoken 'All right?' and wasn't sure if she received an acknowledgement.

'*Mrs* Simpkins –?' Julien enquired.

Mrs Simpkins pursed her lips. 'They told me there were other fish in the sea,' she said briefly.

'Were you happy?'

'For a while, yes.'

'Marguerite . . .' he began.

She shook her head firmly. 'No, Julien.'

'If I were to come back to England?'

'I don't think it would be sensible, or practical, or realistic –'

'When was it ever sensible, or practical, or realistic to need somebody?'

'– or even a particularly good idea.'

She had spoken more quickly than her mind had formed the words. She had listened to herself turning him down. She was older now, clearer headed. She could feel him staring at her and so she concentrated on the circus performance taking place in front of them. Her eyes did not take anything in. Was this the reason he had returned to Shillingbury; was *she* the reason? It would be too easy to believe him, too easy to be hurt again.

Julien was a self-confessed playboy. He had a tried and trusted way of sweeping aside the creeping insecurities – it was the smothering of them with loud bravado. One day it would fail to work, he knew that all too well. But, that night, he would have to make it work for him just once more.

The clown act was reaching the final slapstick sequence and suddenly he was in the middle of it. He joined in with great boisterousness, extravagant *joie de vivre,* infectious laughter, determined to shut away unhappiness for a few hours longer. With an extravagant pantomime gesture Sally held a white-gloved hand towards him; he caught the cue and, bowing deeply, removed the glove and kissed her hand. She affected great pleasure and promptly offered her other gloved hand. He bowed again and tried to remove the glove, but this one was several yards long and, by the time her hand was free, she was well out of range of any kiss. The crowd applauded, Chantale watched her father, happily unaware that anything could be amiss.

Then the bucket routine. Sally balanced a water bucket on a pole high above her head and trod a precarious path towards her husband and Julien. At the last moment she faked a trip and the bucket upturned, only to spill nothing damper than multi-coloured confetti. Then Peter found a similar bucket and began to approach with equal caution. This time Julien stood confidently. Again the trip; but now it was real water, cascades of it, all over the Frenchman. The crowd loved it. Julien shouted with surprise and laughter. Sally mimed great concern, and proffered a hopelessly inadequate pocket handkerchief.

Mrs Simpkins found herself running. She would never know the motivation. She made vain attempts to mop away at least some of the water. 'You're absolutely drenched!'

'Do not worry,' he said. 'I carry always a spare pair of trousers in case I wet myself.'

'You really are going to have to brush up your English.' She led him away from the scene and out of the limelight. Behind them Clown and Auguste took several calls. 'I think it would be absolute madness for you to think about returning to England,' she told him. 'But I would quite like to come to France . . . just to visit, mind.'

Peter crossed to Chantale, she laughed at him and quite unaffectedly stuck her arm through his. Sally noticed it and, behind the ludicrously comic make-up, decided this was the moment to play her ace. With a Marcel Marceau-type mime she took the centre of the Green and held her arms wide apart, beckoning into the light fifty members of the Shillingbury Boys Choir. They assembled before her, smart cassocks and cottas, combed hair, innocent, pure. She turned towards her husband, gave an exaggerated bow, then faced the young choristers. Arms raised, a chord from Reggie, and Sally began to conduct.

She had taught them Peter's jingle. The soprano voices floated through the night air. It was the right sound. There was no question about it. It was indisputably the right sound, the sound which had evaded Peter, the sound which would sweep any client clean off his feet, the sound which could produce a small fortune. Peter slowly slipped away from Chantale's arm and moved towards Sally.

Chantale stood alone. She moved towards her father but stopped when she saw that Mrs Simpkins had taken his arm. On her other side Jake had an arm around Mandy's shoulder. She gave a slight shrug. What did a girl do? She remembered the 'French Baker' and thought she might fancy a pastry after all. Why not? To his unconcealed delight she crossed to him.

Horrible Humphrey sat in the shadows on the very edge of the Green. Not far away from him his attention was caught by an enormously seductive French poodle. She seemed quite favourably disposed – he thought he might even get lucky.

CHAPTER FOURTEEN

ON THE first Sunday in August the Reverend Arthur Norris listened to the singing during the Harvest Thanksgiving service and wondered whether the organ was sounding quite as it should. His church was spectacularly decorated by the good people of Shillingbury who had brought fine examples of fruit, vegetables, cereals and flowers; now they stood before him, joyous voices raised in song, praising the Lord. Normally it was an annual occasion which gave him real pleasure but that morning the vicar was not feeling himself. He could not dispel shafts of cynicism which invaded his thoughts and spoiled his enjoyment.

Whereas many English customs dated back six hundred years and more, he had been amazed to discover one day that the Harvest Thanksgiving Festival, which he had always assumed to be as old as the harvest itself, was not thought of until Victorian times. It seemed odd to him that farmers had sown and reaped through the centuries without an offering of thanks to God until, in 1843, the vicar of a church in a Cornish village, one Robert Hawker, began the festival. Norris felt that the August date was too early and the prayers spoken were more in the nature of advance insurance against last-minute catastrophe than genuine gratitude. The more realistic festival of Michaelmas coincided with the *end* of harvesting and would be an opportune moment, but by then countryfolk were busy selling their produce at fairs and markets without even a passing thought for the deity. It occurred to him, as he looked down on his parishioners, that an inordinate number had brought with them to church a sizeable collection of shopping baskets and, even as they sang, eyes were scanning the generous display around the altar.

Worst of all, St George's Church was far from full. There had been only two occasions during the year when every pew had been occupied; one was when The Close Encounters gave their concert, and the other had been the previous week when Mandy married David the vet. Of course there was nothing more appealing than a village wedding, and a good-looking young man marrying an

190

attractive local girl was a joyful occasion of warm wishes coupled with romantic nostalgia. Mandy and her new husband had sailed for Australia and Jake had journeyed with them to Southampton to see his daughter off. Now he carried with him the all-too-fresh memory of a ship leaving harbour and taking with it a part of his heart. He'd returned alone to the farmhouse and now he wandered lost among the suddenly meaningless treasures of a lifetime, manfully trying to establish a new pattern.

Norris remustered his meandering thoughts. There was positively something wrong with the organ. When Frank Bellows had arrived first thing he had been unable to coax a note out of the instrument for a full half-hour, and had loudly opined that Farmer Hudson had been up to his tricks again. It was true that the two organists, who took turn and turn about playing for Sunday service, jealously guarded the special occasions of Christmas, Easter, Harvest Thanksgiving, and the like. Occasionally the calendar would favour one more than the other and, when Farmer Hudson became the loser, a particularly mean streak would overcome him whereupon he was not beyond removing a vital part of the organ and taking it home with him. The vicar found himself praying that maybe one of them might change his religion to become a Methodist and play *their* organ on the other side of the village, before he pulled himself together and cancelled the prayer by sending up a brief act of contrition in its wake.

He looked around the fourteenth-century church, which had itself replaced an even earlier Norman church, and wished passionately that more people would share his deep enjoyment of the inspiring history contained within its walls. The mighty timbers, bracing each other in criss-cross fashion inside stone columns, related to the Scandinavian building method adopted in the area. The belfry walls were slitted with embrasures through which bowmen could fire, indicating the border skirmishes which raged around the church, and the east wall was chipped and the main door bullet-scarred from a Civil War attack. His enthusiasm knew no bounds but he had come to recognise and take note of the stiffening smile of a listener when he allowed his outpourings to become boring beyond belief.

Nevertheless, Norris was right in surmising the purpose

of the parishioners' shopping baskets. By four o'clock that afternoon the altar looked like Covent Garden at the end of a day's trading. It was clear that the harvest had not realistically been offered up to God – with shop prices what they were his flock did not mind Him looking at the results of their labours, and even blessing it, but they drew the line at Him *nicking* it. The vicar stood in the middle of heaped-up debris, trying to summon enough energy to tackle the mammoth task of clearing up. He recalled how Jake had once said to him, 'Harvest Festivals are all right in their way, although there's some farmers – wild horses wouldn't drag the name from me – who should be hiding it from God, not taking it to church and *showing* it to Him.'

'Farmer Hudson?' Norris had asked, innocently.

'How did you know?'

'It always is.'

'Now the cereals,' Jake had continued, warming to his theme, 'They're a different matter. Quality! Plain for all to see.'

'Who grew those? Or wouldn't wild horses drag that name from you either?'

'As a matter of fact it was me.'

Norris took hold of himself. He began to wonder if he was sickening for something, the daydreams had crowded in on his mind almost uncertainly throughout the day. He set to work, and ten minutes later he had made some inroads on the vegetable refuse when he saw Cuffy the Tinker enter through the main doors and walk hesitantly towards him. 'Ah, do I see a helper?' he enquired. 'Better yet, do I see a return of the prodigal son?'

'I was just wondering – ' began the tinker. He'd been intending to suggest that he might help the vicar out by taking a widely varied selection of fruit and vegetables off his hands, but Norris spoke again.

'The faithful are departed, Cuffy. We are left with nothing more than over-ripe fruit and rotting cabbage leaves.'

'It'll make good compost,' said Cuffy who had knowledge of such things.

'We did not raise our voices in song to celebrate the completion of a compost heap.' Cuffy became slightly ill at ease when he saw the vicar was so out of humour. 'My flock has loaned us the fruit of their labours but since returned for the more commercial reason of flogging it on the open market in the morning.'

Cuffy looked round quickly. 'Didn't anybody save . . .'

'Yours is over there.'

'Oh. Well –'

'Help yourself,' Norris said. 'Everybody else has.'

Cuffy was distinctly uncomfortable. 'If you don't want it . . .' he tried, knowing that Norris had almost certainly set a basket aside specially, but seeing the vicar didn't rise as usual to his conditional acceptance, he asked tentatively, 'Are you all right, Reverend, Vicar, sir?'

'Perfectly.' The answer was unconvincing. An inner voice warned Cuffy against leaving Norris alone while he was in his present mood so, after a moment, he took the broom, the vicar giving it up without demur, and began to sweep up the rubbish.

'You seem a bit depressed,' he remarked after a while.

'Disillusioned.' Cuffy didn't know the difference between the two words so he continued to sweep in silence. 'They come to church as if it is a duty,' Norris continued, almost to himself. 'Like visiting the sick.'

'Well, you don't come in here expecting a good laugh, do you?'

The vicar pulled a rueful face. 'Perhaps that is where I am at fault.'

'You wouldn't be thinking of putting on a string of comics? Not in church?'

'No, no,' smiled Norris, 'but sometimes I wonder, Cuffy. The world advances but the Church stands still. Take the Harvest Festival, for instance. The time was when a farmer ploughed his field with only the aid of his horse, and six months later harvested the crop by hand. He *needed* God to provide rain to moisten, sunshine to ripen, strength to combat disease. Whereas today the farmer attacks his field with machinery, fertilisers, helicopters with chemical spray, combine harvesters to gather in and parcel up. Who needs God? Yet we come together to praise him as if nothing has changed in a hundred years.'

Cuffy was looking at him in wonderment. 'That's not all play-acting you do in the pulpit, is it?' he enquired shocked.

'Of course not,' Norris replied curtly. 'My belief in God

193

in unshaken.' The tinker continued sweeping, moving a couple of chairs to one side so that he could reach more easily. 'It's the people I begin to doubt. There are Sundays when I look down on a thin sprinkling of worshippers sitting as meek as lambs. And I shout at them – ' The vicar faced out towards the body of the church and raised his voice to a mightly volume: '. . . and the wicked shall perish in the flames of hell . . .' As his bellow echoed round and around, he dropped his voice down to a whisper. 'And I watch them cower in fear. But I'm shouting at the wrong people, do you see? Those who should hear are out of earshot.'

'They'd need to be the other side of Banbury to miss hearing that,' Cuffy assured him.

'Where is Jake?' continued Norris without pause. 'Where are you? Where are those whom the church could help most? Sometimes I look at my half-filled House and pray that He might give some sign.' He heaved a deep sigh. 'What Shillingbury needs is a miracle.'

Cuffy shrugged as if the vicar had suggested nothing that was in the least unreasonable. 'Well, if that's what they need, you give it to them, Reverend, Vicar, sir.'

'What do you mean?'

'You've got everything you need in here to set up a spanking good miracle.'

'Oh, Cuffy!' Norris sounded irritated again. Then, slowly, he relaxed and smiled at the old tramp. 'Thank you for your help,' he said honestly.

Cuffy thought he meant the sweeping. 'I don't seem to have done very much.'

'You have allowed me to blow off steam.'

'Oh,' said Cuffy, understanding. 'Well, everyone's allowed to do that once in a while, Reverend, Vicar, sir. Even Reverend Vicar sirs.'

'You must take no notice of what I've said.'

'That's all right. I've never taken any notice of anything you've said,' Cuffy assured him in a comforting voice. Then he looked at the sizeable heap of rubbish he'd swept together. 'What do I do with this?'

'We sweep it under the carpet, Cuffy,' replied Norris, cynicism returning for a brief moment. 'Something at which the church is most adapt,' he continued uncharacteristically. 'Out of sight, out of mind.'

'It does that with tinkers too,' said Cuffy who normally was not given to philosophising. 'In winter, when the nights grow cold, it thinks we hibernate into our old buses and don't come out again till spring.' He handed the broom back to the vicar. 'I'll take my little box of vegetables if that's all right with you.'

The weather continued fine and warm well into October. Crops were gathered, stubble burned, fields ploughed – it had been a good season. Perhaps a drop more rain would have filled out the fruit and vegetables but then the farmers would have been given nothing to complain about, a situation unheard of in the history of agriculture. Suddenly, one night, there was an air frost and it was as if an unearthly paintbrush had painted great sweeps of golden red across the woodlands and hedgerows. The English autumn entered with awe-inspiring magnificence, covering endless miles in breathtaking colours as countless millions of leaves blazed briefly before falling silently to the ground.

In his bus Cuffy found himself thinking of the harder night frosts to come, the long months of damp cold, short days, and interminable nights. He worried, not for himself but for Yorky; since Bernard had died he had become aware of the vulnerability of friends and for the first time in his life he feared loneliness.

Not far away similar thoughts were besetting Jake. Mercifully, the rigours of harvesting had driven most of his misery to the back of his mind but when the clocks went back he was less able to fend off unwelcome memories. It was all too easy to look back on the good times, winter evenings would provide too many hours for thinking . . . and comparing.

He had lit a fire in the fine old living-room fireplace on the evening of the first frost. Sam and Harvey had looked in for a nightcap. Now he knelt to sweep together the ash and dead embers, leaving the grate clean as Martha had once and then Mandy after her. He carried the dustpan out of the room but passing the window he saw Cuffy outside in the yard. He opened it and called out, 'What are you doing?'

'Good morning, Mr Jake. I was just looking.'

'What at?'

'Well, nothing really. I can't say I was looking at anything in particular.'

'Then go away. It's Sunday morning.' Jake closed the window and left the house to empty the ashes on a patch of ground he was attempting to dry out. When he returned through the yard the tinker was standing by the barn.

'I was just noticing,' said Cuffy, 'as I was standing here looking at everything in general, you know, that you can hear them singing in the church.'

'That's the morning service you can hear going on,' commented the farmer gruffly. He went back inside the house and, to his surprised annoyance, found that the tinker followed him.

'It must be a comfort to you now that Mandy's gone,' commented Cuffy. 'It's a long way, Australia.' He watched Jake working for a few moments then adopted a carefully contrived casual tone of voice. 'I dare say you must be a bit lonely here, all by yourself. With her gone . . . to Australia.' Jake continued working in silence and Cuffy moved to look out of the window. 'I could not help observing, as I stood in the yard looking at nothing in particular, how much space there is out there.' Behind him Jake looked up with sudden suspicion but the tinker continued along the line he'd worked out. 'Room enough for a caravan, I shouldn't wonder.'

'I shouldn't wonder either, if I were you,' Jake advised him. 'If it's your bus you're hinting at I shouldn't bother even thinking about it.'

Cuffy turned from the window and abandoned all pretence of subtlety. 'It's just that if you was missing the company I wouldn't mind helping you out.'

'I'm not missing anything,' Jake assured him. 'And if I was, it doesn't mean I'd want a dirty old tinker's bus parked in my backyard.'

Cuffy was stung into mild belligerence. 'And I'm not lonely either. I'm as happy as a sandboy up on top of my hill and don't you be thinking anything different.'

'Then get back up there, Cuffy, and leave me to do my housework.'

The tinker watched him a moment longer before commenting sarcastically, 'A woman's work is never done.' Then, on a more helpful note, 'You wouldn't like me to join you in a cup of tea, would you?' Jake made it amply clear that no such thought had been uppermost in his mind and Cuffy left, shutting the door firmly behind him. A small shower of soot fell from the chimney into the clean grate.

'Now look what you've done,' Jake shouted after him.

In Rose Cottage Peter was writing a score. Sally sat nearby polishing horse brasses. It was late that Sunday night but neither of them saw anything odd in working at such an hour. Peter's life in show-business had accustomed him to working while others relaxed, and sleeping until the audience was ready to relax again; if anything, his hours had become more normal since he gave up performing and took to writing full time. For her part, Sally was used to fitting in with the exigencies of a free-lance career – she was calmer than he when work was slack, and quietly contented when the rush was on. She understood his world; more important, she understood him. She was sympathetic to the insecurities which so often went hand in hand with creativity. The reaction throughout the industry to his jingle was typically instantaneous; his period in the doldrums was forgotten overnight and success brought a flood of commissions. The 'simple sound' was the 'in thing' and would enjoy a season of remunerative popularity until others jumped on the bandwagon and caused the fashion to die from overkill. Meanwhile its originator would benefit most and, for a while at least, Peter was fashionable. At no time would either of them make comment on the fact that it was Sally who actually inspired it.

She watched him writing and marvelled again at his ability to transfer the sounds in his brain to scorepaper via a stubby pencil. Certainly the sound of boy sopranos had been her idea, but his delicate orchestration which made use of recorders, an instrument rarely used professionally, leant a special quality which had epitomised the 'country feeling' the client was seeking. It had not been a good summer so far as they were concerned, either for work or relationship, but they had survived it and their love for each other was that much stronger as a result.

In Jake's kitchen the farmer was pouring hot milk from

a saucepan into a glass, stirring the chocolate powder as he did so. The wind was getting up outside and he paused to listen, mentally checking that nothing had been left insecure in the yard. He washed and put away the saucepan, picked up the glass together with a couple of biscuits, and left the room, switching off the light as he went. At the foot of the stairs he became sharply aware of each and every one of a thousand noises. A man alone, he heard things which with company would have remained as background. A creak, a distant rumble, the mournful note of rising wind – each took on a significance which, because so many were unidentifiable, became singularly disquieting. Quite near him there came a sudden loud slam causing a rush of ice-cold adrenalin to spread through his body. He put the glass down on the hall table and walked firmly into the living-room. Immediately the calming flood of relief as he saw the window was open and moving with the wind. He closed it, and was about to leave, when something made him look at the fireplace. It had been nearly out when he'd left ten minutes earlier but now the flames had re-gathered and flickered strangely as if being blown by a draught from one side. Jake was nervous – there was no other word for it. Perhaps if he had not been on his own it would never have occurred to him that he was in the presence of a manifestation. There was no apparent reason why the flames should react in quite the way they were doing and, anyway, he'd lived in the house all his life without seeing such a sight. He approached the fireplace slowly, cautiously, almost fearfully. Suddenly his nose wrinkled as 'the smell' filled the room. An evil, obnoxious smell. He backed away, very frightened indeed. Then, as suddenly as it had begun, the materialization ended – the flames returned to normal, the smell cleared.

Jake hurried out into the hall where he squared his shoulders as if to dispel any insurgence of cowardice. The wind rose to a new crescendo. He burst into song, his voice uttering a loud, falsely cheerful, tuneless ditty, as he scuttled upstairs. In bed he lay listening to the noises of the farmhouse, eyes wide open, sleep impossible. He did not see the flames rekindle in the fireplace below as an echoing, rushing wind blew around the room. Nor did he see the last flame flicker into extinction but, coincidentally or not, it was at that moment Jake pulled the sheet over his head.

The next morning dawned brightly and daylight thrust aside the mystery of night. Although the air was still, shadows hurried across fields and hills as fast-moving clouds continued to flee before a high altitude wind. Jake had passed a sleepless night and now he hurried across the Green towards Rose Cottage. He was oblivious of time as he hastened up the garden path and pressed the doorbell. Several moments passed before the window above his head opened and a slightly bemused Peter peered down. 'Jake!' he exclaimed in surprise. 'Whatever time is it?'

'A bit early yet,' admitted the farmer, 'but can I have a word with you?'

'What, now?' Peter glanced back into the room at the bedside clock. 'It's only quarter-to-seven.'

'It's urgent.'

'Okay. Hang on a moment.' The window closed and a minute later Peter opened the front door, still tying the sash of his dressing gown. He led the way into the kitchen and, as he followed, Jake's fear began to appear foolish in these everyday surroundings. Nevertheless, it had seemed real enough the previous night. He sat at the kitchen table and watched Peter fill the kettle from the tap. 'My farmhouse is haunted,' he announced.

Peter turned from the sink trying, without success, to subdue a smile of ridicule. 'Haunted? You mean, you've seen something?'

'I didn't exactly *see* anything.'

'But you heard it.'

'I didn't exactly hear it either.' Peter lit the gas with a loud 'pop' and Jake gave a startled leap. 'I wish you wouldn't do that – I'm still a bit jumpy.'

'How did this thing –' Peter searched for the word, '– manifest itself?'

'By means of a musty, malodorous smell.'

'A smell?'

'A smell.'

'You mean a ghost walks around the house letting off smells?'

Jake gave an embarrassed stir. 'Don't mock me, Young

Upstart. It may sound silly now but last night, on the stroke of midnight, my living-room was filled by an all-pervading smell.' His conviction suffered another knock as Sally entered the kitchen, young, fresh from sleep and very real.

'Hullo, Jake,' she greeted him cheerfully. 'You're bright and early this morning. We were talking about you last night.'

'What time, Mrs Higgins?'

'When we were going to bed.'

'Ah!' Jake, grasping at straws, attempted a triumphant look at Peter. 'You see? Telepathy.'

Peter was setting teacups on the table. 'Jake's got something to tell you, Sal.'

'Not if she's going to laugh like you did,' declared the farmer, trying to reassert himself.

'I won't laugh, Jake,' said Sally seriously. 'Why should I?'

'Because – ' Jake began to feel foolish again and looked up at Peter. 'You tell her.'

'He reckons there's a ghost up at the farm.' Sally tried, she really did. She looked directly at Jake, without expression, eyebrows raised in polite enquiry. Then, slowly, a smile broke through.

'There you are. You're laughing. I knew you would.'

'I'm not,' promised Sally, regaining control. 'What did it look like – this ghost?'

Peter was taking milk from the fridge. 'It didn't look like anything,' he said disparagingly. 'Nor did it rattle any chains. It just floated around the room emitting awful smells.' All Sally's resolutions deserted her and she laughed aloud. 'What a very rude ghost!'

'You can laugh, Mrs Higgins,' said Jake, annoyed, 'but it gave me a nasty turn, I can tell you.'

'Of course it did,' replied the girl soberly. 'Darling, we're being very thoughtless.'

'It came through the window with a terrible crash and went straight to the fireplace.'

'It was quite chilly last night,' commented Peter, missing Sally's warning glance. 'Probably wanted to warm its – whatever a ghost warms.'

Jake rose to his feet. 'Are you trying to rile me, Young Upstart?'

'No, of course he's not, Jake,' said Sally soothingly. 'It's just that in the cold light of day these things always sound melodramatic.'

'I didn't know where to turn so I came to where I thought I'd get some good sense,' grumbled the farmer.

'We'll do our best, won't we, darling?' she promised.

'I don't think I know very much about ghosts,' said her husband, who was not at his best before eleven o'clock.

'Would you like some breakfast, Jake?' she enquired.

'I'm not sure I could eat anything,' he sulked.

'Coffee?'

'All right. And perhaps a little porridge.'

'Very well.'

'Followed by bacon and eggs,' Jake suggested.

'Fine.'

'And toast and marmalade to round off,' he finished, mollified.

Sally exchanged a private grin with Peter as he abandoned the tea-making and allowed her to set to.

Later that morning the three of them stood in Jake's living-room. None of them knew quite how to tackle the problem. 'What do we do first?' asked the farmer.

'Well –' began Peter uncertainly.

'Well –' echoed Sally when nothing more was forthcoming from her husband.

'Very good,' interrupted Jake grumpily. 'And what do we do after that?'

'We need a moment to think, Jake,' said Peter with slight heat. 'To start with, I suppose we're quite sure it *was* a ghost? I mean, we only have . . .'

'My word for it?' asked Jake dangerously.

'It's not that,' Sally stepped in quickly. 'Peter's only asking if you could possibly be mistaken. After all, the window blew open, the fire flickered, and there was a smell.'

'If you don't believe me come out with it and say so.'

It was going to prove extremely difficult to make any kind of progress while Jake was so sensitive. Peter thought he might walk round to the vicarage and see Norris; church records often contained evidence of previously unexplained mysteries while not, of course, admitting there could be any psychical connection. This led Sally to think of the public library and she promised to pay a visit to the less populated bookshelves in the reference section and search through the history of Shillingbury for any mention of hauntings.

'My farm is in the history books,' declared Jake suddenly.

'Well, that's relevant. Why didn't you say so before?'

'I only just thought of it. Parts of the farm date back to the fifteenth century. That fireplace in particular. And the south barn is very old; it's been rebuilt several times but there's supposed to be some sort of cellar under the original, though we've never been able to find it.'

'It's worth taking a look,' said Peter.

'Mandy was in there just before she left. Looking out some books her grandfather had left her.'

Sally said, 'Could she have disturbed something? Something supernatural?' Peter stared at her, amazed. It was as if the atmosphere of the room, and the talk of hauntings, had got through to her.

Jake replied simply, 'I don't know. Maybe she did at that.' It seemed as if the ghost hunt had begun.

When Peter called on Norris, the vicar proved more than willing to discuss the history of his parish. The information about the early years of St George's Church had turned out to be fairly sketchy because the building had been ransacked several times after it had been built in 1392. It had been a rough area living in quarrelsome times. Consecrated originally as a Catholic church, it had managed to survive the hazards of a religious obstacle course right up to the Reformation. Henry the Eighth had been keen to change several aspects of Catholic teachings, to suit his own sexual pursuits, as was generally known, and the church had become involved. In fact, there was a great deal of history contained within the boundaries of Shillingbury. Peter told the vicar that parts of Jake's farm dated back to the fifteenth century. 'So he does have a link with the church, if only in longevity,' smiled Norris. 'Strange that a man like him will fall for things that go bump in the night whilst stolidly resisting beliefs of a more redemptive nature.'

'Well, thanks for giving me your time,' said Peter as he rose to leave.'

'I'm afraid to little avail. If you're after a sort of historical gossip column there's nobody better than Ma

Cronin to supply that. She's a positive mine of supernatural whimsies.' Privately Norris thought that Jake was probably suffering from a bad attack of loneliness. It was something he saw all around him – loneliness was practically an epidemic in the village, reaching a point where old people began talking to themselves. He'd seen a man in the supermarket only the day before having a terrible argument with his trolley. 'I must say,' he commented aloud, 'I wouldn't like to live at Jake's farm by myself.'

'I wouldn't like to live anywhere by myself,' Peter agreed.

'But if you had to?'

'I'd probably invent myself a friendly ghost.'

Back at the farm Cuffy was loading manure onto a cart from the large heap behind the stables, and wondering as he worked why animals could not do what they have to do a little nearer to where it was going to be needed. He looked up and saw the farmer approaching him, unusually subdued, strangely diffident. 'I – er . . ' Jake spoke hesitantly. 'I hope you weren't offended yesterday when I sent you away.'

'Me? Offended?' The tinker shook his head. 'I been told to go away all my life. It's only when they say "Don't come back" that I get upset.'

'What exactly did you have in mind?' asked Jake. 'I mean about the yard?'

'Didn't have anything in mind. Not really. Just that the evenings are getting darker, and longer. And that you were here all alone.'

'So you thought you'd move into the farm with me.'

'Not personally.' Cuffy had never slept inside and certainly didn't want to try it. He couldn't imagine how it was possible to hear all the sounds of the night from inside brick walls. He'd reckoned instead on parking his bus in the yard where it was nice and sheltered, and where Yorky could be put in a stable when the weather became bad. 'A horse gets awful rheumaticky up that hill,' he explained to Jake.

'The wheels of your bus are all to pot,' objected Jake. 'You'd tear the bottom off trying to move it.'

'I wouldn't want to move without my bus,' said Cuffy obstinately.

Jake stuck his hands in his pockets and remarked

over-casually, 'Maybe it's not impossible at that. We'll have to chat about it.'

Cuffy paused in his labours and leaned on his fork. 'Well now,' he mused, 'that gives me reason to think, that does,'

'What about?'

Cuffy wasn't sure 'what about' but his sharp survival instincts prompted him to suspect a sudden change of attitude by someone like Jake. 'Me not having any great brainpower – you've often said that, haven't you, Mr Jake, about me being a bit slow when it comes to thinking. But when I remembers that yesterday you said you didn't want any dirty old tinker's bus messing up your backyard and here you are today . . . I got to have a *think* about that.'

'It came as a bit of a surprise, that's all,' shrugged Jake. 'You don't make an instant decision about someone moving in to live alongside of you.'

The tinker narrowed his eyes. 'Nothing happened to sort of hurry it up, like?'

'Look,' flashed Jake with a return of his old spirit, 'do you want to come on the farm or not?'

'I'll think about it.' The farmer hadn't expected any of this. He'd thought Cuffy would be a pushover but, now that there seemed some uncertainty on the tinker's part, he realised it was getting dark and another night was approaching. 'How long have I got?' he heard Cuffy ask. 'I mean, when would you want me to move in?'

'Tonight?' suggested Jake.

CHAPTER FIFTEEN

It was the longest evening Peter had ever known.

The card game had been bad enough. They'd sat in front of the fireplace for what seemed an eternity mindlessly laying down one card after another and listening to the periodic shout from Cuffy. 'Snap!' As he gathered up the heap and added them to those in his hand the tinker looked triumphantly at Peter, Sally, and Jake. 'I'm getting good at this game, aren't I? You didn't none of you think I'd be as good as I am.'

'No, Cuffy,' agreed Sally dully.

'I seen pictures of people playing cards but I've never done it myself. Not till tonight. I don't know why they make it look so difficult.'

'There are other games, slightly more complicated than this one,' said Peter, thinking something as involved even as Beat Your Neighbour Out of Doors would douse Cuffy's boastfulness.

'Ah yes, I dare say there are. Those would be the games you dress up for; ladies in long dresses and all that. Shall we play another round?'

'Must we?' asked Jake.

Sally asked quickly, 'What do you do in the bus, Cuffy? When you're on your own?'

What did he do? The tinker had never thought about what he did. One way or another the night would pass without his ever making a conscious effort to do anything. He liked to sit in the doorway and look out. Not being able to read or write, he'd mainly look. Then, of course, there was an awful lot to see, folk didn't realise how much. If people spent more time looking and thinking . . . and less time rushing off and *doing,* they wouldn't make so many mistakes. He could see fifty or sixty miles from the top of his hill, across fields and meadows where his imagination pictured him sowing and harvesting . . . On a summer's night he'd lie back in the grass looking up at the stars for hours on end. Someone had explained the speed of light to him once, and told him about stars and galaxies being 'light years' away, but his mind would not take it in. It meant that the light he was looking at had started its journey before Shillingbury existed . . . no, his thought process did not have the capacity to cope. He became aware of the other three watching him. 'Nothing much,' he answered Sally at last.

Peter glanced at the fire. 'Well, it's half past ten and not a whiff of our smelly friend.'

'It was there last night,' declared Jake, immediately becoming defensive. 'I know you don't believe me but I tell you it was there.'

'I'm not saying I don't believe you,' said Peter.

'Don't let's have another argument,' Sally admonished.

'There's no saying it'll turn up tonight,' warned Jake.

'Or ever again.'

'Pete!'

Cuffy half listened to the conversation going back and forth. Other people often spoke in his company about things on which he had no knowledge, and he was used to allowing it to float over him. Jake was saying, 'Maybe card games aren't the right thing for it. A seance might be more the thing.'

The words caused Cuffy to look up sharply. 'Just a minute. What's going on? Seance?' He sounded nervous. 'What was there last night?'

Sally told him, 'Jake thinks there's a ghost haunts the farm.'

Cuffy was frightened of ghosts. Very frightened. Ghosts only came into houses, and he felt safer out in the open air: he couldn't abide closed-in places. 'A ghost?' he queried. 'Nobody said anything about a ghost.' He turned accusingly to Jake. 'You never said anything about a ghost.'

'It slipped my mind.'

'When you told me I could come and stay it was because you were frightened.'

The farmer swung round on him. 'I'm not frightened. Me? Frightened? Catch me being frightened.'

'It's nothing to be ashamed of,' Sally said, trying to pacify him. 'I think it would be a good idea for Cuffy to move in. Keep you company.'

Jake gave a half nod of acquiescence but the expression on the tinker's face clearly showed that he thought it was a terrible idea. He wasn't sharing a bed with sorcerers, witches, black magic, and mumbo-jumbo. 'I'm going home,' he announced.

Sally suggested they should all go home. It was getting late, and Peter was writing against a deadline. Jake looked haplessly at the deserters and tried a last tack. 'What about one more hand? For Cuffy here?' he tried weakly.

Cuffy picked up the pack. 'You never said about a ghost,' he muttered to Jake.

They didn't notice it at first but as they laid the cards, the fire began to flicker as it had the night before. The flames played a dancing game of their own and the sound of wind crept around the chimney.

'Snap!' called Peter dutifully.

'That wasn't fair,' cried Cuffy. 'I wasn't watching proper. He's put me off now, I can't concentrate.' The hand was played in silence. The wind rose and the flames cowered in fear.

'Snap!' called Jake. Cuffy scowled ill-humouredly. He was not from the playing fields of Eton.

'Wind's getting up,' observed Peter.

Suddenly a startled shout from Cuffy. 'Look at the fire!' The instant he uttered his warning the flames returned to normality.

'What's wrong with it,' from Peter.

'I thought I saw something.' The voice uncertain.

'What?' from Sally.

Jake asked, as if sensing an ally, 'Did the flames flicker? Like they were being blown from one side?'

'I'm not sure. Maybe I imagined it.'

'It were how it started last night.'

'It's burning quite normally now,' Peter said practically.

'Then,' said Jake, 'there was this terrible smell.'

Cuffy left the card table and stooped in front of the fire. He advanced his face towards the chimney and gave an exploratory sniff. Jake joined him. 'Anything?' The tinker looked at him, puckered up his face and sneezed violently.

'Soot!' he explained sheepishly.

'Here, let me have a go.' Jake directed his nostrils towards the fireplace and sniffed deeply several times. He frowned. There was a positive odour, recognisable, but different from the night before. He sniffed again before turning slowly to look at the tinker. 'Would you mind moving back a bit? You're confusing things.'

Cuffy returned to the others, offended. 'He never said

anything about a haunting.'

'I know, Cuffy,' agreed Peter. 'You already said that.'

It was getting late, the evening had been far from entertaining. Sally said. 'I really think we should be getting home.'

Cuffy commented, 'Ma Cronin says she hears voices regularly coming up through the floor of her cottage.'

Peter nodded agreement. 'The vicar mentioned her. He told me she spends her days dabbling in the occult, trying to contact her dear departed husband.'

Jake gave up attempting to track down the mysterious smell. Maybe he had imagined it because, with the others present, the room didn't even *feel* strange. Anyway, no self-respecting spectre would haunt a party playing 'Snap', for heaven's sake. It was probably best if they called it a day.

Sally left the room to collect her coat from the bedroom and, walking upstairs, she became aware of the wind. It howled around the farmhouse and among the outbuildings with a series of moans, which rose and fell as blustery squalls buffeted into corners. Peter's duffle coat lay on the bed beside hers. She tidied her hair in the mirror. Something moved in a dark area of the reflected background causing her to spin round with a sudden contraction of the stomach. It had been a trick of the glass, but her heart beat a little faster and she felt for Jake as she realised how easily the imagination plays tricks. Somewhere, very near, there came a creak. Again the chill of fear. Nothing. She began to whistle a jaunty tune as she slipped on her coat, collected Peter's, and hurried out of the room. The others waited in the hall below. 'You'll be all right up that hill, all by yourself?' Jake was asking Cuffy.

'I'll be a sight less frightened than I am down here.'

The guests made their goodnights and departed, leaving the farmer alone. He closed the front door, conscious of the empty house around him. He collected a tray of coffee cups from the living-room, washed them up in the kitchen, tidying everything away. Back in the living-room, he collected together the playing cards and was folding the table when his eyes jerked to the fireplace.

In a howling black tumult, echoing and re-echoing outside, the wind had risen as if it were trying to force a way into the room with him. The flames flickered, ducking and weaving in a dance of death, the draught threatening them with extinction. Above the roaring gale he could hear an added sound of rushing air. With a crash the window behind him flew open and the curtains billowed into the room, reaching for him, as the wind screamed out its success. He hurried over and fastened it closed. Terrified now, he turned back towards the fireplace. It was out – just a wisp of smoke remained.

There came a sudden lull. An unnatural stillness. With it, the 'smell' returned. Jake wrinkled his nose in disgust. Finally, with a building crescendo, the booming, rushing, echoing wind noise, and behind it, indistinct but indisputable, the sound of an organ.

Enough was enough. Jake rushed away, through the hall, a glance up the stairs . . . but no. Rather, he grabbed a torch, hurried through the kitchen and out of the back door. The wind tore at hair and clothing as he ran across the yard and into the barn. If the pigs and cows were surprised to see him they gave no sign. He pulled the door shut behind him, secured it, fashioned a bed from bales of straw, and settled down alongside his animals, grateful for their company.

Early next morning Cuffy arrived at the farm to continue clearing away the heaped collection of stable refuse and fresh manure. He had it in mind to put in a good spell of work during the morning in order to leave the afternoon clear for a visit to Banley market. There were good bargains available, more often than not, when the stallholders were packing up for the day. By good bargains Cuffy meant that mostly they weren't too keen on carting fresh foodstuffs and perishables away with them and he was willing to take any leftovers off their hands if it would help them.

He peered in through the kitchen window but seeing no sign of Jake proceeded to the barn, one end of which was given over to the storage of miscellaneous tools of the type Cuffy used – fork, spade, shovel. He collected those he needed for his work but as he turned his eye lit upon the farmer's deserted bed space, with the torch, jacket, and other personal belongings lying in the straw. There was a step behind him and Jake stood there. 'What happened?' Cuffy asked.

'What happened?'

The tinker nodded towards the bed. 'Something must have happened.'

'Immediately you left,' nodded Jake. 'The very moment. As if it had been waiting.'

Cuffy was immensely relieved to have missed it. Relief brought courage – 'If only we'd stayed longer!'

'No good,' said Jake dramatically. 'Whatever it was . . . biding its time . . . until I was alone.'

'Spooky.'

'It was the same as before. The wind, a crash as the window blew open, the flickering flames, the all-enveloping smell. Only this time there was something more.'

'What?'

'An organ.'

'An organ?' repeated Cuffy. 'A church organ?'

'Great majestic chords.' The farmer spread his hands to illustrate the majesty of sound. 'Echoing. Now near, now distant.'

'If only I'd been there!'

'Why do you keep saying that? The moment you heard there was a ghost you couldn't wait to beat it back to your bus.'

Cuffy recalled that it hadn't seemed so frightening once he was out in the fresh air, but he could certainly understand how Jake would prefer to spend the night with his animals than sleep alone in the confines of a haunted house. 'Were they disturbed?' he asked.

'Only by me.'

'Sometimes animals sense the supernatural quicker than what we do.'

'Not stupid ones like I've got.' Cuffy had wondered whether the farmer was putting it on. He'd never known him be frightened of anything before but it was plain to see that something was worrying him. He commented that Jake couldn't possibly go away and leave the farm to look after itself. 'Can't I?' said the farmer grimly. 'You just watch me! I'm not sleeping in that house again.'

In Rose Cottage Cuffy had a partner who equally wondered whether Jake was playing some mystical game.

Peter was trying to guide his wife towards the path of common sense, and he was becoming irritated by her sudden obsession with the supernatural.

'Somebody's got to help him,' declared Sally.

'Okay, find him an exorcist. Try the Yellow Pages,' said Peter shortly. 'Why us?'

'Because there's no one else.'

He stopped his work and stood over her with an exaggerated air of patience. 'Look, Sal. Let's start off with the premise that there is not a ghost.'

She flashed back at him. 'I've got a better idea. Let's start off with the premise that there *is* a manifestation of some sort.'

He was surprised by her fiery response. 'Okay. He's experiencing *something*. But, because there is no immediate rational explanation, he's allowed his imagination to run away with him.'

She pulled him down onto the settee beside her. 'Listen to this.' She thumbed through the pages of a reference book from the library until she found a marked passage. ' "The reported incidences of manifestation by smell increased considerably during the latter part of the nineteenth century" ,' she read. ' "A country house in Sussex was well known for an evil odour which became apparent at midnight whenever the moon was full." ' He started a sigh but she put a hand over his mouth and continued reading: ' "The house stood on a site once occupied by the hangman's gibbet, and the sudden smell was accompanied on occasions by the sound of the villain's last strangled gasp." '

'Undoubtedly, the gentleman would have received a very considerable fright.'

Sally slammed shut the book. 'You don't want to know, do you?'

'It's claptrap, Sal. Jake's having us on.'

'He's not. I learned a great deal in the library. It's enormously interesting.'

'You're surely not going to fall for all that cant, are you?' He took the book from her and found the passage she'd quoted, and adopted the most scornful tone. ' "Latter part of the nineteenth century . . . country house in Sussex . . . at midnight when the moon is full . . ." Cliche-ridden rubbish. They never write, "At

211

four-thirty on the sixth of October in the semi-detached number four, Cheyne Walk, in the middle of the rush hour, a comic figure in a false moustache did a great impression of Groucho Marx." '

Sally was already reaching for a second book and flicking through the pages. 'All right, then. How about this?' She found the place. ' "There was the story of a poltergeist in Streatham . . ." '

'Oh come on, Sal!' interrupted Peter impatiently.

'You can be wrong, you know,' exclaimed Sally who was in full cry now. She picked up a third book – her trump card. 'In a chapter on Priestholes. "During the reign of Henry the Eighth many of the faithful built concealed priestholes in their homes. Some of these constructions were cunning in the extreme and a few exist to this day." Jake said his farm dated back to the sixteenth century, and the living-room fireplace is a significant feature. Because here –' Sally reached for a fourth book, '– are listed towns and villages with meritorious monuments . . . and Shillingbury is mentioned! Peter, you can't just ignore it.'

He shook his head in wonderment. 'You're really into this, aren't you?'

She rose and crossed the room away from him, a trick she used when he annoyed her. 'I'm interested.'

'Quite a little researcher,' continued Peter unwisely. 'Four books and you're convinced.'

Sally swung round, eyes glinting. 'Four books and I'd like to learn more about it. I don't believe Jake's the kind of man who frightens easily, and I'd like to see for myself what he saw last night.'

'Smelt,' he corrected.

'Smelt then. If you don't want to come then stay at home, although I can't see how you can be so pompous if you don't at least investigate the facts.'

'I'm not being pompous,' he objected. 'I'm just being practical.'

'What do you suggest then?' It was a challenge.

'To start with, has anybody thought of taking that fireplace to pieces?'

She raised her arms and appealed to heaven for patience. Like he'd gone mad. 'It's a *priceless relic!*'

'All the more reason,' he said calmly.

There was a pause between them. Then Sally indulged in another of her habits – she grinned at him, suddenly and unpredictably. 'So at least you're coming with me.'

He smiled back, relieved that the tension was broken. 'I'm not going to be left alone in Rose Cottage. I might start talking to myself.'

Jake was not in the least happy about the young couple messing about in his living-room. He wasn't at all sure they had any regard for genuine antiques and in particular feared the do-it-yourself clumsiness of Peter. However, they were his only friends, it seemed. There had been a significant lack of interest from Harvey, Sam or Reggie, indeed his entire world seemed to have turned topsy-turvy since Mandy had left. So he went about his business on the farm and left them to it. If they managed to solve the mystery his life would be a sight more comfortable than it was at present.

Sally carefully removed the ornaments and photographs and laid a dust-sheet over each piece of furniture. She covered the floor with newspapers, particularly around the fireplace. Both wore their oldest clothes and Sally had tied a scarf around her hair. Peter was standing in the fireplace examining the chimney. He found he was able to stand upright, so that his legs were visible up to the waist while the upper half of his body was hidden in the surprisingly large chimney. The heat loss must have been tremendous. He experienced a distinctly weird feeling; not fear, but . . . awe. The workmanship was extraordinary. Even through several thick layers of soot it was possible to admire the perfection of building, and be entirely amazed by the sheer age of the construction.

Sally experienced much the same feeling as she stood close to the hearth surround examining the incredibly beautiful woodwork.

When Peter spoke to her his voice took on an inhuman quality, seeming first to echo but immediately becoming deadened by the black space surrounding him. 'I'll tell you something.'

'What?'

'I hate to admit it,' his invisible voice continued. 'But there *is* a smell. Faint, but distinctive.'

213

'May I have a look?'

'Go ahead.' His knees bent and he carefully lowered himself to a stoop in order to climb from the huge grate into the room. He stepped aside and Sally ducked into the fireplace. She straightened up until she too could be seen only from the waist downwards. 'Spooky, isn't it?' Her voice echoed momentarily, then became at once muffled.

'We're not using words like that. Remember?' he admonished.

'Are we right to meddle with the supernatural?' her voice asked, sounding strangely unlike her.

Peter walked across the room to look more closely at the catch on the window. 'Nobody has yet shown me evidence of anything supernatural,' he said pompously, raising his voice, now his back was to her. 'All I've been told is that there's a nasty smell and the wind blew out the fire.' But precisely during that comment, Sally had disappeared. The lower half of her body just went clean up the chimney. He turned back from the window and gave a start as he stared into the empty fireplace. 'Sal – Sally? Come on . . don't play silly games . . . Sally!!' He hurried back across the room, peered into the grate, and partially up the chimney. He stepped back a couple of paces, uncertain. Nervous.

Then he panicked. 'JAKE!' he shouted. And rushed from the room.

Cuffy was returning his tools to the barn when Peter hurtled in. 'Jake –' he called. Then, seeing the tinker, 'Oh, Cuffy. Sally – my wife. She's disappeared.'

'Disappeared?' echoed the tinker, a sudden fear flooding his body.

'Gone.'

'Gone?'

'She just went clean up the chimney.'

'Clean up the chimney?'

'Don't repeat everything I say. Get Jake.'

Cuffy sprang into action; but it was meaningless action. He simply ran about like a headless chicken. 'What can Mr Jake do?'

'I don't know. Just get him.'

'What we need is a chimney sweep,' advised the tinker thoughtlessly.

'GET JAKE!' shouted Peter. As he turned to run from

the barn he stopped dead in his tracks as there came a stifled sound – it was a chuckle. It was Sally. The smothered echoing laugh came from . . everywhere . . . The two men looked around wildly. Then, with quick anger, Peter called, 'Sally . . .!' before he strode purposefully from the barn and back into the farmhouse.

He marched quickly and crossly into the living-room and shouted firmly up the chimney. 'Sally . . .!'

Her legs slowly reappeared. Her knees bent, and his wife stooped out of the chimney. Her face smudged with soot, brown eyes over a sheepish grin. 'I'm here,' she said needlessly.

'That was the stupidest damn thing you ever did.'

'Well, you *are* pompous,' she said, smilingly defensive. 'I couldn't resist it.'

'You frightened the living daylights out of me,' he admitted. She put her arms round his neck, her kiss transferring a quantity of soot.

'I'm sorry. Really I am.' Her expression belied her words. The trouble was she always looked so devastatingly beautiful when she tried to appear contrite.

'Where were you anyway?' he demanded, softening.

'There's a bar stretches across the chimney. And a stone ledge. I pulled myself up.' She took his hand. 'Come on, I'll show you.'

'Is there room for two?'

'Sort of.'

He grabbed hold of the torch and ducked into the fireplace after her as she reached up into the chimney, grasped the bar, and hauled herself up. When her head was above her hands she swung her body sideways towards a recess, not much wider than a shelf. She showered soot down onto Peter who seemed neither to notice nor care. She crouched back into the recess as he reached up for the bar and pulled himself up with several grunts and cascades of soot. He was not as fit as she and considerably less lithe. After several scrabbling attempts he swung himself into the recess and she guided his foot onto the narrow platform. He settled beside her.

'Good Lord,' he exclaimed, shining the torch around the area. 'This was no builder's accident.'

'It's a paradise for Father Christmas.' Their voices seemed to whirl around the confined space, then fly off into some distant part whence the echo returned seconds later. 'Whatever could it have been used for?'

'I haven't the faintest idea,' he said, continuing his careful study. 'How strange it is, sitting here trying to fathom out the mind of a builder four hundred years ago.' He discovered it was possible for him to understand a small fear of the unknown. His good sense resisted it, trying instead to find a plausible explanation, but the strange echo which dominated their speech, added to the mysterious atmosphere, was compellingly awe-inspiring.

Cuffy had pulled himself together. Having conducted a systematic search for Jake, he hurried nervously into the living-room to keep Peter abreast of the news. 'There's no sign of Mr Jake anywhere . . .' his voice faltered as he looked around the deserted room. 'I said there's no sign . . .' His eyes widened as fear turned to stark terror and, with a brief plea to the deity, he scurried from the house.

In the chimney the light from Peter's torch paused and hovered on a section where the soot appeared to cling less thickly. He leaned forward and brushed some aside. At first it seemed he had revealed a small grille but, as he cleared a larger area, it was something much wider. Window size, almost certainly an air vent through which the feeble light showed a flight of stone steps leading downwards. Sally eased herself up beside him and their two blackened faces peered through into the murky blackness like a pair of Victorian chimney sweeps. He grasped one of the grille cross-members and pushed hard. It gave slightly. They looked at each other, a slight nod, and they both pushed with all their strength. The aged construction offered little resistance; with a crash that released cascades of dirt and soot, they fell through and found themselves tumbling headlong down a dozen steps or so before coming to rest in inky blackness. Peter had maintained a hold on the torch and when he gave it a shake the lamp responded with a dull beam.

They were in a rough-hewn, tunnel-like passage which stretched ahead before curving round into the unknown. Once again an exchange of looks, again the quick nod, and the couple started on a journey of dark exploration. Sally felt her heart pounding with nerves while at the same time being wholly possessed by an intense curiosity. They rounded the bend slowly and felt rather than saw the tunnel continuing indefinitely.

In the barn Cuffy was pushing aside a group of animals in order to reach his coat lying by the tools. 'Come on, animals,' he gasped, 'Cuffy's in a hurry.' As he stooped to pick it up he heard a disembodied voice call his name – a call that reached him across a thousand years, an echoing, distorted, faint pronouncing of his name.

'C-u-f-f-y . . .!'

It was a conversation he had no intention of entering into. If there was one place he wanted to be more than anywhere else on earth it was safely back in his little bus. He grabbed his coat and, waving it round his head in a determined effort to cast aside demons and hell-hounds, he charged out of the barn. By the door he crashed into Jake. 'Where are you in such a hurry to get to?' asked the farmer.

'Home.'

'Where's Mr and Mrs Higgins?'

'They've been taken. Heaven knows where.' Cuffy had always lacked diplomacy.

'Stop it. You're making me nervous.'

'I'm frightening myself to death.'

The voice again. 'C-u-f-f-y . . . J-a-k-e . . .!' Jake stopped dead in his tracks. He moved cautiously towards the centre of the barn and, without knowing precisely where to look, addressed the spirit. 'It is I. Jake. Where are you?'

The voice replied. 'In the chimney.'

Cuffy decided to wait no longer, and fled from the barn.

Jake looked around, puzzled and petrified at the same time. He remembered the old ventilation shaft that ran up the back wall of the barn and began climbing the bales of hay stacked in front of it. 'What chimney?' he called.

The voice echoed back, 'Y-o-u-r c-h-i-m-n-e-y . . .

Immediately the farmer realised his mistake. The voice was coming from *below* him. He jumped down from the bales bracing himself for the shock of an eight-foot drop. It never came. The floor splintered almost without resistance and he disappeared clean through and out of sight. For a full minute there was total silence. Cuffy's frightened face appeared around the side of the door, scared eyes scanning the deserted area. First Mr and Mrs Higgins, now his old friend Jake – it was more than his simple mind could understand. He hadn't moved from the outside of the barn. Now he did. 'Call the Fire Brigade! Everyone's been taken!' he shouted as he hotfooted it to the village.

In the tunnel Peter and Sally stood frozen to the spot until the sound of the crash finished echoing back and forth, dying at last into a silence of black totality. 'What on earth was it?' she asked.

'I don't know.' He called again. 'Jake!' There was no response. Sally moved forward slowly, still shining the torch. 'Hold it!' he said suddenly. 'Shine the torch there again.'

'Where?'

'To your left.' She obeyed. 'There!'

It was a second grille. She hurried forward and tapped it with the torch. The sound echoed a dozen times, through a long distance. He came up beside her, grasped the grille, and was about to heave when a new sound reached them. It was a rushing noise, rising and falling. 'We've released something,' she whispered. 'Released some kind of energy.'

'Nonsense. Shut up and listen.'

'Peter . . . the smell . . .'

Suddenly it engulfed them, a reeking, noxious, frowsty odour, stinking of decomposition. 'We've got to know what's the other side of that wall,' he said quietly.

'It seems to go on for ever. Some kind of cave, or a black hole stretching back into time.'

'Will you stop being so dramatic?' he instructed curtly.

She was overwhelmed by the black atmosphere, both physical and insubstantial. A feeling in no way improved by the added sound of a man groaning – somewhere nearby. 'Listen,' she breathed. 'Voices. Echoing. Trying to tell us something.'

'If we could get this grille off . . .'

'We're interfering with something we don't understand,' she warned.

'Shut up and shine the torch up here.' He heaved and, like the first, the grille seemed to move relatively easily. As if the wall across the tunnel was not part of the original structure. She helped him and this time, as the wall disintegrated, they were ready. They picked their way forward, Sally clinging tightly to his hand, until a dull glow coming from ahead and above caused them to hurry their step. It was a faint light filtering from a splintered break in the ceiling. They almost fell over the body of a man and their hearts came into their mouths as Jake sat up, shaking his head. 'Jake, Jake, can you hear me?'

The farmer resigned himself to an unknown fate as he regained consciousness. 'Who is that calling me?'

'It's Peter, you fool!' They helped the man to his feet. One part of the mystery was at once solved. What Jake had always referred to as a cellar beneath the barn was, in fact, a tunnel connecting it with the living-room fireplace. The farmer's head cleared slowly, and Peter investigated the new space they had discovered. The tunnel seemed to continue but was blocked almost completely by a fall of rubble. It would take days to dig through. There was a small space between the top of the heap and the roof of the tunnel and it was through here that the rushing sound could be heard and was the emission point of the fetid smell. Behind him he heard Sally say in a strangely level voice, 'Jake. Who's your friend?'

He turned to see them both staring at the floor. In the gloomy light issuing from the hole in the barn floor above, they were looking at the distinct remains of a human skeleton.

'I must say the skeleton is tremendously interesting,' said the Reverend Arthur Norris. 'For as many years as I can remember Ma Cronin has been claiming the existence of the remains of a man.' They were sitting in his study at the vicarage, Peter and Sally were bathed, changed, and not a little pleased with themselves. 'It is true that the persecutions during the Reformation were far-reaching and cruel – nowhere more so than in this part of the country,' Norris went on. 'In this case a criminal, fleeing from the law, sought shelter in a local house. The owner took pity and hid him in a cellar. The authorities came, searched the place, and found the unfortunate man. The wretched criminal was told he had chosen his own final resting place.'

Sally was considerably impressed. 'You mean he was walled in and left to die?'

'So the story goes.'

'How awful.'

Peter spoke up scornfully. 'And to this day, when the wind is in the west, his faint cries can be heard as even now he screams for his release . .!'

'I beg your pardon?' requested Norris politely.

'I'm sorry, but although it has a good archaic ring to it, the story just doesn't fit the facts. Someone, four hundred years ago, had gone to the not inconsiderable trouble of building a tunnel from the old barn to the living-room fireplace. He's surely not going to waste all that work on a passing criminal.'

If one relied on information culled from reference books the entire country seemed to have been riddled with secret tunnels. Smugglers bored a route from sheltered coves to illegal warehouses, special constructions for mistresses to secretly visit their lovers were a standard fitting in the best appointed castles and, as Peter sarcastically observed, the original owner of Jake's farm had gone one better; when he fancied a spot of roast suckling pig he whistled up the chimney to the barn and the next in line walked up the steps and threw himself on the spit.

Sally no longer objected to his frivolous comments. She felt closer to her husband then than she had since moving into the village. His dogged perseverance in logically pursuing the truth while those around him were immersed in mystical drama was courageous. As a composer he was prone to all the insecurities of the creative mind but, when it came to sorting out the practicalities from the occult, he was strong, secure, and wonderful to be with. He was keen to continue along the road of making the story fit the facts although, now the news was out, he was going to find himself in competition with hordes of historians and students of psychical research, not to mention a friendly police investigation assuring itself the skeleton was as old as they thought. Peter had taken a slightly possessive pride in the tunnel he and Sally had unearthed and wanted to get to the bottom of the mystery. What was the rushing noise? Where did the smell come from? And which bright spark built a full-size organ in the bowels of the earth?

Two unwilling disciples of the demoniacal met outside the bus at the top of the hill late in the afternoon. Cuffy, wearing only one boot, was walking back and forth experimentally when Jake climbed up to pay him a visit that was to be so unique in its rarity as to be the very first time ever.

'Have you lost a shoe,' Jake enquired by way of introduction.

'No. I *found* one.'

The farmer cleared his throat, perhaps a trifle nervously. 'We'd been talking about you spending a day or two down at the farm . . .' he began hesitantly.

'Not me, Mr Jake.' The statement was accompanied by an unduly solemn shake of the head. 'That was some other tinker who hadn't been told anything about a haunting.'

'Well, it didn't seem important at the time.'

'I wouldn't be seen dead down at your place,' Cuffy assured him. Then, more realistically, 'I'm too afeared I *might* be seen dead down at your place.'

Jake squared his shoulders in an attempt to adopt his customary superior attitude towards the tinker. 'I can see that a man of your mentality might be frightened at first. You not having the education to take a philosophical view.'

'Do you take a philosophical view, Mr Jake?'

'I like to think so.'

'I don't know what philosophical means.'

'It means –' It had been intended as a grand and patronising explanation but Jake suddenly abandoned all pretence and came clean. 'It means being scared out of your wits, that's what it means!'

'No, I didn't know that, you see,' admitted Cuffy innocently. 'I thought it meant something deeper than that.'

'It means I'm not sleeping in that house until someone's got rid of all the evil spirits,' exclaimed Jake as the truth poured from him.

'They seem to have got rid of you already.' Even the jibe failed to rile Jake; he was too scared to be riled. Cuffy gave up the pretence at last as he confessed that the great fear left him only when he returned to his bus. Jake said, 'I wondered . . .' He swallowed, then tried again. 'I suppose you wouldn't have room for another one, would you? I mean, just for a night or two?' With that single enquiry a lifetime spent in antagonistic partnership melted into mutual understanding. The tinker looked at him as a first foundation for a new and different friendship was laid.

'You don't mean that,' he observed quietly. 'You'd never leave the animals. You'll just have to sleep in the barn with them. And, if you want, I'll maybe join you there.'

'Would you?'

'If I could park my bus in your yard for the winter.'

'Of *course* you can. You should've said before.'

'And I'll tell you something else,' continued Cuffy whilst he was on a winning streak. 'You ask Mr and Mrs Higgins to stay in the house – *they'll* do it. They're as puzzled as we are but nothing like so frightened. Especially him.'

'They're educated, you see,' explained Jake. A thought crossed his mind prompting a brief return to his old self. 'If they slept in the house I wouldn't need you in the barn.'

'But you got me, haven't you?' Cuffy grinned slyly. 'After repeated invitations to bring my bus down to your farm I finally accepted. Just to help you out!'

Jake nodded, turned, and began to walk down the hill. The tinker looked after him thoughtfully. When he was several yards distant the farmer called back to him. 'There's something about you that's always been a mystery to me.'

'What's that, Mr Jake?'

'You've no intelligence, not much education, and you're none too fresh bodywise . . . but you always seem to get your own ruddy way.'

Late that night, thick grey clouds with silvered edges scudded across the sky, occasionally blanketing out the light of a crescent moon. The clock on St George's Church chimed the half-hour before midnight as a figure emerged from the shadows and walked steadily through the cemetery.

Five minutes later the door of the vicarage opened and a second figure stepped out into the night air. It was Norris.

Peter lay in the old-fashioned iron bedstead of Jake's bedroom watching Sally brush her hair in front of the dressing-table mirror. Although he had never expected mystical happenings to manifest themselves to order he was quite positive he could not take another evening of cards with Jake and Cuffy. 'You'd have thought with all the racket we were making this afternoon the ghosts would have been rushing about like mad things,' he commented.

'Perhaps we frightened *them*.'

'Maybe we did at that. Broken the atmosphere.' Jake had said that on the two previous nights the wind had been blowing – moaning and groaning he'd said. 'It's a pity we couldn't have rustled up some stage wind tonight - just to keep the momentum going.'

Sally stopped brushing as a schoolgirl memory returned to her. The words of a childhood poem. With a slight smile she climbed on the bed and knelt beside him. She looked down, utterly beautiful in the subdued light from the bedside lamp.

'Have you ever heard the night wind go Yooooh?
'Tis a pitiful sound to hear.
It seems to thrill you through and through
With a strange and speechless fear.
'Tis the voice of the night
That broods outside when folks should be asleep,
And many and many's the time I've cried
To the darkness brooding far and wide
Over the Land and Deep,
Oh, whom do you want, oh lonely night,
That you wail the dark hours through?
And the night would say in its ghostly way,
Yooooooooooh – Yooooooooooh – Yooooooooooh –!'

She slowly lowered her head to his as she spoke the last line until, gently, their lips met and she kissed him softly and lingeringly. Then she rested her head on his shoulder, content, secure, and deeply in love.

'I didn't know you could do that,' he murmured.

'Did I frighten you?'

'Much more than Stinky Spectre downstairs.'

She slid an arm round his neck. 'If it wasn't for your practical common sense we'd all be frightening ourselves to death.'

'There has to be a *reason* for everything,' he said soberly.

'Suppose the reason is, quite simply, that a presence

223

does exist?'

'Then we would learn about it, understand it, and cease to be frightened of it.' She nodded, satisfied. He was right. Totally, thoroughly, and completely right.

He was about to switch off the light when their reverie was interrupted by footsteps pounding up the stairs, followed by an urgent knocking on the door. 'Young Upstart! Mrs Higgins'!' It was Jake's voice. 'Something's happening. I can hear things.'

They leapt from the bed, grabbed gowns, and piled downstairs. As they went Jake explained from behind them, 'It started off with this rushing sound – same as before. Then the smell. And just as I came to call you, I heard an organ . . .' They hurried into the living-room, past the cowering figure of Cuffy, and straight to the fireplace. The flames were flickering in their strange and frightening way but at least they knew the adjacent tunnel was the cause of that. The evil smell was stronger than in the afternoon and, positively, there could be heard quite clearly the sound of a church organ. Rising and falling, somewhere far away. 'What is it, Pete?' cried Sally. 'Whatever can it be?' He raised a hand for silence and listened carefully. Suddenly he stiffened, and gave her a faint smile. 'Have you heard something?' she asked.

He nodded smugly. 'Yes.'

'What?' asked Jake.

'A wrong note.'

'This is no time to worry about the tune,' exclaimed Cuffy.

'Don't ghosts play wrong notes?' from Sally.

'Not that particular wrong note.' Peter rose to his feet. 'There's only one person I know who never fails to mess up that particular phrase. If I've told him once I've told him a dozen times – it's C-sharp in the left hand!' He hurried from the room. 'Come on,' he called to his wife.

'Where are we going?' she asked.

'To bloody well tell him again.' He and Sally were at the top of the stairs by the time Jake and Cuffy reached the hall.

'Are you going out?' Jake called up to them.

'Won't be long,' Peter replied.

Jake looked round, still uncertain. Then a nervous glance back into the living-room. 'I'll just check the animals are all right,' he decided.

'I'll help you, Mr Jake,' said Cuffy following him closely as he left the house.

The young couple reached the churchyard ten minutes later and, holding hands, moved past the tombstones towards the sacristy door. They could hear the organ playing and the last vestige of fear was fading from Sally The two let themselves in quietly and made their way towards the organ console. They could see a solitary lamp burning, and throwing long shadows across the empty pews. The grand majestic chords filled the darkened church, and the sheer incongruity of an organ playing in the middle of the night gave the music an added mystique. They came abreast of the chancel screen and could clearly see the organist, Frank Bellows, finishing the work. Beyond him, half-hidden in the shadows, Norris sat alone. They reached him as Bellows held the final chord and the aftermath of silence seemed the more intense for the mighty sound which had preceded it.

'A fine work,' declared Norris. 'Splendid stuff. I could listen to him all night.'

'How long has this been going on?' asked Peter. 'Organ recitals in the small hours?'

Norris shook his head in mock sadness. 'There seems no end to the rift between Frank Bellows and Farmer Hudson. Frank would rather play at night than cause another argument.'

Sally sat down beside him and said in a casual voice, 'The sound of his playing is coming out of Jake's fireplace.'

Norris looked at her incredulously before switching his gaze to Peter. 'A tunnel to the barn didn't seem to make sense. But a tunnel to the *church* –!' the young man explained.

The vicar switched his amazed concentration back to Sally as she asked, 'Your story about the criminal hiding from the law. Could he not have been a priest fleeing from his persecutors?'

'A secret tunnel to the priesthole?' added Peter.

'If that's true I think I know where the tunnel starts,' said Norris.

'Where?'

'Immediately behind the font.' He rose to his feet and

lead the way as the other two followed. 'I've been particularly stupid not to think of it before.' At the back of the church the vicar lifted aside a strip of carpet, revealing an iron ring let into one of the flagstones. He grasped it with both hands and slowly heaved the stone clear.

'What's down there?' enquired Peter.

'I thought a cellar,' answered Norris. 'Or an unused tomb. There seemed nothing else.'

'May we take a look?'

'By all means.'

They would need a light. Sally looked round and, seeing a collection box with a container of new candles above it, she took out a couple and handed them to Peter. Catching a quick look from the vicar she dutifully dropped a fifty-pence piece into the box. Peter had spotted a flight of stone steps leading down into the cavern and, having lit the candles, lowered himself into the space. Sally followed him and Norris knelt to get a better view of their progress. As they reached the foot of the steps a rush of air caused the candles to gutter. Peter called up to Norris, 'Could you ask Frank to switch off the organ pump?'

'Yes, of course.'

Peter and Sally felt their way across the confined space to the wall opposite, holding the candles high in an attempt to penetrate the darkness. They seemed to be walking in a rubbish tip which, looking down, turned out to be exactly what it was. Remnants of numerous Harvest Festivals, and goodness knows what else, because their Reverend friend above found the cavern more convenient than the long trudge to the dustbins. The rush of air subsided to silence as the organ was switched off and the stench at once became strong. Obviously the draught was blowing the smell away somewhere, and, a second later, they spotted the grille simultaneously – it was identical to the other two. 'We were right. One tunnel stretching from the church to the farm. What an incredible achievement for those days.'

Even with the mystery solved they could not prevent themselves leaping in sudden fear when a distorted voice, befuddled by a thousand echoes, came from the grille. 'Is anybody there?' Sally clung to Peter suddenly.

'Where are you?' Peter spoke into the grille.

'Say who you are!' demanded the deep-toned reverberant voice.

'It's Peter and Sally. Is that you, Jake?'

The voice sounded relieved despite the added sepulchral overtones. 'Yes. I'm speaking into the fireplace. Where are you?'

'Under the church,' announced Peter. 'I think we've finally solved the mystery.'

Norris had followed them down the steps and by the light of the flickering candles could be seen staring awe-struck at the grille. But the mystery *wasn't* solved. The two men and the girl started visibly when the air was rent with a closer voice, quavering, old, enquiring . . . the voice of a woman.

'H-u-l-l-o!!?'

Both ends of the tunnel were stunned into deathly silence. The woman's 'Hullo' boomed around the cavern, frightening the living daylights out of Peter, Sally and Norris whilst, in the living-room, Cuffy and Jake clutched each other. After a long moment Jake spoke to the fireplace in a much subdued voice. 'Was that you?'

'No, it wasn't,' Peter's voice came back nervously. Then he asked, 'Did somebody call?'

The woman's voice came again. 'H-u-l-l-o!!?'

Peter asked, 'Speak to me! Who are you calling?'

'I'm trying to talk to my dear departed husband!' said the voice.

Norris suddenly relaxed. 'It's Ma Cronin,' he declared. He moved right up to the grille and spoke slowly and distinctly, 'You're on a crossed line, Mrs Cronin. Hang up and try later.'

It began raining on the Sunday.

A light drizzle at first from clouds which had carried threats for several hours. Then the drops thickened and became heavier until, by breakfast time, it settled down into good, solid, autumnal rain. Apart from the freak cloudburst it was the first real downpour the village had seen throughout the long hot summer. It dripped and gurgled from eaves, trees, gutters, and streams. Dust was washed from roofs and roads, it soaked into parched lands reaching down to the deepest roots, the air was cool and moist, the reservoirs began to fill. The countryside which had gloried under an English sun welcomed a return of the friendly rain.

The vicarage telephone had scarcely stopped ringing over several days. Jake and his fireplace had been photographed from every angle, various official societies had examined every inch of the tunnel, and paid particular attention to the air-vent concealed within Ma Cronin's old cottage. The venerable lady had been especially resentful of the public interest expressed in the grille above her living-room fireplace which she had always regarded as a personal voicepipe to the spirits.

Sally also harboured a slight pique towards those who were violating the secrecy of their tunnel. It was Peter's and her place; they'd discovered it; and, in its own supernatural way, it had brought them together again.

By eleven o'clock the parish church was full to over-flowing. The rain had kept no one away and the Reverend Arthur Norris looked down from the pulpit and relished the sight of a complete congregation. There was Young Upstart and his pretty wife, Old Saltie, Jake, Mr Charles, Harvey, Sam and the entire Shillingbury Brass Band, Mrs Simpkins, George Langton and his good lady, Ma Cronin, Meadows and . . . wait a minute, just one person missing. There was not a sign of Cuffy. Norris felt an extraordinary surge of disappointment – better to lose the whole world than suffer the loss of one sinner. 'Just a few weeks ago,' he said to them, 'we celebrated the Harvest Festival in the presence of a congregation which caused the church to be a little less than half full. I prayed for some sign which might point the way towards larger attendances. Today my simple mind tells me that somewhere Somebody heard my call. We are gathered here to praise God rather than to marvel at the wonders of man but, whatever your reasons for joining us today, I welcome you. This week we have witnessed a miracle – the Shillingbury Miracle.'

Frank Bellows played an introduction on the organ. Peter nudged Sally, 'Considering it was Cuffy who suggested a miracle in the first place, you'd have thought he would turn up today.'

'It's a rotten rainy day,' she whispered back. 'Cuffy was never one for putting himself out.'

As hymn books were opened and voices raised in song a flagstone, quite near the font, began to rise from the ground of its own accord. Sally saw it first and pulled Peter's arm. He stared and nudged Jake. The eyes of the congregation swivelled fearfully. The flagstone rose into the air before settling itself to one side of the cavern opening. The figure of Cuffy the Tinker slowly rose from the depths. Spruce, smart, washed, hair brushed, wearing the check trousers Norris had given him. He was the only person in St George's Church who was bone dry.

Cuffy stepped up into the aisle, saw Peter, Sally and Jake, smiled a bashful smile, and joined them. He knew the hymn and added his voice to the rest – he was always glad to help out.

TIMES OF TRIUMPH
by Charlotte Vale Allen

Spanning more than three decades in the turbulent history of our century, Charlotte Vale Allen's magnificent saga traces the life and loves of a woman born to struggle against every adversity with dauntless courage and unflinching love.

Leonie came to New York with all the world against her and built her tiny eating-house into a mighty business empire.

Gray, the London journalist who followed her across the ocean, was the father of her children and the love of her lifetime.

Through the First World War, the hard and hungry years that followed, through love and pain and bitter sadness, through the growing years of their son and daughter destined to retrace their mother's footsteps into a Europe once again torn apart by war — Leonie's life was a time of triumph.

NEW ENGLISH LIBRARY

MEET ME IN TIME
by Charlotte Vale Allen

Meet Me in Time is a story about love, its intensity and destructiveness, its needs and satisfactions. It is also the story of the Burgesses, a brilliant, tormented family.

Gaby : bitter and unstable, cheated by the failure of her marriage and resenting the child she never wanted . . .

Dana : a talented playwright who recoiled from the truth about himself . . .

Glenn : the artist, haunted by her mother's death, expecting more love than anyone could humanly give her . . .

All three had dreams of fame, and passions that demanded fulfilment. All three shared the bittersweet inheritance from their mother, whose need to love had been overwhelming, and whose need to be loved was an inescapable legacy to her children.

NEW ENGLISH LIBRARY

THE RICH AND THE RIGHTEOUS

by Helen Van Slyke

Joseph Haylow, the dynamic, well-meaning founder of a billion-dollar empire, faces his testimonial retirement dinner with trepidation. Unwilling to retire from the company that is his creation, he must name his successor, a decision still unresolved as the dinner begins. Haylow's world, faith and family are examined as, in his last year of office, he learns the truth about those who surround him — the weak, the ruthless, the loving and the fallible.

NEW ENGLISH LIBRARY

Book Tokens

**Give them
the pleasure of choosing**

Book Tokens can be bought
and exchanged at most
bookshops in Great Britain
and Ireland.

NEL BESTSELLERS

T037061	BLOOD AND MONEY	*Thomas Thompson*	£1.50
T045692	THE BLACK HOLE	*Alan Dean Foster*	95p
T049817	MEMORIES OF ANOTHER DAY	*Harold Robbins*	£1.95
T049701	THE DARK	*James Herbert*	£1.50
T045528	THE STAND	*Stephen King*	£1.75
T065475	I BOUGHT A MOUNTAIN	*Thomas Firbank*	£1.50
T050203	IN THE TEETH OF THE EVIDENCE	*Dorothy L. Sayers*	£1.25
T050777	STRANGER IN A STRANGE LAND	*Robert Heinlein*	£1.75
T050807	79 PARK AVENUE	*Harold Robbins*	£1.75
T042308	DUNE	*Frank Herbert*	£1.50
T045137	THE MOON IS A HARSH MISTRESS	*Robert Heinlein*	£1.25
T050149	THE INHERITORS	*Harold Robbins*	£1.75
T049620	RICH MAN, POOR MAN	*Irwin Shaw*	£1.60
T046710	EDGE 36: TOWN ON TRIAL	*George G. Gilman*	£1.00
T037541	DEVIL'S GUARD	*Robert Elford*	£1.25
T050629	THE RATS	*James Herbert*	£1.25
T050874	CARRIE	*Stephen King*	£1.50
T050610	THE FOG	*James Herbert*	£1.25
T041867	THE MIXED BLESSING	*Helen Van Slyke*	£1.50
T038629	THIN AIR	*Simpson & Burger*	95p
T038602	THE APOCALYPSE	*Jeffrey Konvitz*	95p
T046850	WEB OF EVERYWHERE	*John Brunner*	85p

NEL P.O. BOX 11, FALMOUTH TR10 9EN, CORNWALL

Postage charge:

U.K. Customers. Please allow 40p for the first book, 18p for the second book, 13p for each additional book ordered, to a maximum charge of £1.49, in addition to cover price.

B.F.P.O. & Eire. Please allow 40p for the first book, 18p for the second book, 13p per copy for the next 7 books, thereafter 7p per book, in addition to cover price.

Overseas Customers. Please allow 60p for the first book plus 18p per copy for each additional book, in addition to cover price.

Please send cheque or postal order (no currency).

Name ....

Address ....

....

Title ....

While every effort is made to keep prices steady, it is sometimes necessary to increase prices at short notice. New English Library reserve the right to show on covers and charge new retail prices which may differ from those advertised in the text or elsewhere.(5)